J. M. YOFFEY   *Photograph: Mrs E. Salomon*

*The Ciba Foundation for the promotion of international cooperation in
medical and chemical research is a scientific and educational charity established by
CIBA Limited – now CIBA-GEIG Y Limited – of Basle. The Foundation operates
independently in London under English trust law.*

*Ciba Foundation Symposia are published in collaboration with
Associated Scientific Publishers (Elsevier Scientific Publishing Company, Excerpta Medica,
North-Holland Publishing Company) in Amsterdam.*

Associated Scientific Publishers, P.O. Box 1270, Amsterdam

Haemopoietic Stem Cells

Ciba Foundation Symposium 13 (new series)
Held in tribute to J. M. Yoffey

1973

Elsevier · Excerpta Medica · North-Holland
Associated Scientific Publishers · Amsterdam · London · New York

ISBN Excerpta Medica 90 219 4014 0
ISBN American Elsevier 0-444-15009-9

Library of Congress Catalog Card Number 73-76975

Published in 1973 by Associated Scientific Publishers, P.O. Box 1270, Amsterdam, and 52 Vanderbilt Avenue, New York, N.Y. 10017.
Suggested series entry for library catalogues: Ciba Foundation Symposia.

Ciba Foundation Symposium 13 (new series)

Printed in The Netherlands by Mouton & Co., The Hague

Contents

Participants

Symposium on Haemopoietic Stem Cells
held at the Ciba Foundation, London, 13th-14th July, 1972

Chairman: J. F. LOUTIT   MRC Radiobiology Unit, Harwell, Didcot, Berks., UK

G. ASTALDI   The Blood Research Foundation Center, Ospedale Civile, I-15057 Tortona, Italy

P. MARY COTES   MRC Division of Biological Standards, National Institute for Medical Research, Hampstead Laboratories, Holly Hill, London NW3 6RB

K. A. DICKE   Radiobiological Institute of the Organization for Health Research TNO, 151 Lange Kleiweg, Rijswijk (ZH), The Netherlands

G. M. GRIGORIU   Centre of Haematology, Str. C-tin Caracas, nr. 2-8, OP 2, CP 1006, Bucharest, Rumania

P. F. HARRIS   Department of Human Morphology, University of Nottingham, University Park, Nottingham NG7 2RD, UK

G. HUDSON   Faculty of Medicine, 304 Western Bank, Sheffield S102TN, UK

N. N. ISCOVE   Friedrich Miescher-Institut, PO Box 273, CH-4002 Basel, Switzerland

B. KUBANEK   Abteilung für Hämatologie der Universität Ulm, Steinhövelstrasse 9, D-79 Ulm (Donau), Germany

L. G. LAJTHA Paterson Laboratories, Christie Hospital & Holt Radium Institute, Manchester M20 9BX, UK

E. A. MCCULLOCH Department of Medicine, Princess Margaret Hospital, 500 Sherbourne Street, Toronto 284, Canada

D. METCALF Cancer Research Unit, The Walter & Eliza Hall Institute of Medical Research, Post Office, Royal Melbourne Hospital, Victoria 3050, Australia

H. S. MICKLEM Department of Zoology, University of Edinburgh, West Mains Road, Edinburgh EH9 3JT, UK

D. G. OSMOND Department of Anatomy, McGill University, PO Box 6070, 101 Montreal, Quebec, Canada

C. ROSSE School of Medicine, Department of Biological Structure, University of Washington, Seattle, Washington 98105, USA

D. P. SHREINER Department of Nuclear Medicine, Veterans Administration Hospital, University Drive, Pittsburgh, Pa. 15240, USA

F. STOHLMAN JR. St. Elizabeth's Hospital of Boston, 736 Cambridge Street, Boston, Mass. 02135, USA

D. B. THOMAS Department of Anatomy, University of Birmingham, The Medical School, Birmingham B15 2TJ, UK

K. H. WINTERHALTER Friedrich Miescher-Institut, PO Box 273, CH-4002 Basel, Switzerland

J. M. YOFFEY Department of Anatomy, The Hebrew University, Hadassah Medical School, PO Box 1172, Jerusalem, Israel

Editors: G. E. W. WOLSTENHOLME and MAEVE O'CONNOR

Chairman's introduction

J. F. LOUTIT

MRC Radiobiology Unit, Harwell

The Ciba Foundation with its world-wide reputation tries to bring people like ourselves together for fruitful discussions, which we must agree is an invaluable form of communication in science. This particular meeting is devoted to Joe Yoffey and the haemopoietic stem cell; it is about work in progress on a problem not yet completely solved. By the end of these two days we shall know better where we stand about the haemopoietic stem cells, but here I shall talk about Joseph Mendel Yoffey whom we are honouring on this occasion.

To start in a rather formal manner, I quote one of his shorter communications —from *Who's Who*, where he writes that he was born on the 10th July 1902, the son of Rabbi Israel Jacob Yoffey and Pere Jaffe. The rest of his career is listed, starting in 1926–1927 as a research fellow, continuing as a research scholar of the British Medical Association, a house surgeon at the Manchester Royal Infirmary, through the usual stages of assistant lecturer of anatomy and senior lecturer at Cardiff, and several Hunterian and Rockefeller professorships until finally he was Professor of Anatomy in Bristol from 1942 to 1967. In this list in *Who's Who* there is a gap and as Yoffey is tremendously interested in numbers and quantification, I am intrigued by this gap: what was he doing in those three years?

I very much regret the absence of Al Gordon, who was to have been chairman on this occasion, because I feel he would have made a very much better job of telling you all about Yoffey than I. In fact, I feel singularly ill-equipped, because there are many people in this room who could have done it very much better from personal knowledge. However, Yoffey and I have, by Brownian movement, met on a number of random occasions over the last fifteen or more years and he seems to me to be the epitome of the dedicated university don; that is, he has two main attributes, teacher and research worker. I cannot speak about his qualities as a teacher but I can speak about his qualities as a research worker.

They can perhaps be summed up by saying that he has spent a lifetime in scholarly work, as is appropriate to a university academic, in a particular field. This is a very large field which includes the lymphoid tissue and its cells, and the related bone marrow and its cells. Therein he is an acknowledged world authority. He is the author of several monographs and co-author of one particularly valuable work, in the latest edition entitled *Lymphatics, Lymph and the Lymphomyeloid Complex* (1970, Academic Press, London, New York). Sophisticated though we may be in this audience, I think that like Goldsmith's yokels in *The Deserted Village* we can say

> '*And still we gazed and still the wonder grew*
> *That one small head could carry all he knew*'.

By contrast, if I can talk about myself for a few minutes, as a government scientist I reckon to be a hired hack and therefore, unlike the professional academic, I have not spent my life in one continued search in one field. Indeed like Dryden's character I 'did everything by shifts and nothing long'. So I can appreciate the dedication of Yoffey to the gradual unfolding and elucidation of this particular and fascinating field, much of the progress in which is due to his own personal work and also to the school that he founded.

Whereas Yoffey and I have met at symposia like this and on visits to each other's laboratories, I am unable personally to speak of him as a university teacher. All that I can judge is the quality of the younger research workers whom he has encouraged and produced. Fortunately Dr Wolstenholme has collected for me letters from members of this group which give first-hand information about Professor Yoffey as a teacher and a professor. The first comment I shall quote is: 'One only gets to know Professor Yoffey if one works with him. The relationship of the most senior person in the department with the most junior members, B.Sc. students, was a unique one. He immediately made us feel very important and by involving us in research straight away encouraged us to dispute and argue with him, making himself an equal member of a group of students. In these discussions we learned an awful lot, not only about blood-forming tissues but about the history of medicine, haematology and the world, anecdotes about leading haematologists of the present and the past, about world affairs, and quite a lot about Professor Yoffey himself. After sitting for long hours with his microscope or going over the draft of a paper in his office or at his home, the conversation might turn to anything, ranging from the beauty of the countryside around Manchester to the interpretation of Beethoven's piano sonatas, which he could play'.

And later on: 'He knows everybody in the area of his research and his knowledge of the literature is unbelievable. In his spirited manner he gets obvious pleasure out of winning an argument or discussion by quoting the previous and long-forgotten work of his 'opponent'. When I said good-bye to him in Bristol in 1967 his advice to me was to stick to my convictions through thick and thin if I feel them to be well founded, even if others laughed at it. Indeed, this advice may have summed up the experience of his life's work. He was among the very first to draw attention to a cell which has become the object of the most extensive investigation and far-reaching importance in modern medicine. Many of the questions he asked decades ago only recently have been hammered home'.

'Perhaps his most outstanding quality was that of infectious enthusiasm in all matters relating to his chosen research field. He is able to impart a feeling of excitement in the chase and an aura of importance to the research problem, which has greatly influenced many who have worked with him and which has painlessly channelled a number of workers into research careers'.

'To generations of medical students, he has appeared as a benign lecturer, examiner and father figure, who could nevertheless entertain them with a ballad at the piano at preclinical students' Christmas parties. His department became their natural home and a base for their other activities during the first year or two of their medical course. He fostered an active B.Sc. honours programme for medical students, of which the major feature was an extensive research project and thesis in the lymphoid problem'.

Those were quotations from Professor Yoffey's own students, now grown up to mature research workers. At the Ciba Foundation symposium on *Haemo-poiesis* in 1960 my own colleague Ossie Trowell, now unfortunately deceased, was present. I shall always remember Ossie when he first came to join me at Harwell insisting that the book by Yoffey and Courtice (*Lymphatics, Lymph and Lymphoid Tissue*) should be on permanent loan to him in his office! As director responsible for the bits and pieces I queried this but he was insistent. He said 'Everything in my field is in there. Everything that is worthwhile, Yoffey has collected and put in this book'. Further, he went on to say, 'I may not agree with all of Yoffey's interpretations [and Yoffey was telling me that he had some good arguments with Trowell in this room] but I am always confident of Yoffey's observations'. I think that is as great a tribute as we can make to any research worker. Interpretations are liable to mutation as time goes on, but as long as the raw material is exact we're all right.

Finally, may I quote another vignette from the letters about Professor Yoffey. 'He is fond of relating a remark of one of his senior colleagues at Bristol on his appointment to the chair of anatomy in 1941. The senior professor evidently was pleased with all the attributes and qualifications of his future junior colleague, but for one: his reservation being "If only he weren't interested in such a completely dull and useless cell" '.

Stem cell role of the lymphocyte – transitional cell (LT) compartment

J. M. YOFFEY

Department of Anatomy, The Hebrew University–Hadassah Medical School, Jerusalem, Israel

Abstract In the fully developed marrow of the normal animal in postnatal life there is no single specific stem cell but rather a stem cell compartment. This is the lymphocyte–transitional (LT) compartment, which in the normal steady state consists of about 80–90% of pachychromatic small lymphocytes and 10–20% of transitional cells. The transitional cells are a spectrum of cells of varying sizes, proliferative capacities and degrees of basophilia. Basophilic transitionals, the immediate precursors of the blast cells, are derived from pale transitional cells which are capable of self-maintenance. These views are embodied in a stem-cell model supported by many lines of evidence, among which one may note: (1) quantitative studies of bone marrow during either stimulation or depression of erythropoiesis; (2) ultrastructural studies of erythroblastic islands in different functional states; (3) changes in the marrow during sublethal irradiation; (4) analysis of marrow suspensions transfused to protect against lethal irradiation; (5) a study of the properties of colony-forming units; (6) data on stem cell migration; (7) the possible existence of truly pluripotent stem cells which can develop along either immunological or haemopoietic pathways. The combination of these and other data makes possible the formulation of a series of stem-cell postulates which can only be met by the cells of the LT compartment.

DIRECT AND INDIRECT METHODS OF APPROACH

When one surveys the vast amount of effort which has been devoted to the investigation of the stem cell, it is evident that there have been two fundamentally different lines of approach, the *direct* and the *indirect*. The indirect approach is to study the haemopoietic tissues in terms of the cells (or the substances—e.g. haemoglobin) which they produce, whether erythrocytes, granulocytes, megakaryocytes, monocytes or stem cells. The direct approach involves, as its name implies, the direct study of the changes in the haemopoietic tissue itself, essentially the bone marrow, both in the normal steady state and in conditions in which this is subject to different types of perturbation. The direct method is the one which was adopted for many years by our Bristol group. It gives me particular pleasure that several members of our old group are participating in this symposium, for in presenting the stem cell scheme which I am now putting forward, I want to acknowledge at the outset that it is based to a large extent on a foundation to which they have all contributed. In making this acknowledgement, may I hasten to add that I do not impute to them any responsibility for the views now expressed. On the contrary, it has given me singular satisfaction to learn from them, and to have them correct some of the quite fundamental errors of much of my earlier work.

For example, at the Ciba Foundation Symposium on *Haemopoiesis: Cell Production and its Regulation* in 1960 one of my chief working hypotheses was that lymphocytes were not formed in the marrow, but were constantly obtaining access to it from the bloodstream (Yoffey 1960). The correction of this error by Dr Osmond made possible—or rather quite categorically necessitated—a completely fresh approach to the stem cell problem. At the 1960 Symposium, furthermore, I presented the first observations, made in conjunction with Drs Everett and Reinhardt (Everett *et al*. 1960), on the high labelling index of transitional cells. However, the significance of this was completely missed at the time, since I then adhered to the view that transitional cells were incapable of division. This error too had to be corrected, on the basis of the comprehensive studies of both Dr Osmond and Dr Harris, before more fruitful lines of investigation could be developed. I cannot do better at this stage than give what my former Bristol associates would expect from me, namely an appropriate Talmudic quotation, from a Jerusalem scholar of the first century: 'Much have I learned from my teachers, still more from my fellow students, but most of all from my pupils'.

The direct method has not been as widely used as the indirect techniques, which are numerous. One of the early indirect methods was to test for the presence of stem cells by their ability to protect lethally irradiated animals. The use of chromosome markers (Ford *et al*. 1956) made it possible to learn much about the subsequent life history of the transfused stem cells. The spleen colony technique introduced by Till & McCulloch (1961) has been the basis of a vast amount of experimentation. The response to erythropoietin has been extensively used by Lajtha *et al*. (1964), while Blackett *et al*. (1964) used a stem cell test based on short-term erythropoietic repopulation. Hellman & Grate (1967) used granulocyte production as a stem cell indicator. Bradley & Metcalf (1966) developed an *in vitro* colony technique for stem cell study. These and other indirect methods of investigating the stem cell problem have recently been reviewed elsewhere (McCulloch 1970; Lajtha 1970; Orlic 1970; Fruhman 1970; Metcalf & Bradley 1970; Sachs 1970). I shall therefore concentrate here on the results obtained by the direct method, and then compare the stem cell scheme founded on these results with the schemes obtained by the more indirect methods. The comparison is an interesting one, since there seems to be an increasing measure of agreement between the various stem cell models which have emerged from the different approaches.

One important difference between the stem cell model now propounded (Fig. 1) and most others is that the stem cells are presented as occupying a compartment which can be morphologically identified, namely the lymphocyte–transitional cell compartment, or LT compartment. But in stating this it is important first to clear up certain misconceptions. To state that the haemo-poietic stem cells are to be found in the LT compartment does not mean that all the cells of the compartment can function as stem cells: just as the small lymphocytes are a functionally heterogeneous population, so in all probability are the transitional cells.

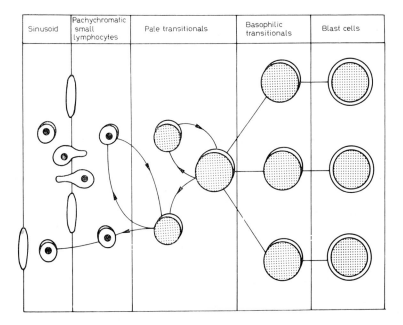

FIG. 1. A stem cell scheme. The most undifferentiated cells are the pale transitional cells. These may either undergo proliferation or leave the compartment. When they proliferate, small transitional cells grow into large ones, which then divide. When they leave the compart-ment, they may either develop basophilia and then become blast cells, or else they may divide to give rise to small lymphocytes, which can leave the marrow by traversing the sinusoidal endothelium and entering the bloodstream. Some lymphocytes may also traverse the sinusoidal endothelium in the opposite direction, i.e. from blood to marrow. Transitional cells can also enter the bloodstream from the marrow (not shown in the scheme). They do so in much smaller numbers than lymphocytes.

Furthermore, it is perhaps misleading to speak of *the* stem cell, for there is not a single specific stem cell throughout life. In the foetus, as is well known, the changing sites of haemopoiesis seem to be associated with different stem cells, though once the definitive myeloid haemopoiesis has become established, the LT compartment is especially prominent, even in foetal life (Yoffey *et al.* 1961). But even in foetal marrow, in the early stages at least, primitive mesenchymal cells have been thought to be the initial stem cells. It may well be that the localized regeneration of marrow under certain experimental conditions (Patt & Maloney 1970; Knospe *et al.* 1972) is associated with a different type of haemopoietic stem cell from that found once myeloid haemopoiesis is fully established. It is even conceivable that any primitive undifferentiated cell can, if appropriately stimulated, undergo haemopoietic differentiation. This does not alter the fact that, once the bone marrow is fully developed, the only stem cells found to be associated with normal erythropoiesis appear to belong to the LT compartment.

A haemopoietic stem cell is here defined as a cell which does not possess any of the signs of differentiation in its cytoplasm or nucleus but is nevertheless capable of differentiating into an erythrocyte, granulocyte, monocyte or megakaryocyte. This broad definition leaves open the further subdivision of stem cells into those which are already committed to a given line of development and those which are not. It also leaves open the source of the stem cells, though in fact the scheme now submitted does envisage self-replication of the stem cell compartment.

As a result of the intensive work of recent years, it now seems that we can eliminate two of the classical contenders for the role of stem cell, namely the sinusoidal endothelium and the so-called reticulum cell. Though reticulum cells have figured so largely in classical haematological theory as the fundamental stem cells, they are a singularly ill-defined group. Rohr (1949), for example, appears to have applied the term reticulum cell to almost any cell in the marrow which could not be clearly identified, and he recognized five types of reticulum cell. In recent years Huhn (1966), on the basis of ultrastructural studies, and Fliedner *et al.* (1968), on the basis of light microscope studies, have distinguished two types of reticulum cell, and in each case one of the two types seems closely to resemble a transitional cell. But so far as reticulum cells can be morphologically defined, the data of both Caffrey *et al.* (1966) and Fliedner *et al.* (1968) indicate that these cells do not possess the labelling or migratory properties required of haemopoietic stem cells on the basis of the experimental data now available (Barnes & Loutit 1967*a*; Loutit 1967).

THE LYMPHOCYTE–TRANSITIONAL (LT) COMPARTMENT

Transitional cells were first noted in rabbit marrow (Yoffey & Parnell 1944), though the term 'transitional' was introduced later by Hudson et al. (1952), who reported that after repeated injections of ACTH '…there appeared to be an increased number of lymphocytes with varying degrees of leptochromasia, which could be interpreted as transitional forms of varying sizes between small lymphocytes and micro-myeloblasts'. After several further investigations we concluded that transitional cells were a normal feature of guinea-pig marrow and comprised all intermediate stages between lymphocytes and blast cells. This point requires emphasis, since the transitional cells are an entire *spectrum* of cells, not a single specific cell. Their morphological features, as seen with the light microscope, were subsequently described in detail and illustrated at a Brookhaven symposium (Yoffey 1957). At one end of the spectrum is the pachychromatic small lymphocyte, whose morphology as seen with the light microscope is characterized by five distinctive features. (1) It is one of the smallest cells in the marrow. (2) It possesses a very high nucleus: cytoplasm ratio, and in smear preparations the cytoplasm often forms only a small tuft at one pole of the cell. (3) There is a well-marked nucleolus with an irregular coating of DNA. (4) The chromatin is dense—*pachychromatic*—forming not only blocks in the interior, but also an irregular dense layer next to the nuclear membrane, the *juxtamembranous condensation*. (5) There is a very high ratio of chromatin to parachromatin. These features combine to give more or less the characteristic appearance of a chromatin ring with a dot in the middle (Yoffey et al. 1965a; Rosse & Yoffey 1967).

When the pachychromatic small lymphocyte enlarges to become a transitional cell, all these elements in its morphology undergo change. (1) The cell undergoes progressive enlargement. The initial growth involves mainly the nucleus, but after a while the cytoplasm also increases, gradually extending all the way round the nucleus, until it finally forms a complete rim. (2) In a varying number of transitional cells basophilia develops, and when the nucleus is completely surrounded by basophilic cytoplasm the appearance is that of a typical blast cell. (3) The dense nucleolar coating of DNA gradually disappears, leaving a less dense nucleolus which gradually becomes more difficult to identify. (4) The dense masses of chromatin, whether juxtamembranous or situated more deeply in the nucleus, gradually break up, so that as seen with the light microscope the nucleus becomes completely leptochromatic. (5) The ratio of chromatin to parachromatin gradually diminishes. These changes can readily be seen in light microscope studies of phytohaemagglutinin (PHA) cultures (Yoffey et al. 1965c).

Ultrastructural examination (Fig. 2) brings out the same essential features but, as might be expected, with rather more detail (Hudson & Yoffey 1966). The polar cytoplasm of the marrow small lymphocyte as seen in smears would appear to be an artifact, since in the electron microscope even the smallest lymphocyte may be seen to possess a complete rim of cytoplasm. The varying degrees of basophilia seen with the light microscope (Rosse & Yoffey 1967) presumably have their counterpart in the changing proportions of monoribosomes to polyribosomes (Ben-Ishay & Yoffey 1972). Furthermore, ultrastructural

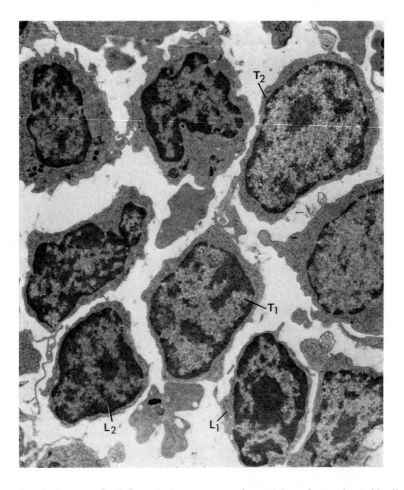

FIG. 2. A group of cells from the bone marrow of a rat 4 days after moderate bleeding. L1 and L2 are pachychromatic small lymphocytes. T1 and T2 are small transitional cells. T1 is a slightly earlier stage in transitional cell development than T2. From Yoffey & Ben-Ishay 1971. × 4900.

examination brings out very clearly the frequent occurrence of one or more indentations in the nuclei of transitional cells, particularly the large ones (Harris & Kugler 1967; Ben-Ishay & Yoffey 1972). Rosse (1971) has recently observed very active nuclear changes in transitional cells in culture, with the repeated formation and disappearance of 'deep invaginations of the nuclear membrane'.

Lymphocyte formation in the marrow

The views presented in the preceding section were our first approach to the problem of the LT compartment. This approach involved two basic assumptions: (1) that small lymphocytes were not formed in the marrow, but were constantly coming to it from outside; (2) that once in the marrow they enlarged, passed through a transitional cell phase, and became blast cells. These assumptions seemed to afford a simple and plausible solution of the stem cell problem. Lymphocytic stem cells in an extramyeloid environment could proliferate, but not differentiate. In this way a constant supply of undifferentiated stem cells was available to enter the marrow. However, the pioneer studies of Osmond & Everett (1964) on the guinea pig, supported by the further studies of Everett & Caffrey (1967) on the rat, together with the results obtained by Harris *et al.* (1963), established that there was in fact active lymphocyte production in the marrow through the division of transitional cells. Even though there is some movement of lymphocytes into the marrow via the bloodstream (Everett *et al.* 1960; Rosse 1972), Rosse believes that these haematogenous cells are recirculating long-lived small lymphocytes.

The maintenance of the LT compartment

The division of transitional cells to produce small lymphocytes raises a number of problems, of which the most obvious concerns the actual maintenance of the transitional cell population. Clearly, if all that transitional cells did was to divide into small lymphocytes, they would very quickly disappear, in which case we would be faced with the further problem of finding some other precursor for the blast cells than the basophilic transitionals. The absence of any other precursor merely serves to emphasize the basic problem of the maintenance of the transitional cell compartment.

If we can disregard the reticulum cell, the only two possibilities here seem to be either self-replication, or the enlargement of small lymphocytes to become transitional cells once again.

Jones et al. (1967) and Moffatt et al. (1967) suggested that the pale transitional cells were the primitive undifferentiated compartment, consisting of completely uncommitted and possibly even pluripotent cells, while the basophilic transitionals were the committed cells which would become blast cells and so pass out of the transitional group. The larger transitionals have a high labelling index with thymidine, and the smaller transitional cells a much lower one.

Re-entry of small lymphocytes into the transitional compartment

One of the basic problems of the LT compartment is the possibility that small lymphocytes formed by the division of transitional cells might enlarge to become transitional cells once again. If this could happen, it would enormously increase the reserve of stem cells, a reserve which in normal marrow is very large indeed (Kubanek et al. 1968). Moffatt et al. (1967) left open the possibility of small lymphocyte re-entry.

There is of course no doubt that in cultures of blood lymphocytes the small lymphocytes enlarge and become blast cells only after passing through a transitional cell stage. This may readily be seen on examination with both the light microscope (Yoffey et al. 1965c) and electron microscope (Inman & Cooper 1963a, b; Tanaka et al. 1963; Firket 1969). But does this also hold good for marrow small lymphocytes? It is true that the PHA blast cells do not normally exhibit any sign of haemopoietic differentiation, though in the present state of our knowledge such a possibility should not be completely ruled out (see Saillen et al. 1969; Doklen et al. 1970; Grigoriu et al. 1971). Micklem (1966) and Scaro et al. (1971) observed an increase in colony-forming units (CFU) in the spleens of mice after administration of PHA. Scaro et al. (1971) further observed that after this PHA stimulation there was a marked increase in erythropoiesis—notably in the spleen—in response to erythropoietin. These observations invite the speculation that there may be two stages in erythropoietic stimulation, the first stage being a non-specific activation, as by PHA, and the second the more specific activation by erythropoietin. If there is any substance in this speculation, it would follow that attempts to treat conditions such as aplastic anaemia by PHA (Humble 1964; Astaldi et al. 1965) might conceivably meet with greater success if the initial non-specific effects of PHA were followed after 48–72 hours by more specific stimulation with erythropoietin.

From a histogenetic point of view, the essential point in all these PHA experiments is that this substance appears to act in the first instance only on the pachychromatic small lymphocyte (Yoffey & Courtice 1970), so that presumably CFU developing after the administration of erythropoietin must have been derived from small lymphocytes. Since the enlargement of small lymphocytes into blast cells necessitates a transitional stage, as already noted, this would be a further argument in favour of the re-entry of small lymphocytes into the transitional compartment.

Osmond & Yoshida (1971) have shown that at least some marrow lymphocytes can be transformed into proliferating blast-like cells in response to a variety of stimuli (cf. Yoshida & Osmond 1971a). But apart from such stimulation, some evidence also suggests that a small number of marrow lymphocytes regularly enter into DNA synthesis. Thus, Yoshida & Osmond (1971b) found 3.8% of marrow small lymphocytes labelled after exposure to thymidine for one hour, while Rosse (1971) found 1% labelled after one hour. An hour seems too short a time for labelled small lymphocytes to have formed from labelled precursors. Furthermore, the morphology of these small lymphocytes is not the same as that of the cells which label when the growth of small lymphocytes is stimulated in PHA cultures. In such cultures thymidine labelling does not become evident until 30 hours after the start of the culture, at which time the transforming cells for the most part have the structure of medium-sized transitional cells. The marrow small lymphocytes that label after one hour seem to be associated with a different labelling pattern altogether, and may conceivably represent a distinctive subgroup of small lymphocytes with haemopoietic potency. The CFU which appear after the administration of PHA (Micklem 1966; Scaro et al. 1971) do not become evident until after 48–72 hours.

Intrinsic proliferation of transitional cells

The stem cell scheme portrayed in Fig. 1, if correct, indicates a very flexible stem cell compartment which can be controlled in several ways. The first of these is concerned with the intrinsic proliferation of the compartment, when the smaller pale transitional cells enlarge and then divide when they have reached the appropriate size. This presumably can happen at different rates, so that if the need for stem cells is diminished a considerable proportion may go out of cycle for several days (Rosse 1970). On the other hand, when there is an increased need for stem cells the intrinsic proliferative cycle may accelerate.

At whatever rate intrinsic proliferation occurs, the effect if nothing else happened would be a progressive increase in the size of the compartment. But there are two major reasons why this does not happen. Some transitional cells, especially the larger ones, can develop basophilia and become blast cells, thus leaving the compartment. The administration of actinomycin, which blocks RNA synthesis and the development of basophilia, prevents this happening and results in the accumulation of large pale cells with leptochromatic nuclei (Hershko *et al.* 1969). Apart from an experimental block of this nature, the efflux of cells from the larger end of the transitional spectrum will vary with the changing stem cell requirements. If these are increased, more cells would leave the transitional compartment, which should therefore diminish unless its size is maintained by either increased intrinsic proliferation, or an augmented influx of cells, or both. If on the other hand stem cell requirements are diminished, fewer pale transitional cells would develop basophilia, so that if the rate of cell proliferation is unchanged, the compartment should increase. It can however also be controlled at the other end, consisting of the small transitional cells. These cells appear to have a two-way choice, as it were, and to be capable either of enlarging to give rise to large transitionals, or of dividing and giving rise to small lymphocytes. Rosse (1971) has observed both these processes *in vitro*. There are thus three basic points of control for the pale transitional cells: (1) their intrinsic proliferation, (2) the development of blast cells, and (3) the formation of small lymphocytes. To these may be added a fourth factor, the possible enlargement of at least some of the small lymphocytes and their re-entry into the transitional cell compartment. We do not know by what mechanisms these controls are exercised, nor do we know whether these mechanisms are interlinked or completely independent.

Before I discuss the experimental data which led to the formulation of the stem cell scheme presented in Fig. 1, one further point requires emphasis. Transitional cells of all sizes can be labelled with thymidine, but the larger cells of the transitional spectrum have a much higher labelling index than the smaller ones. A typical count in guinea-pig marrow on the seventh day of rebound (see p. 17) showed that one hour after thymidine administration, out of a total of 300 lymphocytes and transitional cells, 95 were pachychromatic small lymphocytes, none of which were labelled. The remaining 205 cells were transitional cells, grouped roughly as small, medium and large. Of the small transitional cells, six out of 80 were labelled; of the medium transitionals, 39 out of 86, and of the large transitionals, 30 out of 41. Thus, nearly 50% of the medium transitionals and 75% of the large transitionals were labelled with thymidine (Yoffey *et al.* 1968; cf. Osmond 1967). These labelling differences have an important bearing on efforts to correlate the results of the direct and the indirect studies.

Nomenclature

The term 'transitional' was originally applied to a series of cells intermediate between the small lymphocyte and the blast cell. In the intrinsic proliferative cycle there are also intermediate forms of a different nature, between the small and the large transitional cells. *Transitional*, therefore, is essentially a morphological term. Other terms have been suggested, e.g. *lymphoid*. But transitional cells are a group with properties (both proliferative and developmental) not possessed by lymphoid cells elsewhere, and the designation lymphoid may therefore prove somewhat misleading. 'Primitive' cell might have been a useful term, had it not been for the previous use of this designation by Cunningham *et al.* (1925) in which the 'primitive' cell was derived from a reticulum cell, and considered to be fundamentally different from the lymphocytic series. This point has been fully discussed elsewhere (Yoffey & Courtice 1970). There is no doubt that transitional cells have been seen by numerous observers, and given a variety of names, from the 'lymphoidocytes' of Pappenheim (1907), to the 'lymphocyte-like' cell of Burke & Harris (1959) and Harris (1961). The 'Q' cells of Davidson *et al.* (1943), the 'X' cells of Simar *et al.* (1968), and the 'candidate stem cell' of van Bekkum *et al.* (1971) are all undoubtedly members of the transitional group. On the whole, therefore, I have preferred to retain the term 'transitional'.

PERTURBATION OF THE STEADY STATE

(1) Quantitative studies of bone marrow in hypoxia and rebound

The first method employed for perturbing the steady state was to subject guinea pigs to hypoxia. Initially, experiments were performed at the Hochalpine Forschungsstation, Jungfraujoch, at an altitude of about 3350 m (11 000 ft) (Yoffey 1956, 1957). These experiments, though in some respects unsatisfactory, led to the conclusion that the augmentation of erythropoiesis involved feeding additional undifferentiated stem cells into the erythropoietic compartment, a conclusion subsequently confirmed by a number of investigators (e.g. Alpen & Cranmore 1959; Erslev 1959, 1964; Lajtha & Oliver 1960). But the experiments did not throw any light on the identity of the stem cells concerned.

Accordingly, more intense hypoxic stimulation was employed, namely a simulated altitude of about 4250 m (14 000 ft) in a decompression chamber (Moffatt *et al.* 1964*a*). This was followed by a study of marrow changes during rebound, i.e. the period of post-hypoxic polycythaemia, when erythropoiesis is markedly depressed (Moffat *et al.* 1964*b*). The term *rebound* was employed because the number of lymphocytes fell during hypoxia but rebounded to the normal level during the period of post-hypoxic polycythaemia. The use of the term was subsequently reinforced when it was observed that, at about 5200 m (17 000 ft), myeloid cells also fell during hypoxia, but rebounded during post-hypoxic polycythaemia to the normal level (Yoffey *et al.* 1968).

The working hypothesis behind these experiments was that after hypoxia had been intensified, so creating an even bigger demand for stem cells, examination of the marrow might indicate which cells were called upon to differentiate. Similarly, during rebound, when erythropoiesis was depressed, there might be an accumulation of stem cells which were no longer called upon to differentiate, and this accumulation too might be a further guide to the identity of the cells concerned. In fact, at 4250 m there was a fall in the marrow lymphocytes (including transitional cells) during hypoxia, and a rise during rebound, though in each case the change only just reached the conventional significance level. If the slight rise in lymphocytes and transitional cells during rebound really represented an accumulation of non-differentiating stem cells, such a marrow ought to be capable of a much more vigorous erythropoietic response if stimulated a second time by hypoxia. Accordingly, we investigated the marrow changes in what was termed 'secondary hypoxia', i.e. hypoxia applied to a marrow in rebound (Yoffey *et al.* 1965*b*) as opposed to what we now termed primary hypoxia, i.e. hypoxia applied to marrow in the normal steady state. The changes in secondary hypoxia gave two quite unexpected results. The erythropoietic response took appreciably longer to develop than in primary hypoxia. Furthermore, there was now a highly significant increase in both lymphocytes and transitional cells. Although there were only slight changes in the LT compartment in primary hypoxia at 4250 m, the striking increase in these cells in secondary hypoxia nonetheless indicated that some very definite alterations must have been taking place, so that there was a remarkable difference in response. The question is, why?

In an effort to answer this question, it was decided to intensify the hypoxia still further (Yoffey *et al.* 1968). Accordingly, animals were kept in hypoxia at a simulated altitude of 5200 m for seven days, at the end of which they were markedly polycythaemic. The polycythaemia persisted even after seven days of rebound, and in consequence the depression of erythropoiesis during rebound was even more pronounced than in the earlier studies at 4250 m. Some additional studies were carried out at 6100 m (20 000 ft) (Yoffey *et al.* 1967; Harris *et al.* 1966), but here the rebound changes were not investigated. Since the changes in rebound provide information of such great value, the following account will be devoted to the experiments on hypoxia at 5200 m, and the subsequent rebound.

Fig. 3 shows the changes in the three main cell groups of the marrow during

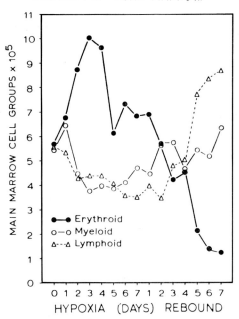

FIG. 3. Changes in the three major cell groups in the bone marrow of the guinea pig during 7 days of primary hypoxia at 5200 m, followed by 7 days of rebound. During primary hypoxia the nucleated erythroid cells rise to almost twice their control number, after which they level off somewhat. During rebound the nucleated erythroid cells fall to about one-fifth their control number, though they never completely disappear. The lymphocytes (including transitional cells) fall markedly below the control level during hypoxia, and then rise to about 50 % of this level during rebound. Rebound marrow is an excellent source of increased numbers of transitional cells. Modified slightly from Yoffey *et al.* (1968).

seven days of primary hypoxia at 5200 m followed by seven days of rebound. There is a highly significant fall in the number of marrow lymphocytes during hypoxia, and a striking increase during rebound. The lymphocyte fall in hypoxia only becomes evident on the second day, not during the first 24 hours. Fig. 4 shows that if one breaks down the lymphocytes into pachychromatic small lymphocytes and transitional cells, the fall in hypoxia affects only the small lymphocytes, while the transitional cells seem actually to be edging upwards. The fall in the marrow lymphocytes could obviously be interpreted as a stress response, but despite the fact that hypoxia is undoubtedly a source of stress, this interpretation was ruled out. Neither light microscopy nor electron microscopy provided any sign of lymphocyte damage, while in several other

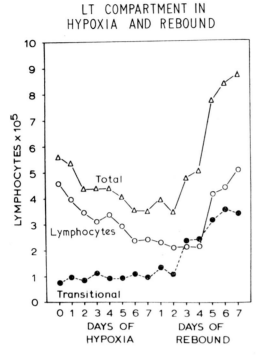

FIG. 4. Differential response of lymphocytes and transitional cells in guinea pig marrow during 7 days primary hypoxia at 5200 m, followed by 7 days of rebound. The pachychromatic small lymphocyte ('lymphocytes' in the figure) fall during primary hypoxia, but the transitional cells seem to be edging upwards. In rebound, on the other hand, both small lymphocytes and transitional cells undergo a highly significant increase. Note that the rise in the transitionals precedes that in the small lymphocytes. Modified slightly from Yoffey *et al.* (1968).

situations a severe fall in marrow lymphocytes could be observed when no question of stress was involved. Furthermore, in the 4250 m hypoxia experiments, the same degree of stress as was associated with a fall in marrow lymphocytes during primary hypoxia (Moffatt *et al.* 1964*a*) was associated with a striking rise during secondary hypoxia (Yoffey *et al.* 1965*c*).

But if stress can be ruled out, how else can the fall in lymphocytes be explained? One explanation is that a considerable number may be discharged from the marrow, while another is that some are being transformed into transitional cells, which then develop into blast cells. The apparently stable level of the transitional cells during hypoxia would thus represent a dynamic equilibrium. But there is also another possible source for the additional stem cells required, namely increased proliferation of transitional cells. If this is the correct explanation, then during rebound, when transitional cells are no longer transforming into proerythroblasts, they should rapidly increase in number, at least until such time as their proliferation can be checked. Such an increase does in fact occur (Fig. 4), reaching a peak on the sixth and seventh days of rebound, while after the fourth day of rebound the lymphocytes also rise rapidly. In terms of the stem cell scheme (Fig. 1), the transitional cells are increasing rapidly during the first three to four days of rebound, but the increase does not continue indefinitely, since from the fourth to seventh day many cells are dividing to give rise to small lymphocytes.

Thus by the seventh day of rebound the LT compartment has increased to more than 50% above its normal level and, if this rate of increase were to continue, the entire marrow would soon consist of lymphocytes and transitional cells. Things do not go quite so far. If rebound is continued for a few days longer, the lymphocytes continue to rise until they form about 70% of the total

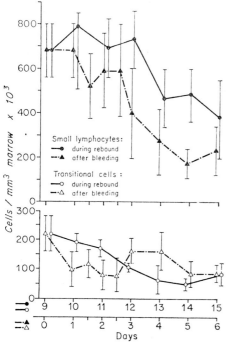

FIG. 5. Distribution of pachychromatic small lymphocytes and transitional cells in the bone marrow of guinea pigs from the 9th to 15th days of rebound, compared with similar animals bled on the 9th day of rebound. The fall in the small lymphocytes is more marked and occurs earlier in the bled than in the unbled animals, but the difference is of degree rather than of kind. The transitionals, on the other hand, differ markedly in the two groups. In rebound alone they steadily fall until day 14, but in the bled animals a sharper fall after the bleeding is followed by a significant rise on days 12 and 13, coinciding with the increase in the earlier erythroid cells. From Rosse et al. (1970).

nucleated cells of the marrow, while the transitional cells steadily fall. But from the ninth to twelfth day of rebound the lymphocytes also fall (Jones *et al.* 1967; Griffiths 1969; Rosse *et al.* 1970). From data of this nature we may conclude that the transitional cells can rapidly increase in numbers (Fig. 4) or diminish (Fig. 5). We do not know the mechanism responsible for either their increase or their decrease.

The data of Rosse *et al.* (1970) (Fig. 5) show the same general trend as those of Jones *et al.* (1967), with a slight difference in the time relationship. But they also bring out one further fact of interest. In animals bled on the ninth day of rebound, the fall in both lymphocytes and transitionals is accelerated for the first two days after bleeding, but on the third and fourth days the transitional cells show a significant increase, coinciding with a marked rise in the number of early erythroblasts.

The fall in the marrow lymphocytes during rebound is in large part, if not entirely, due to their discharge from the marrow, since it is in such cases that one finds well-marked lymphocyte loading, i.e. the accumulation of lymphocytes in increased numbers in the bone marrow sinusoids (Fig. 6) (Z. Ben-Ishay, D. Ben-Ishay & J. M. Yoffey, 1971, unpublished work). Blood withdrawal in addition to rebound can give rise to particularly heavy loading, which accords with the finding of Harris *et al.* (1966) that blood withdrawal is associated with some degree of lymphocytosis. It should be emphasized that the marked fall in marrow lymphocytes in the later stages of rebound cannot be attributed to stress. The animals at this time are in particularly good condition, eating well and gaining weight rapidly.

Whether in hypoxia or in rebound, the marrow response always seems to be associated with quantitative changes in the LT compartment. These changes are consistent with the view that the haemopoietic stem cells are to be found in the LT compartment, in which the immediate precursor of the proerythroblast seems to be the basophilic transitional cell. It is noteworthy that Hurst *et al.* (1969) found a correlation between the number of transitional cells in rebound marrow, and the number of stem cells in terms of CFU (cf. Okunewick & Fulton 1970). The data also indicate that the proliferating members of the LT compartment, the transitional cells, can undergo marked changes both in their proliferative capacity and in their total numbers.

(2) Ultrastructural studies of erythroblastic islets in hypoxia and rebound

The quantitative studies of the bone marrow during hypoxia and rebound demonstrate that the LT compartment undergoes marked changes which strong-

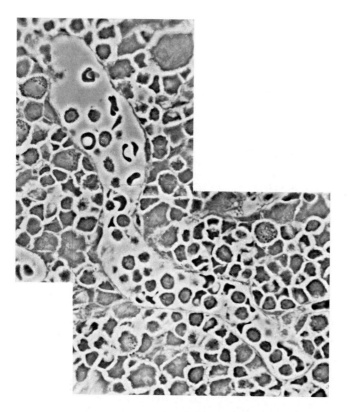

FIG. 6. Heavy lymphocyte loading of dilated marrow sinusoids in rats, 24 hours after bleeding on the 7th day of rebound, after 7 days of hypoxia at 5200 m. From Z. Ben-Ishay, D. Ben-Ishay and J. M. Yoffey (1971, unpublished). × 870.

ly suggest an association with erythropoiesis. Unfortunately, the technique used necessitates breaking up the marrow in order to obtain a suspension of free cells which can be counted. During this process the relation of cells to one another is completely lost, so that it is not possible to establish precisely where these cellular changes are in the marrow. In order to remedy this deficiency, the quantitative studies have recently been supplemented by ultrastructural studies of the erythroblastic islets. If it is true that increased erythropoiesis involves the feeding in of additional stem cells, the obvious place in which to look for these is the region where erythropoiesis occurs, namely the erythroblastic islets. These were studied in rats, in which the islets are easier to identify than in guinea pigs.

The erythroblastic islet in the normal steady state

In the normal steady state the erythroblastic islet consists of a more or less centrally placed phagocytic reticular cell, which contains a varying number of

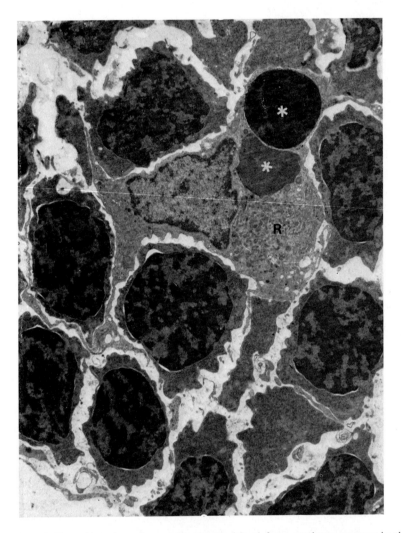

FIG. 7. Central portion of an erythroblastic island from rat bone marrow in the normal steady state. The phagocytic central reticular cell ('R') contains two large ingested bodies (*), the uppermost of which is the extruded nucleus of a mature red cell. In an active erythroblastic island the central reticular cell has characteristic long and slender processes which extend between the surrounding erythroblasts and come into close contact with them. From Ben-Ishay & Yoffey (1971*b*). × 5400.

inclusions and possesses numerous branching processes, extending between and coming into close contact with the surrounding erythroid cells. Though the islands are never absolutely uniform in structure, one usually finds that for a given functional state of the marrow one particular pattern tends to predominate.

In the normal steady state most of the erythroid cells are either basophilic erythroblasts or later stages; proerythroblasts are infrequent. Now and again a granulocyte seems to find its way into the island, while very occasionally a plasma cell may also be seen. But in most cases the island consists only of the central reticular cell and the surrounding nucleated erythroid cells (Fig. 7). Among the inclusions in the central reticular cell the extruded nuclei of mature red cells can be easily recognized before they have undergone digestion. Now and again the so-called 'central' reticular cell seems to be eccentric in position, and may even be found at the edge of an island.

The erythroblastic islet in hypoxia

When rats are subjected to 5200 m hypoxia, the earliest sign of change is seen at five hours, when mainly lymphocytes, but also occasional transitional cells, appear, both around the island and in its interior, between the erythroid cells and in the vicinity of the central reticular cell. Following the conventional use of Greek in bone marrow terminology, we term the LT cells at the periphery of the island 'perinesic', while those in its interior are 'endonesic' (*nesos*: island). In one animal examined after five hours, several cells with typical transitional structure were seen, perinesic in distribution. But at this early stage, as a rule, most of the cells which are in evidence are pachychromatic small lymphocytes. At 12 hours, appreciable numbers of both lymphocytes and smaller transitional cells may be seen. Fig. 8, from an animal after 12 hours of hypoxia, depicts the edge of an erythroblastic island, adjacent to which are four small lymphocytes and an early transitional cell. This transitional cell is typical of the early stages of lymphocyte transformation as seen in cultures, when the lymphocytes are passing from the inactive to the active phase. Many of the transitional cells at this stage contain almost exclusively monoribosomes in their cytoplasm, and these presumably correspond to the pale transitional cells of light microscopy. The varying proportions of monoribosomes and polyribosomes account no doubt for the differing degrees of basophilia in the transitional spectrum.

The presence of LT cells in and around the islands during hypoxia must be due to an actual influx, since the islands do not contain cells from which they could be derived. We do not know whether the influx is random, or whether some biotactic mechanism is at work. The appearance of the LT cells in the erythroblastic islets is short-lived. After 24 hours of hypoxia, both the small lymphocytes and the transitional cells have almost entirely disappeared and the characteristic feature of the islets at this stage is the relatively large number of proerythroblasts. As the proerythroblasts are among the largest cells in the

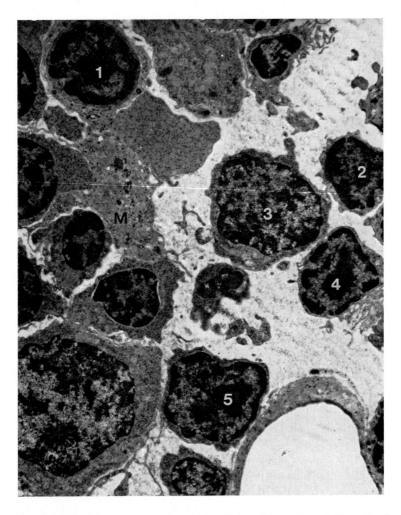

FIG. 8. From the bone marrow of a rat after 12 hours' hypoxia at 5200 m. The figure depicts the edge of an erythroid island, including part of the central reticular cell (M). Cells 1, 2, 4 and 5 are small lymphocytes, while cell 3 is a typical stage in early lymphocyte activation. The nucleus of cell 3 is somewhat more leptochromatic than that of the pachychromatic small lymphocyte, and the cell is slightly larger, due to commencing growth of both nucleus and cytoplasm. This cell is one of the smallest—and probably earliest—stages in the cell spectrum forming the transitional group. From Ben-Ishay & Yoffey (1971a). × 4400.

erythroid series, the islands now appear to be considerably bigger. The erythroid cells are more tightly packed, in close contact with one another and also with the processes of the central reticular cells. The enlargement of the islets seems to be even more marked by three days, when the proerythroblasts are being replaced by increasing numbers of basophilic erythroblasts and later erythroid stages. From four to seven days, it is mainly the more mature erythroblasts, poly-chromatic and orthochromatic, which dominate the picture (Ben-Ishay & Yoffey 1971a).

One negative finding needs to be emphasized. After the first 24 hours, when the erythropoietic response is well under way, lymphocytes and transitional cells are hardly ever seen. In comparison to the first 12–24 hours they are conspicuous by their absence.

Erythroblastic islands in rebound

For the first few days of rebound, the position does not seem to undergo any very striking change, since some erythropoiesis is still in progress, though on a steadily diminishing scale (Turner et al. 1967; Yoffey et al. 1968). But by the fifth day of rebound erythropoiesis has been depressed long enough for most of the nucleated red cells to have disappeared, although they never disappear completely from all the islands however long rebound continues. Between the fifth and eighth days of rebound, an increasing number of islets are seen at the end of a wave of erythropoiesis, and they contain few or no erythroid cells. Such islands then consist of a shrunken central reticular cell, with its processes progressively retracting, and surrounded to an increasing extent by lymphocytes and transitional cells (Fig. 9) (Ben-Ishay & Yoffey 1971b). When a new wave of erythropoiesis begins, the first cells to show any erythroid development are large transitional cells (Fig. 10).

The role of the central reticular cell

The central reticular cell is undoubtedly actively phagocytic and, apart from its scavenger role in ingesting extruded nuclei, which so prevents the erythro-blastic islands from being cluttered up with masses of such nuclei, it seems to ingest quite readily inert particles such as India ink (Hudson & Yoffey 1963). The close contact of its long and slender processes with the developing erythroid cells, and also with many of the perinesic and endonesic LT cells, raises the question of other possible functions, e.g. the transfer of ferritin or of some form

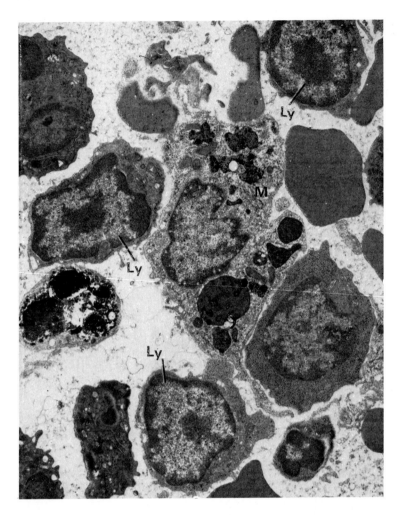

FIG. 9. Bone marrow of rat on day 8 of rebound after 7 days of hypoxia at 5200 m. A typical depleted erythroblastic island, containing a central reticular cell (M) with numerous inclusions. There are also three small lymphocytes (Ly) and an early erythroblast (E). The processes of the central reticular cell have for the most part disappeared. From Ben-Ishay & Yoffey (1971b). × 5800.

of information which might influence the development of neighbouring cells. The transfer of material has been suggested (Policard & Bessis 1958), disputed (Berman 1967) or left open (Weiss 1965). But apart from this, the general biological properties of the central reticular cell are poorly understood. Is it a specific type of macrophage, or can any macrophage function in this capacity?

Mitosis in these cells must be very infrequent, yet presumably they must need replacement sooner or later.

The erythropoietic cycle

The changes in erythroblastic islands in hypoxia and rebound demonstrate an erythropoietic cycle which reaches its peak after a few days of hypoxia, and then fades away during rebound. However, in the normal steady state depleted islands are virtually never seen. It must be assumed, therefore, that before one erythropoietic cycle is completed, additional stem cells begin to differentiate and a new cycle commences. The developmental pattern suggested by Matoth (1968) in the spleen does not seem to occur in bone marrow on hypoxic stimulation, though it is not possible to rule it out entirely in the normal steady state.

The role of the perinesic and endonesic LT cells

As far as the stem cell problem is concerned, the only non-erythroid cells which appear in the erythroid islands when erythropoiesis is stimulated are lymphocytes and transitional cells. Presumably, then, the stem cells must be sought among these. But many new questions arise. Do they all function as stem cells? Can any of the small lymphocytes rapidly enlarge in this situation, or is it only cells entering as transitional cells which can function as stem cells? Is the influx of LT cells purely random, or is it a specialized group of cells, actuated by some biotactic mechanism, which is here involved? What happens to the cells which enter the island, and then move out? Are they conditioned in some way? These and many other questions we are not yet able to answer. But, whatever the ultimate role of the perinesic and endonesic small lymphocytes may be, the immediate precursor of the proerythroblast seems to be the large basophilic transitional cell.

SUBLETHAL IRRADIATION

A number of studies have been made of the effects of sublethal irradiation. The most comprehensive direct studies of bone marrow are those of P. F. Harris and his associates, beginning with a preliminary communication by Harris (1956). In guinea pigs given whole-body irradiation (150 R) the nucleated erythroid and LT cells fall to very low levels during the first two days. Lymphocyte regeneration begins to be evident by the fourth day and continues until the 16th day, by which time the LT cells are more than 50% above their control level, only to fall abruptly from 16–20 days (Harris 1960). This fall is at a time when intense erythropoietic regeneration is quickly followed by a tremendous spurt of granulopoiesis. This sequence of events would fit in well with a stem cell role for the LT cells. It is interesting to note that a transitional cell peak immediately precedes the appearance of blast cells (Harris 1956; Harris *et al.* 1963). The increase in transitional cells before the new crop of blast cells was also noted in rats after sublethal irradiation by Hulse (1963)—who refers to them as 'atypical mononuclear cells'—and by Blackett *et al.* (1964). In dogs given the radiomimetic nitrogen mustard, Thomas *et al.* (1965) found that the first indication of haemopoietic recovery was the appearance of small lymphoid cells, followed 24 hours later by blast cells. Presumably some of the 'small lymphoid cells' seen at the outset were transitional cells, or else a transitional stage intervened later between the small lymphocytes and the blast cells. Transitional cells are found in the marrow of the dog (Keiser *et al.* 1967).

As in other experimental situations in which there is a sharp fall in marrow LT cells, the problem arises of whether this may in part be due to cells leaving the marrow. This possibility is supported by the observation of Lajtha *et al.* (1969) that 12–24 days after total body irradiation in mice more stem cells migrate from bone marrow to spleen, as measured by the overshoot in spleen colony formation.

Lajtha *et al.* (1964), using the erythropoietin response as their criterion (in mice), observed in the marrow a stem cell overshoot with the same kind of time relationship as the LT overshoot in guinea pigs (Harris 1956). The fact that these two overshoots coincide does not of course constitute proof that any of the LT cells are stem cells. However, there are additional lines of evidence favouring this interpretation. If the LT cells are stem cells, even in part, then marrow which contains them in increased numbers should protect very effectively against lethal irradiation. This was found to be the case by Harris & Kugler (1963, 1967), who used for protection guinea-pig marrow 13 days after 150 R whole-body irradiation, at which time the marrow contained about 75% of LT cells, of which 15% were transitional cells. Morrison & Toepfer (1967) obtained a concentrated suspension of LT cells from normal rat marrow by gradient centrifugation and this too protected effectively against lethal irradiation. Osmond & Yoshida (1970) used sucrose-serum density gradients to obtain a slowly sedimenting lymphocyte-rich fraction, which seemed to be responsible for haemopoietic regeneration.

A similar conclusion seems to emerge from an analysis of the composition of marrow used for repeated transplantation. Cudkowicz *et al.* (1964), working with mice, noted that after primary marrow transplantation the proliferative and protective capacity of the marrow falls markedly but is restored after 30 days or more. This restoration coincides with the reappearance in the marrow of normal numbers of 'lymphocyte-like' cells, which, from their morphology and labelling properties, were evidently transitional cells. This also seems to be the only group of cells capable of meeting the experimental requirements for proliferation.

On the whole, then, the irradiation studies all seem to point to a stem cell role for the LT compartment. The accumulation of LT cells before haemopoietic regeneration, the high protective efficiency of these cells when given to lethally irradiated animals, and the association of the LT overshoot with that in erythro-poietic stem cells, are all consistent with such a role. But whether all these LT cells are stem cells, or whether only a specific subpopulation functions in this manner must be left open for the time being.

COLONY FORMATION

In recent years much attention has been devoted to the study of haemopoiesis in colonies, both *in vivo* and *in vitro*. The general problems of colony formation have recently been reviewed (McCulloch 1970; Lajtha 1970; Metcalf & Bradley 1970; Sachs 1970), so I shall only deal here with some aspects relevant to stem cell identification.

Following the early observations of Till & McCulloch (1961), Becker *et al.* (1965) noted that colony-forming cells could exist in two forms, one proliferat-ing, as indicated by DNA synthesis, and the other not. With increased stem cell requirements, the proportion of cells in synthesis could rise from less than 10% to 65%. This order of proliferative variation is well exemplified by the LT com-partment (see Fig. 4). As already noted, the non-synthetic stage could be repre-sented by small transitional cells, most of which do not label. However, if one accepts that CFU can be increased by PHA (Micklem 1966; Scaro *et al.* 1971), then the small lymphocyte—or at least some small lymphocytes—could also be members of the non-synthetic group, since as far as is known the action of PHA is primarily on the pachychromatic small lymphocyte (for literature see Yoffey & Courtice 1970). Lajtha *et al.* (1969) have shown that the distinction between the proliferating and the non-proliferating stages of the colony-forming cells can be made by applying the so-called 'thymidine suicide' test *in vivo*.

Turner *et al.* (1967) described in murine marrow an increased number of lymphocytes and transitional cells in rebound, after which Hurst *et al.* (1969) found that this increase in transitional cells paralleled an increase in the number of CFU. Murphy *et al.* (1971), evidently unaware of this earlier work, arrived independently at a similar conclusion, and then proceeded to inject the enriched suspension of transitional cells into the exteriorized spleen of lethally irradiated mice. As might be expected from the studies of Hurst *et al.* (1969), the injected cells formed colonies and conferred protection. Robinson *et al.* (1967), using an *in vitro* colony-forming system, found that with increasing doses of whole-body radiation the number of marrow cells capable of colony formation progressively decreased. This seemed to suggest that the *in vitro* colony-forming cells are members of the small lymphocyte population. However, the transitional cells are also highly radiosensitive, probably even more so than the small lymphocytes. More recently, Moore *et al.* (1972) have expressed the view that the *in vitro* colony-forming cells are in fact transitional cells.

Wu *et al.* (1968) postulated a relationship between colony-forming units and cells in the thymus and lymph nodes, but were not sure whether CFU gave rise to lymphoid cells, or whether both were derived from a common unidentified precursor. Niewisch *et al.* (1967) fractionated the cells from spleen colonies and concluded that the stem cell was a large cell with a leptochromatic nucleus and intensely basophilic cytoplasm. The intensity of the basophilia, however, makes it necessary to consider the possibility that these cells are early blast cells. Orlic *et al.* (1968) studied the changes in splenic erythropoiesis after administering erythropoietin and tritiated thymidine to polycythaemic mice. Within an hour they observed thymidine labelling of cells with the general configuration of transitional cells. More recently, van Bekkum *et al.* (1971) devised a technique for enriching the CFU content of mouse bone marrow by a factor of up to 30. They were then able to identify a 'candidate stem cell' whose ultrastructure (see van Bekkum *et al.* 1971, Fig. 3, p. 554) is almost identical with that of a medium transitional cell (see this volume, p. 67).

STEM CELL MIGRATION

The pioneer studies of Jacobson *et al.* (1949) first drew attention to the migration of stem cells to and from the spleen. The use of chromosome markers (Ford *et al.* 1956) made it possible to identify with considerable precision the fate of transfused stem cells and there is copious literature about this (Barnes & Loutit 1967a, b). Of the many problems involved, I propose to deal very briefly with two. What is the identity of the migrating stem cells? At what rate does migration occur?

Hanks (1964) investigated the outflow of CFU from a shielded thigh in animals given whole-body irradiation (900 R) and concluded that there was a uniform continuous release of CFU from the marrow. Lajtha *et al.* (1969) on the other hand, emphasized that the seeding of CFU from the marrow could undergo marked variation. In either case, the question arises whether in the normal steady state, when one is dealing with marrow not depleted by irradiation, migration of CFU occurs to the same extent. Micklem *et al.* (1968) transfused marrow cells from normal male CBA-T6T6 mice into normal male CBA recipients. They found some donor cells in bone marrow and spleen, but it is difficult to know whether they injected more stem cells than would normally be entering the bloodstream. The experiments of Harris *et al.* (1964) with parabiotic rats seem to be free from this objection. It is interesting therefore that although there was only a limited uptake of cells by the marrow, the splenic migration stream was considerably larger. These experiments confirmed the earlier findings of Ford *et al.* (1966) that far fewer cells are taken up by normal than by irradiated marrow. The conclusion of Ford *et al.* (1966) was that circulating stem cells do not normally settle out and proliferate in the marrow to any great extent, and the recent studies of Tyler & Everett (1972) seem to be in agreement with this. This of course still leaves open the possibility that the marrow may be constantly discharging a varying surplus of stem cells whose subsequent fate is largely unknown, though in the mouse they may in part be taken up by the spleen.

According to Hodgson *et al.* (1968) stem cells disappear from the blood with great rapidity, and have a half-life in the blood of six minutes. However, the number in the blood is small. Barnes & Loutit (1967a, b) give figures of the order of 50 000 CFU in the marrow, 1000 in the spleen and 20 in the blood of the normal adult mouse. It is not known to what extent CFU may recirculate. These data are based on the normal steady state. If however haemopoiesis is strongly stimulated, the number of stem cells in the marrow may rapidly increase, and presumably the outflow from the marrow may increase also. Thus increased numbers of stem cells may be found in the blood during the intense proliferative changes associated with the period of marrow regeneration after sublethal irradiation (Lord 1967) or in phenylhydrazine anaemia (Hodgson *et al.* 1968). Harris & Kugler (1971) have made a careful study of the unusual mononuclear cells appearing in the blood of guinea pigs during phenylhydrazine anaemia. Of these mononuclear cells 39% were transitional cells, 37% blast cells, and about 25% large cells with the features of early monocytes or monoblasts. These latter recall the 'monocytoid' cells of Tyler & Everett (1966). From the later studies of Everett & Tyler (1968) it would appear that some of the monocytoid cells could equally well be described as 'lymphocytoid', while others could well be transitional cells. At the same time it must be admitted that one occasionally sees in either blood or marrow non-granular cells with horseshoe-shaped nuclei which label heavily with thymidine. The origin and life history of these cells require further investigation.

PLURIPOTENT STEM CELLS

Pluripotentiality in the haematological sense, i.e. the derivation of various blood cells from a common ancestral cell, has been postulated since the early days of haematology. The introduction of chromosome marking (Ford *et al.* 1956; Barnes *et al.* 1959) made it possible to demonstrate that stem cells of this type existed. The existence of a common stem cell raises the question of *stem cell competition*. If there is an unusually strong stimulus for the formation of a particular group of cells, many more stem cells will be stimulated to differentiate in that direction, and the development of other cell lines will diminish. Thus, for example, increased erythropoietic stimulation is associated with diminished granulopoiesis (Harris *et al.* 1966; Yoffey *et al.* 1967; Yoffey *et al.* 1968; Rosse *et al.* 1970). Rickard *et al.* (1971) have independently described this phenomenon.

Severe stimulation of granulopoiesis causes an increase in myeloblasts and a marked fall in proerythroblasts (Yoffey *et al.* 1964). Under the experimental conditions in question, the proerythroblasts were returning towards normal levels by 48 hours. But it is possible that sustained stimulation of granulo-poiesis in chronic infections may be responsible for the development of anaemia through long-continued diversion of stem cells from erythropoiesis to granu-lopoiesis.

The evidence for a common haemopoietic stem cell seems fairly definite. Is there an even more primitive cell, an immuno-haemopoietic stem cell, which can be diverted either into haemopoiesis or into immune reactions? A full discussion of this intriguing problem is beyond the scope of this paper. It is not clear why antigenic substances, such as pertussis vaccine, should result in an increase in circulating CFU (Barnes & Loutit 1967a). One of the effects of *Bordetella pertussis* is to cause a massive discharge of lymphocytes and transi-tional cells from the marrow (Morse & Riester 1967). Hanna *et al.* (1967) observed in irradiated animals an increase in CFU (with increased survival rate) after treatment with a macroglobulin fraction of *Salmonella typhimurium* endotoxin. It is particularly interesting in this connection to note that the slowly sedimenting lymphocyte-rich fraction of marrow, obtained by centrifugation in sucrose–serum density gradients, contains not only the haemopoietically protective cells of the marrow, as already noted (Osmond & Yoshida 1970), but also the cells capable of mounting a blastogenic response to allogeneic lymphoid cells *in vitro*. It remains to be established whether these lymphocyte-rich fractions (of which about 20% are transitional cells) react in this way because they contain different cell strains, or whether one and the same cell is capable of responding either haemopoietically or immunologically, depending on the nature of the stimulus which reaches it.

STEM CELL POSTULATES

From the various experimental data which have accumulated a number of stem cell postulates appear to emerge, among which one may note the following:

(1) Stem cells must either be present in appreciable numbers, or be capable of rapid proliferation, or both, so that when there are heavy demands for them exhaustion will not ensue.

(2) Stem cells exist in two forms, proliferating and non-proliferating.

(3) Within the stem cell compartment, the proportion of proliferating to non-proliferating cells can vary, depending upon stem cell requirements.

(4) Stem cells must be capable of remaining in a dormant state for lengthy periods.

(5) Stem cells must be capable of mobilization and migration into or out of haemopoietic tissues. The rate at which stem cells can be mobilized and caused to migrate must be capable of variation, depending on the functional requirements of the haemopoietic tissues.

(6) The identification of stem cells is aided by searching for them in haemopoietic tissues at a time when stem cell requirements are known to be increased, and new stem cells may be expected to appear (stem cell phanerosis).

The lymphocyte–transitional cell compartment appears to meet all these requirements, including that of stem cell phanerosis.

ACKNOWLEDGEMENTS

It is a pleasure to thank Mrs Eva Salomon for the preparation of the stem cell scheme (Fig. 1), and the montage (Fig. 6). Thanks are also due to the Leverhulme Foundation, as this paper was written during the tenure of a Leverhulme Emeritus Fellowship.

References

ALPEN, E. L. & CRANMORE, D. (1959) Observations on the regulation of erythropoiesis and on cellular dynamics by Fe⁵⁹ autoradiography. In *The Kinetics of Cellular Proliferation* (Stohlman F., ed.), Grune & Stratton, New York

ASTALDI, G., AIRO, A., SAULI, S. & COSIA, G. (1965) Phytohaemagglutinin in treatment of aplastic anaemia. *Lancet* 1, 1070–1071

BARNES, D. W. H. & LOUTIT, J. F. (1967a) Haematopoietic stem cells in the peripheral blood. *Lancet* 2, 1138–1141

BARNES, D. W. H. & LOUTIT, J. F. (1967b) Migration streams of haematopoietic stem cells. *Haematol. Lat.* 10, 1–11

BARNES, D. H. W., FORD, C. E., GRAY, S. M. & LOUTIT, J. F. (1959) Spontaneous and induced changes in cell populations in heavily irradiated mice. *Prog. Nucl. Energy Ser. VI*, 2, 1–10

BECKER, J. E., MCCULLOCH, E. A., SIMINOVITCH, L. & TILL, J. E. (1965) The effect of differing demands for blood cell production on DNA synthesis by hemopoietic colony-forming stem cells of mice. *Blood J. Hematol.* 26, 296–308

BEN–ISHAY, Z. & YOFFEY, J. M. (1971a) Erythropoietic islands in rat bone marrow in different functional states. I. Changes in primary hypoxia. *Isr. J. Med. Sci.* 7, 948–962

BEN–ISHAY Z. & YOFFEY, J. M. (1971b) Reticular cells of erythroid islands of rat bone marrow in hypoxia and rebound. *J. Reticuloendothel. Soc.* 10, 482–500

BEN–ISHAY, Z. & YOFFEY, J. M. (1972) Ultrastructural studies of erythroblastic islands of rat bone marrow. II. The resumption of erythropoiesis in erythropoietically depressed rebound marrow. *Lab. Invest.* 26, 637–647

BERMAN, I. (1967) The ultrastructure of erythroblastic islands and reticular cells in mouse bone marrow. *J. Ultrastruct. Res.* 17, 291–313

BLACKETT, N. M., ROYLANCE, P. J. & ADAMS, K. (1964) Studies on the capacity of bone marrow cells to restore erythropoiesis in heavily irradiated rats. *Br. J. Haematol.* 10, 453–467

BRADLEY, T. R. & METCALF, D. (1966) The growth of mouse bone marrow cells in vitro. *Aust. J. Exp. Biol. Med. Sci.* 44, 287–300

BURKE, W. T. & HARRIS, C. (1959) Total cell counts of the bone marrow of normal albino rats from one to fifty weeks of age. *Blood J. Hematol.* 18, 691–701

CAFFREY, R. W., EVERETT, N. B. & RIEKE, W. O. (1966) Radio-autographic studies of reticular and blast cells in the hemopoietic tissue of the rat. *Anat. Rec.* 155, 41–55

CUDKOWICZ, G., UPTON, A. C., SMITH, L. H., GOSSLEE, D. G. & HUGHES, W. L. (1964) An approach to the characterization of stem cells in mouse bone marrow. *Ann. N.Y. Acad. Sci.* 144, 571–582

CUNNINGHAM, R. S., SABIN, F. R. & DOAN, C. A. (1925) The development of leucocytes, lymphocytes and monocytes from a specific stem cell in adult tissues. *Contrib. Embryol.* 16, 227–276

DAVIDSON, L. S. P., DAVIS, L. J. & INNES, J. (1943) Studies in refractory anaemia. I. The technique and interpretation of sternal puncture biopsies. Classification. *Edinb. Med. J.* 50, 226–236

DOKLEN, A., VARTERESZ, V. & VARGA, L. (1970) Effect of haematopoietic humoral factors on PHA-transformed leucocytes. I. Haem-synthesis in PHA-stimulated lymphocyte cultures. Role of factors controlling erythropoiesis. *Haematologia* 4, 203–211

ERSLEV, A. J. (1959) Effect of anemic anoxia on nucleated red cells. *Blood J. Hematol.* 14, 386–398

ERSLEV A. J. (1964) Erythropoietin in vitro. II. Effect on 'stem cells'. *Blood J. Hematol.* 24, 331–342

EVERETT, N. B. & CAFFREY, R. W. (1967) Radioautographic studies of bone marrow small lymphocytes. In *The Lymphocyte in Immunology and Haemopoiesis* (Yoffey, J. M., ed.), pp. 108–119, Arnold, London

EVERETT, N. B. & TYLER, R. W. (1968) Studies on lymphocytes: Relationship to mononuclear cells of inflammatory exudates. *Biochem. Pharmacol.*, Suppl., 185–196

EVERETT, N. B., RIEKE, W. O., REINHARDT, W. O. & YOFFEY, J. M. (1960) Radioisotopes in the study of blood cell formation with special reference to lymphocytopoiesis. In *Haemopoiesis: Cell Production and its Regulation (Ciba Found. Symp.)*, pp. 43–66, Churchill, London

FIRKET, H. (1969) L'évolution de l'ultrastructure du lymphocyte humaine en culture sous l'influence de la phytohémagglutinine. Comparaison avec le lymphocyte en culture mixte. *Nouv. Rev. Fr. Hématol.* **9**, 159–176

FLIEDNER, T. M., HAAS, R. J., STEHLE, H. & ADAMS, A. (1968) Complete labelling of all cell nuclei in newborn rats with H³-thymidine. *Lab. Invest.* **18**, 249–258

FORD, C. E., HAMERTON, J. L., BARNES, D. W. H. & LOUTIT, J. F. (1956) Cytological identification of radiation chimaeras. *Nature (Lond.)* **177**, 452–454

FORD, C. E., MICKLEM, H. S., EVANS, E. P., GRAY, J. G. & OGDEN, D. A. (1966) The inflow of bone marrow cells to the thymus: studies with part-body irradiated mice injected with chromosome-marked bone marrow and subjected to antigenic stimulation. *Ann. N.Y. Acad. Sci.* **129**, 283–296

FRUHMAN, G. J. (1970) Splenic erythropoiesis. In *Regulation of Hematopoiesis* (Gordon, A. S., ed.), vol, 1, pp. 339–368, Appleton-Century-Crofts, New York

GRIFFITHS, D. A. (1969) Radioautographic studies of the lymphocytic bone marrow. *Blood J. Hematol.* **34**, 696–700

GRIGORIU, G., ANTONESCU, M. & IERCAN, E. (1971) Evidence for a circulating stem cell. Newly formed erythroblasts found in autologous leukocyte-filled diffusion chambers inserted into bled rabbits. *Blood J. Hematol.* **37**, 187–195

HANKS, G. E. (1964) In vivo migration of colony-forming units from shielded bone marrow in the irradiated mouse. *Nature (Lond.)* **203**, 1393–1395

HANNA, M. G., JR., NETTESHEIM, P., FISHER, W. D., PETERS, L. C. & FRANCIS, M. W. (1967) Serum alpha-globulin fraction: Survival and recovery effect in irradiated mice. *Science (Wash. D.C.)*. **157**, 1458–1461

HARRIS, C. (1961) The lymphocyte-like cell in the marrow of rats. *Blood J. Hematol.* **18**, 691–670

HARRIS, J. E., FORD, C. E., BARNES, D. W. H. & EVANS, E. P. (1964) Evidence from parabiosis for an afferent stream of cells. *Nature (Lond.)* **201**, 886–887

HARRIS, P. F. (1956) Quantitative examination of bone marrow in guinea pigs after gamma irradiation. *Br. Med. J.* **2**, 1032–1034

HARRIS, P. F. (1960) A comparison of cell depletion in irradiated guinea pig bone marrow studied by a quantitative technique. *Acta Haematol. (Basel)* **23**, 293–305

HARRIS, P. F. & KUGLER, J. H. (1963) The use of regenerating bone marrow to protect guinea pigs against lethal irradiation. *Acta Haematol. (Basel)* **32**, 146–167

HARRIS, P. F. & KUGLER, J. H. (1967) Transfusion of regenerating bone marrow into irradiated guinea pigs. In *The Lymphocyte in Immunology and Haemopoiesis* (Yoffey, J. M., ed.), pp. 133–148, Arnold, London

HARRIS, P. F. & KUGLER, J. H. (1971) Unusual mononuclear cells in guinea pig peripheral blood during anaemia. *J. Anat.* **108**, 1–12

HARRIS, P. F., HAIGH, G. & KUGLER, J. H. (1963) Quantitative studies of mitoses and DNA-synthesizing cells in bone marrow and blood of guinea pigs recovering from sublethal whole-body gamma irradiation. *Br. J. Haematol.* **9**, 38 5–405

HARRIS, P. F., HARRIS, R. S. & KUGLER, J. H. (1966) Studies of the leucocyte compartment of guinea pig bone marrow after acute haemorrhage and severe hypoxia. Evidence for a common stem cell. *Br. J. Haematol.* **12**, 419–432

HELLMAN, S. & GRATE, H. E. (1967) Production of granulocytic progeny by transplanted bone marrow in irradiated mice. *Blood J. Hematol.* **30**, 103–111

HERSHKO, G., SCHWARTZ, R. & IZAK, G. (1969) Morphological-biochemical correlations in

rabbit red cell precursors synchronized by actinomycin administration. *Br. J. Haematol.*
17, 569–579

HODGSON, G., GUZMAN, E. & HERRERA, C. (1968) Characterization of the stem-cell population
of phenylhydrazine-treated rodents. In *Symposium on the Effects of Radiation on Cellular
Proliferation and Differentiation*, pp. 163–170, International Atomic Energy Agency,
Vienna

HUDSON, G. & YOFFEY, J. M. (1963) Reticulo-endothelial cells in the bone marrow of the
guinea pig. *J. Anat.* **97**, 409–416

HUDSON, G. & YOFFEY, J. M. (1966) The passage of lymphocytes through the sinusoidal
endothelium of guinea pig bone marrow. *Proc. R. Soc. Lond. B. Biol. Sci.* **165**, 486–496

HUDSON, G., HERDAN, G. & YOFFEY, J. M. (1952) Effect of repeated injections of ACTH upon
the bone marrow. *Br. Med. J.* **1**, 999–1002

HUHN, D. (1966) Die Feinstruktur des Knochenmarks der Ratte bei Anwendung neuerer
Aldehydfixation. *Blut Z. Gesamte Blutforsch.* **13**, 291–304

HULSE, E. V. (1963) Lymphocytic recovery after irradiation and its relation to other aspects of
haemopoiesis. *Br. J. Haematol*, **9**, 376–384.

HUMBLE, J. G. (1964) The treatment of aplastic anaemia with phytohaemagglutinin. *Lancet* **1**,
1345–1349

HURST, J. M., TURNER, M. S., YOFFEY, J. M. & LAJTHA, L. G. (1969) Initial investigation of
the changes in the stem-cell compartment of murine bone marrow during post-hypoxic
polycythaemia. *Blood J. Hematol.* **33**, 859–864

INMAN, D. R. & COOPER E. H. (1963*a*) Electron microscopy of human lymphocytes stimulated
by phytohaemagglutinin. *J. Cell Biol.* **19**, 441–445

INMAN, D. R. & COOPER E. H. (1963*b*) The relation of ultrastructure to DNA synthesis in
human leucocytes. *Acta Haematol. (Basel)* **33**, 257–278

JACOBSON, L. O., MARKES, E. K., GASTON, E. O., ROBSON, M. & ZIRKLE R. E. (1949) The role
of the spleen in radiation injury. *Proc. Soc. Exp. Biol. Med.* **70**, 740–742

JONES, H. B., JONES, J. J. & YOFFEY, J. M. (1967) Studies on hypoxia. VII. Changes in lymphocytes and transitional cells in the bone marrow during prolonged rebound. *Br. J. Haematol.*
13, 934–941

KEISER, G., COTTIER, H., BRYANT, B. J. & BOND, V. P. (1967) Origin and fate of bone marrow
lymphoid cells of dog. In *The Lymphocyte in Immunology and Haemopoiesis* (Yoffey,
J. M., ed.) pp. 149–159, Arnold, London,

KNOSPE, W. H., GREGORY, S. A., HUSSEINI, S. G., FRIED, W. & TROBAUGH, F. E., JR. (1972)
Origin and recovery of colony-forming units in locally curretted bone marrow of mice.
Blood J. Hematol. **39**, 331–340

KUBANEK, B., TYLER, W. S., FERRARI, L., PROCELLINI, A., HOWARD, D. & STOHLMAN, F., JR.
(1968) Regulation of erythropoiesis. XXI. The effect of erythropoietin on the stem cell.
Proc. Soc. Exp. Biol. Med. **127**, 770–776

LAJTHA, L. G. (1970) Stem cell kinetics. In *Regulation of Hematopoiesis* (Gordon, A. S., ed.),
vol. 1, pp. 111–131, Appleton-Century-Crofts, New York

LAJTHA, L. G. & OLIVER, R. (1960) Studies on the kinetics of erythropoiesis: A model of the
erythron. In *Haemopoiesis: Cell Production and its Regulation (Ciba Found. Symp.)*, pp.
289–314, Churchill, London

LAJTHA, L. G., GILBERT, C. W., PORTEOUS, D. D. & ALEXANIAN, R. (1964) Kinetics of a bone
marrow stem cell population. *Ann. N. Y. Acad. Sci.* **133**, 742–752

LAJTHA, L. G., POZZI, L. V., SCHOFIELD, R. & FOX, M. (1969) Kinetic properties of haemopoietic stem cells. *Cell Tissue Kinet.* **2**, 39–49

LORD, B. I. (1967) Improved erythropoietic recovery in lethally irradiated mice after transfusion
of buffy coat cells from the blood of partially shielded, heavily irradiated donors. *Nature
(Lond.)* **214**, 924–925

LOUTIT, J. F. (1967) Grafts of haemopoietic tissue: the nature of haemopoietic stem cells.
J. Clin. Pathol. (Lond.) **20**, 535–539

McCulloch, E. A. (1970) Control of hematopoiesis at the cellular level. In *Regulation of Hematopoiesis* (Gordon, A. S., ed.), vol. 1, pp. 132–158, Appleton-Century-Crofts, New York

Matoth, Y. (1968) Studies in mitotic activity in vitro and kinetics of proliferation of erythroid cells from splenic colonies in irradiated marrow-transfused mice. *Ann. N.Y. Acad. Sci.* **149**, 445–448

Metcalf, D. & Bradley, T. R. (1970) Factors regulating in vitro colony formation by hematopoietic cells. In *Regulation of Hematopoiesis* (Gordon, A. S., ed.) vol. 1, pp. 185–216, Appleton-Century-Crofts, New York.

Micklem, H. S. (1966) Effect of phytohemagglutinin-M (PHA) on the spleen-colony-forming capacity of mouse lymph node and blood cells. *Transplantation* **4**, 732–741

Micklem, H. S., Clarke, C. M., Evans, E. P. & Ford, C. E. (1968) Fate of chromosome-marked mouse bone marrow cells transfused into normal syngeneic recipients. *Transplantation* **6**, 299–302

Moffatt, D. J., Rosse, C., Sutherland, I. H. & Yoffey, J. M. (1964a) Studies on hypoxia. I. The response of the bone marrow to primary hypoxia. *Acta Anat.* **59**, 23–36

Moffatt, D. J., Rosse, C., Sutherland, I. H. & Yoffey, J. M. (1964b) Studies on hypoxia, II. A quantitative study of changes in the bone marrow of the guinea pig during post-hypoxic polycythaemia (rebound). *Acta Anat.* **59**, 188–197

Moffatt, D. J., Rosse, C. & Yoffey, J. M. (1967) Identity of the haemopoietic stem cell. *Lancet* **2**, 547–548

Moore, M. A. S., Williams, N. & Metcalf, D. (1972) Purification and characterization of the in vitro colony forming cell in monkey hemopoietic tissue. *J. Cell. Physiol.* **79**, 283–292

Morrison, J. H. & Toepfer, J. R. (1967) Survival of lethally X-irradiated rats after treatment with isogenic marrow lymphocytes. *Am. J. Physiol.* **213**, 923–927

Morse, S. I. & Riester, S. K. (1967) Studies on the leukocytosis and lymphocytosis induced by *Bordetella pertussis*. I. Radioautographic analysis of the circulating cells in mice undergoing pertussis-induced hyperleukocytosis. *J. Exp. Med.* **125**, 401–408

Murphy, M. J., Bertles, J. P. & Gordon, A. S. (1971) Identifying characteristics of the hematopoietic precursor cell. *J. Cell Sci.* **9**, 23–47

Niewisch, H., Vogel, H. & Matioli, G. (1967) Concentration, quantitation and identification of hemopoietic stem cells. *Proc. Natl Acad. Sci. U.S.A.* **58**, 2261–2267

Okunewick, J. P. & Fulton, D. (1970) Comparison of erythropoietin response in mice following polycythaemia induced by transfusion and hypoxia. *Blood J. Hematol.* **36**, 239–245

Orlic, D. (1970) Ultrastructural analysis of erythropoiesis. In *Regulation of Hematopoiesis* (Gordon, A. S., ed.), vol. 1, pp. 271–296, Appleton-Century-Crofts, New York

Orlic, D., Gordon, A. S. & Rhodin, J. A. G. (1968) Ultrastructural and autoradiographic studies of erythropoietin-induced red cell production. *Ann. N.Y. Acad. Sci.* **149**, 198–216

Osmond, D. G. (1967) Lymphocyte production in the bone marrow. Radioautographic studies in polycythaemic guinea pigs. In *The Lymphocyte in Immunology and Haemopoiesis* (Yoffey, J. M., ed.), pp. 120–130, Arnold, London

Osmond, D. G. & Everett, N. B. (1964) Radioautographic studies of bone marrow lymphocytes in vivo and in diffusion chamber cultures. *Blood J. Hematol.* **23**, 1–17

Osmond, D. G. & Yoshida, Y. (1970) Post-irradiation haemopoietic repopulating ability of lymphocyte-rich fractions of guinea-pig bone marrow. *Proc. Can. Fed. Biol. Sci.* **13**, 152

Osmond, D. G. & Yoshida, Y. (1971) Blastogenic transformation in lymphocyte-rich fractions of guinea pig bone marrow. In *Proc. Fourth Ann. Leucocyte Culture Conference* (McIntyre, O. R., ed.), pp. 97–109, Appleton-Century-Crofts, New York

Pappenheim, A. (1907) Über die Stellung der akuten grosszelligen lymphozytären Leukämie im nosologischem System der Leukämien und die Bedeutung der grossen Lymphozyten Ehrlichs an und für sich und für die Pathologie dieser Erkrankung. *Folia Haematol.* (*Leipz.*) **4**, 1–53, 142–201

PATT, H. M. & MALONEY, M. A. (1970) Influence of time of X-irradiation on the regenerative process after localized bone marrow depletion. *Proc. Soc. Exp. Biol. Med.* **133**, 527–531

POLICARD, A. & BESSIS, M. (1958) Sur une mode d'incorporation des macromolecules par la cellule, visible au microscope électronique: la rhopheocytose. *C. R. Hebd. Séances Acad. Sci. (Paris)* **246**, 3194

RICKARD, K. A., RENCRICCA, N. J., SHADDUCK, R. K., MONETTE, F. C., HOWARD, D. E., GARRITY, M. & STOHLMAN, F., JR. (1971) Myeloid stem cell kinetics during erythropoietic stress. *Br. J. Haematol.* **21**, 537–547

ROBINSON, W. A., BRADLEY, T. R. & METCALF, D. (1967) Effect of whole body irradiation on colony production by bone marrow cells in vitro. *Proc. Soc. Exp. Biol. Med.* **125**, 388–391

ROHR, K. (1949) *Das menschliche Knochenmark*, 2nd ed. Thieme, Stuttgart

ROSSE, C. (1970) Two morphologically and kinetically distinct populations of lymphoid cells in bone marrow. *Nature (Lond.)* **227**, 73–75

ROSSE, C. (1971) Lymphocyte production in the bone marrow. In *Proc. Sixth Leucocyte Culture Conference* (Schwarz, M. R., ed.), Academic Press, New York

ROSSE, C. (1972) Migration of long-lived lymphocytes to the bone marrow and to other lymphomyeloid tissues in normal and parabiotic guinea pigs. *Blood J. Hematol.* **40**, 90–97

ROSSE, C. & YOFFEY, J. M. (1967) The morphology of the transitional lymphocyte in guinea-pig bone marrow. *J. Anat.* **102**, 113–124

ROSSE, C., GRIFFITHS, D. A., EDWARDS, A. E., GACHES, C. G. C., LONG, A. H. L., WRIGHT, J. L. W. & YOFFEY, J. M. (1970) Identity of erythroblast precursors in rat bone marrow. *Acta Haematol. (Basel)* **43**, 80–88

SACHS, L. (1970) In-vitro control of growth and development of hematopoietic cell clones. In *Regulation of Hematopoiesis* (Gordon, A. S., ed.), vol. 1, 217–233, Appleton-Century-Crofts, New York

SAILLEN, R., JEQUIER, E. & VANNOTTI, A. (1969) Porphyrin synthesis by the phytohaemag-glutinin-transformed lymphocytes in vitro. *J. Reticuloendothel. Soc.* **6**, 175–183

SCARO, J. L., CARRERA, M. A., TERUEL, J. E. & DE TOMBOLESI, R. A. P. (1971) Phytohemag-glutinin and hematopoietic stem cells in the mouse. *Acta Haematol. (Basel)* **46**, 275–281

SIMAR, I. J., HAOT, J. & BETZ, E. H. (1968) Etude ultrastructurale de la moelle hématopoietique au cours de la régénération après irradiation. *Eur. J. Cancer*, **4**, 529–535.

TANAKA, Y., EPSTEIN, L. B., BRECHER, G. & STOHLMAN, F. JR. (1963) Transformation of lymphocytes in cultures of human peripheral blood. *Blood J. Hematol.* **22**, 614–629

THOMAS, E. D., FLIEDNER, T. M., THOMAS, D. & CRONKITE, E. P. (1965) The problem of the stem cell: observations in dogs following nitrogen mustard. *J. Lab. Clin. Med.* **66**, 64–74

TILL, J. E. & McCULLOCH, E.A. (1961) A direct measurement of the radiation sensitivity of mouse bone marrow cells. *Radiat. Res.* **14**, 213–222

TURNER, M. S., HURST, J. M. & YOFFEY, J. M. (1967) Studies on hypoxia. VIII. Effect of hypoxia and post-hypoxic polycythaemia (rebound) on mouse marrow and spleen. *Br. J. Haematol.* **13**, 942–948

TYLER, R. W. & EVERETT, N. B. (1966) A radioautographic study of hemopoietic repopulation using irradiated parabiotic rats. *Blood J. Hematol.* **28**, 873–890

TYLER, R. W. & EVERETT, N. B. (1972) Radioautographic study of cellular migration using parabiotic rats. *Blood J. Hematol.* **39**, 249–266

VAN BEKKUM, D. W., VAN NOORD, M. J., MAAT, B. & DICKE, K. A. (1971) Attempts at identification of hemopoietic stem cell in mouse. *Blood J. Hematol.* **38**, 547–558

WEISS, L. (1965) The structure of bone marrow. Functional interrelationships of vascular and hematopoietic compartments in experimental hemolytic anemia: An electron microscope study, *Blood J. Hematol.* **36**, 189–208

WU, A. M., TILL, J. E., SIMINOVITCH, L. & McCULLOCH, E. A. (1968) Cytological evidence for a relationship between normal hematopoietic colony-forming cells and cells of the lymphoid system. *J. Exp. Med.* **127**, 455–463

YOFFEY, J. M. (1956) The mobilisation and turnover times of cell populations in blood and blood-forming tissues. *J. Histochem. Cytochem.* **4**, 516–530

YOFFEY, J. M. (1957) Cellular equilibria in blood and blood-forming tissues. In *Homeostatic Mechanisms (Brookhaven Symp. Biol.* No. 10*)*, pp. 1–25

YOFFEY, J. M. (1960) The lymphomyeloid complex. In *Haemopoiesis: Cell Production and its Regulation (Ciba Found. Symp.)*, pp. 1–36, Churchill, London

YOFFEY, J. M. & COURTICE, F. C. (1970) *Lymphatics, Lymph and the Lymphomyeloid Complex.* Academic Press, London

YOFFEY, J. M. & BEN-ISHAY, Z. (1971) The non-immunological role of lymphocytes in bone marrow and their association with erythropoiesis, in *Proceedings, 1st Meeting European Division Int. Soc. Haematol.* (Polli, E. E. & Maiolo, A. T., eds.), pp. 61–94, Arti Grafiche Fratelli Ferraro, Milan

YOFFEY, J. M. & PARNELL, J. (1944) The lymphocyte content of rabbit bone marrow. *J. Anat.* **78**, 109–112

YOFFEY, J. M., THOMAS, D. B., MOFFATT, D. J., SUTHERLAND, I. H. & ROSSE, C. (1961) Non-immunological functions of the lymphocyte: In *Biological Activity of the Leucocyte (Ciba Found. Study Group* No. 10), pp. 45–54, Churchill, London

YOFFEY, J. M., MAKIN, G. S., YATES, A. K., DAVIS, C. J. F., GRIFFITHS, D. A. & WARING I. S. (1964) The discharge of granulocytes from guinea-pig bone marrow in response to intravenous T. A. B. vaccine: a quantitative study. *Ann. N.Y. Acad. Sci.* **113**, 790–799

YOFFEY, J. M., HUDSON, G. & OSMOND, D. G. (1965a) The lymphocyte in guinea-pig bone marrow. *J. Anat.* **99**, 841–860.

YOFFEY, J. M., ROSSE, C., MOFFATT, D. J. & SUTHERLAND, I. H. (1965b) Studies on hypoxia. III. The differential response of the bone marrow to primary and secondary hypoxia. *Acta Anat.* **62**, 476–488

YOFFEY, J. M., WINTER, G. C. B., OSMOND, D. G. & MEEK, E. S. (1965c) Morphological studies in the culture of human leucocytes with phytohaemagglutinin. *Br. J. Haematol.* **11**, 488–497

YOFFEY, J. M., SMITH, N. C. W. & WILSON, R.S. (1967) Studies on hypoxia. V. Changes in the bone marrow during hypoxia at 10,000 and 20,000 feet. *Scand. J. Haematol.* **4**, 145–157

YOFFEY, J. M., JEFFREYS, R. V., OSMOND, D. G., TURNER, M. S., TAHSIN, S. C. & NIVEN P. A. R. (1968) Studies on hypoxia. VI. Changes in lymphocytes and transitional cells in the marrow during the intensification of primary hypoxia and rebound. *Ann. N.Y. Acad. Sci.* **149**, 179–192

YOSHIDA, Y. & OSMOND, D. G. (1971a) Blastogenic response of lymphocytes separated from bone marrow to allogeneic lymphoid cells in vitro. *Immunology*, **21**, 767–779

YOSHIDA, Y. & OSMOND, D. G. (1971b) Identity and proliferation of small lymphocyte precursors in cultures of lymphocyte-rich fractions of guinea-pig bone marrow. *Blood J. Hematol.* **37**, 73–86

Discussion

Harris: You said that the phenomenon of lymphocyte loading in the sinusoids occurs both during hypoxia and after bleeding. Do these animals show lymphocytosis in the peripheral blood?

Yoffey: Yes, they do. We (Yoffey *et al.* 1966) reported a marked lymphocytosis on the second, third and fourth days of hypoxia at 6100 m, and you also reported an increase in blood lymphocytes after three days' hypoxia at 6100 m (Harris *et al.* 1966).

Harris: We certainly found a marked lymphocytosis in guinea pigs given repeated injections of phenylhydrazine. We found that thymectomy immediately before the injections essentially abolishes this lymphocytosis.

Rosse: There is a lymphocytosis, particularly if one takes into account the reduction in blood volume and subsequent haemodilution after the bleeding. But even without such corrections one can detect an increase in circulating lymphocytes (Rosse *et al.* 1970).

Astaldi: Have you done any studies with erythropoietin, Professor Yoffey?

Yoffey: No. It took us practically three years before we were satisfied that our quantitative techniques were repeatable and reliable, as confirmed by Hudson *et al.* (1963). When I wanted to use erythropoietin I could not get it in the quantities we needed, but it ought to be studied.

Astaldi: Apparently the effects of hypoxia and of erythropoietin are exactly parallel. Before erythropoietin was discovered I found (Astaldi *et al.* 1952, 1954) that erythropoiesis was depressed in bone marrow in hypoxic tissue culture. But *in vivo* hypoxia stimulates erythropoiesis and lymphocyte increase, as you have so well shown, and you have seen some relationship between the increases in lymphocytes and erythroblasts. I wonder whether one could put bone marrow in a tissue culture system and see whether hypoxia stimulates proliferation of transitional cells which go to erythroblasts or to small lymphocytes and so on? That would be a completely closed system, with no traffic of lymphocytes from the peripheral blood or from other lymphoid areas, and would be a very important contribution.

Hudson: It may be useful to compare the features of an erythroblastic island in the normal monkey (Fig. 1) with those noted by Professor Yoffey in the rat (Ben-Ishay & Yoffey 1971). Fig. 1 shows a typical central reticular cell, with a nucleus, a large vacuole and numerous cytoplasmic inclusions, as well as the usual ring of erythroblasts. Around the island are quite a number of what I think Professor Yoffey would call perinesic members of the LT compartment, and the interesting thing is that at least some of these lymphocytes are in close contact with the processes of the central reticular cell. This might of course be due to chance, as so many members of the LT compartment are present anyway. But this is something we have seen not infrequently (K. N. Chin and G. Hudson, unpublished findings, 1972), and the question obviously is whether this type of relationship has some functional significance in the normal monkey.

Yoffey: I am very intrigued by this different situation in the monkey, as you can imagine, Dr Hudson, particularly since in the normal rat in a steady state we do not get that large accumulation of perinesic lymphocytes. In fact, in your figure they seem to be partly perinesic, partly endonesic. It is only when we put our rats in the decompression chamber at 5200 m that we get this temporary

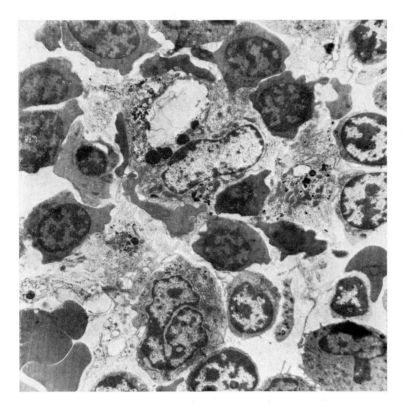

FIG. 1 (Hudson) Electron micrograph of a typical erythroblastic island in the bone marrow of normal monkey, to show a central reticular cell with a ring of erythroblasts of rather dense appearance surrounding it. A number of cells of the lymphocyte–transitional (LT) compartment may be seen at its periphery, two of these cells (midway down the extreme right of the picture) being in close contact with one of the reticular cell processes. (× 3400; stained with lead citrate)

inflow during the first 12 hours, and then the lymphocytes and transitional cells go away again. Now and again the processes of the reticular cells seem to be almost enclosing the lymphocytes and pulling them in, though that is probably wild imagination since the lymphocyte is quite capable of moving under its own steam. There is no doubt about the closeness of the relationship, but I do not know how to explain it.

Stohlman: Can the rebound lymphocytosis be attributed to the hypoxic stimulus applied? In the mouse and the rat—I do not know about the guinea pig—if one hypertransfuses the animal erythropoiesis will be shut off completely. In these circumstances the total cellularity of the bone marrow may decline slightly but really not appreciably. Lymphoid elements move in. Might not your observations just reflect the fact that the bone marrow does not just 'collapse' but rather that, when production of one cell line is shut off, there is an influx of other mononuclear cells. Have you looked at the changes in these compartments in the guinea pig after hypertransfusion?

Yoffey: No, but Al Gordon and his group hypertransfused polycythaemic mice and got a big increase in the lymphocytes and transitional cells (Weitz-Hamburger *et al.* 1971). The question is, is it necessary for cells to migrate into the marrow? Normally the marrow is a big lymphocyte producer. You are saying that when you hypertransfuse the marrow it stops producing its own lymphocytes and then a lot of new lymphocytes come in so that two processes are involved. You may be right, but I do not know of any evidence that there is a shut-down of marrow lymphocyte production in hypertransfusion.

Also, the marrow has very thin-walled vessels—the larger veins have walls just as thin as those of the sinuses—and it is the easiest thing on earth for these to dilate and take up spare space. For that physical reason, I do not think a lot of lymphocytes need to come in from outside. I know that does not prove or disprove it, but in marrow-depleted animals certainly we have seen quite widely dilated sinusoids. One sees this after severe bleeding when lots of red cells are discharged. That is the simple circulatory fact governing conditions in a rigid casing like the solid outer bone.

Stohlman: In the hypoxic animal the cellularity does not change that much: the loss of erythroid elements is compensated for by an increase either through migration or replication of mononuclear cells.

Yoffey: Just to drive home the point, let us say that precursor cells—transitionals—are both constantly dividing in large numbers to form small lymphocytes, as is evident from the work of Osmond & Everett (1964), Harris & Kugler (1965), Craddock (1965), and Everett & Caffrey (1967), and also that at the same time some are entering the blast cell compartment. If one stops this from happening, either by transfusion polycythaemia or by what I call active polycythaemia, then the transitional cells increase. In rabbits the same effect has been observed after giving actinomycin D, which blocks RNA synthesis and therefore also prevents blast cell formation. In these circumstances Hershko *et al.* (1969) observed in rabbits a marked increase in large pale cells which doubtless are pale transitional cells. After a while this increase would swamp the marrow unless there were an escape mechanism, which in this instance seems to be the division of transitional cells to form small lymphocytes and leave the marrow. In this system, in which there is no obvious reason why the polycythaemia should stop division of precursor cells into small lymphocytes, I do not know why you should suddenly get a large number of small lymphocytes coming in from the blood, as you were suggesting, Professor Stohlman.

Stohlman: There are clearly two possibilities, both subject to experimental clarification. The point I was trying to make was that this is not necessarily a phenomenon associated with hypoxia.

Yoffey: I quite agree. We used hypoxia as a preliminary stage to getting rebound and depressing erythrocyte production. We deliberately settled for hypoxia rather than transfusion because we felt that whatever the stem cell was, it would be forming in increased numbers during the active hypoxic stimulation. Therefore, if one then cuts off red cell formation, one would have a larger number of proliferating stem cells to play about with. That was what we saw in rebound, where there was a rapid rise first in transitional cells and then a massive increase in small lymphocytes. But I suppose, on a lesser scale, one should get precisely the same thing in transfusion polycythaemia.

Lajtha: Hypoxia or bleeding essentially perturbs the system. When one bleeds an animal or exposes it to high altitude, simulated or otherwise, one induces not only erythropoietin production but also some other ill-defined physiological stresses. These physiological stresses in fact hide the response pattern of the stem cell population in an undesirable fashion. If we stimulate the system with good quality preparations of exogenous erythropoietin, or if we bring the animal immediately down to normal pressure after transient hypoxia or provide it with extra red cells so that the hypoxic stress is abolished, then the number and cycling of stem cells oscillates in a way that is not visible if the animal is *kept* hypoxic. In other words, I am proposing that for such perturbations one should try to avoid a prolonged state of hypoxia which produces a stress which prevents the response of the population. In your system, I wonder what the population changes would be like, morphologically.

Yoffey: I would like to see the detailed data before expressing even a tentative opinion. I did not know about those marked swings.

I am glad you raised the point of stress. Hypoxia obviously produces all sorts of changes in the conditions for stimulating red cell formation. There is some evidence, for example, that hypoxia, even at 3650 m, can produce slightly impaired liver function, in some but not all rabbits (Reese 1960). With the remote metabolic effects so produced, one does not know what the whole chain of metabolic changes would be. I agree with all that. We were bothered about stress primarily in the sense in which it is concerned with a fall in the lymphocytes— the classical steroid hormone business. Even with 5200 m hypoxia, though lymphocytes decrease markedly, there is definitely no evidence from ultrastructural studies of lymphocytes dying. Furthermore, whatever stress or perturbation is affecting the changes in hypoxia, there is no question whatever of the rebound changes being influenced in this way.

The phrase 'ineffective erythropoiesis' has frequently been used, but although we were constantly on the lookout for it, we never, on ultrastructural examination, saw any evidence of abnormal changes in the erythropoietic line. I do not know what the indirect effects are, but even at 5200 m or 6100 m there is still a massive and apparently normal erythropoietic response. Professor Stohlman is probably going to say that even with prolonged hypoxia the erythropoietin level goes down after about 16 hours (Stohlman 1959).

Stohlman: I don't think the hypoxic stimulus can be directly compared with repeated injections of erythropoietin. We were formerly unaware that as part of the adaptation to hypoxia there are quite striking shifts in the oxygen dissociation curve, due to shifts in pH and 2,3-diphosphoglycerate, which result in changing patterns of erythropoietin production. Dr M. E. Miller in our laboratory is working on this to see exactly what the changes are and how they affect erythropoietin production. The hypoxic animal is not the exact counterpart of an animal getting repeated injections of a standard dose of erythropoietin.

Osmond: In the guinea pig a hypertransfusion polycythaemia results in increased numbers of marrow lymphocytes, particularly when preceded by erythropoietic stimulation in the form of repeated haemorrhage (D. G. Osmond, unpublished observations). As regards the post-hypoxic polycythaemic guinea pig, the rate of renewal of the unusually large number of lymphocytes in the bone marrow is as rapid as that in normal animals (Osmond 1967). Moreover, autoradiographic studies with [³H]thymidine, in conjunction with limb occlusion techniques, have shown that these rapidly renewing small lymphocytes are mainly locally produced rather than being immigrants (Osmond 1967). The observations of Professor Yoffey, that transitional lymphocytes increase in numbers before small lymphocytes in the bone marrow of hypoxic animals, are also consistent with the idea of intense marrow lymphocytopoiesis during post-hypoxic polycythaemia.

References

ASTALDI, G., BERNARDELLI, E. & REBAUDO, G. (1952) La prolifération de l'érythroblaste en dépression. *Sang* **23** (4), 293–310

ASTALDI, G., BERNARDELLI, E., REBAUDO, E. & PARMENTIER, R. (1954) With reference to the relations between proliferation activity of erythroblasts and their sensitivity to hypoxia. *Experientia* **10** (5), 220–222

BEN-ISHAY, Z. & YOFFEY, J. M. (1971) Reticular cells of erythroid islands of rat bone marrow in hypoxia and rebound. *J. Reticuloendothel. Soc.* **10**, 482–500

CRADDOCK, C. G. (1965) An investigation of lymphocyte production in guinea pig bone marrow. *Acta Haematol. (Basel)* **33**, 19–27

EVERETT, N. B. & CAFFREY, R. W. (1967) Radioautographic studies of bone marrow small lymphocytes. In *The Lymphocyte in Immunology and Haemopoiesis* (Yoffey, J. M., ed.), pp. 108–119, Arnold, London

HARRIS, P. F. & KUGLER, J. H. (1965) An investigation of lymphocyte production in guinea-pig bone marrow. *Acta Haematol. (Basel)* **33**, 351–369

HARRIS, P. F., HARRIS, R. S. & KUGLER, J. H. (1966) Studies of the leucocyte compartment in guinea-pig bone marrow after acute haemorrhage and severe hypoxia. Evidence for a common stem cell. *Br. J. Haematol.* **12**, 419–432

HERSHKO, G., SCHWARTZ, R. & IZAK, G. (1969) Morphological-biochemical correlations in rabbit red cell precursors synchronized by actinomycin administration. *Br. J. Haematol.* **17**, 569–579

HUDSON, G., OSMOND, D. G. & ROYLANCE, P. J. (1963) Cell-populations in the bone marrow of the normal guinea-pig. *Acta Anat.* **53**, 234–249

OSMOND, D. G. (1967) Lymphocyte production in the bone marrow: radioautographic studies in polycythaemic guinea pigs. In *The Lymphocyte in Immunology and Haemopoiesis,* (Yoffey, J. M., ed.), pp. 120–130, Arnold, London

OSMOND, D. G. & EVERETT, N. B. (1964) Radioautographic studies of bone marrow lymphocytes *in vivo* and in diffusion chamber cultures. *Blood J. Hematol.* **23**, 1–17

REESE, A. J. M. (1960) The effect of hypoxia on liver secretion studied by intravital fluorescence microscopy. *Br. J. Exp. Pathol.* **41**, 527–535

ROSSE, C., GRIFFITHS, D. A., EDWARDS, A. E., GACHES, C. G. C., LONG, A. H. L., WRIGHT, J. L. W. & YOFFEY, J. M. (1970) Evidence for the identity of erythroblast precursors in bone marrow. *Acta Haematol. (Basel)* **43**, 80

STOHLMAN, F., JR. (1959) Observations on the physiology of erythropoietin and its role in the regulation of red cell production. *Ann. N. Y. Acad. Sci.* **77**, 710–724

WEITZ-HAMBURGER, A., LOBUE, J., SHARKIS, S. J., GORDON, A. S. & ALEXANDER, P., JR. (1971) Quantitative studies of peripheral blood and bone marrow in transfusion-induced plethoric mice. *J. Anat.* **109**, 549–557

YOFFEY, J. M., SMITH, N.C.W. & WILSON, R. S. (1966) Studies on hypoxia. IV The differential haemopoietic responses to moderate and severe hypoxia. *Scand. J. Haematol.* **3**, 186–192.

Attempts at morphological identification of the haemopoietic stem cell in primates and rodents

K. A. DICKE, M. J. van NOORD, B. MAAT, U. W. SCHAEFER and D. W. van BEKKUM

Radiobiological Institute TNO and Institute for Experimental Gerontology TNO, Rijswijk, The Netherlands

Abstract The colony-forming unit–culture (CFU–C) in the thin-layer agar colony technique is considered to be representative of haemopoietic stem cells, according to our studies in mouse and monkey bone marrow. This makes it feasible to attempt morphological identification of haemopoietic stem cells in the primate by using stem cell concentrates prepared from suspensions of human and monkey bone marrow by repeated density separation. The numbers of CFU–C could be concentrated up to 100-fold and in these enriched fractions the content of CFC–C representing the total number of stem cells was calculated to be 10–20%. Using a May-Grünwald-Giemsa staining method and electron microscope techniques, a fair correlation was demonstrated between the calculated number of stem cells and the number found of a cell type with morphological characteristics identical to that of the candidate stem cell in the mouse. In both primates and mice the candidate stem cell was quite distinct from the so-called 'small lymphocyte'.

In mice the existence of a pluripotent haemopoietic stem cell (HSC) has been established. It was proved that one cell originates a spleen colony consisting of differentiated cells of the erythroid, granuloid and thromboid cell lines (Till & McCulloch 1961). Furthermore, Trentin & Fahlberg (1963) demonstrated that complete repopulation of the haemopoietic as well as the lymphoid tissues of lethally irradiated mice was effected by descendants from *one* spleen colony. Finally, lymphoid cells in mouse and rat radiation chimeras have been shown to carry chromosome markers of the donor (Ford & Micklem 1963; Nowell *et al.* 1970).

Many attempts have been made to identify the HSC by morphological criteria (Bennett & Cudkowicz 1968; Niewisch *et al.* 1967; Haas *et al.* 1971). None of these investigations yielded convincing results, because correlative studies with functional haemopoietic stem cell tests were not done. The greatest difficulty encountered in such identification studies is the low concentration of stem cells in haemopoietic tissues. The highest concentration seen in the mouse bone marrow is only four to six per 1000 cells. Using density gradients we have prepared stem cell concentrates from mouse bone marrow in which the proportion of CFC–S* was calculated to be up to 25%.

In these preparations a new and dominant cell type, not recognized before, was identified. The morphological characteristics of this cell type were defined with the aid of the electron microscope.

Cells meeting these criteria were enumerated in a number of preparations containing different concentrations of CFU–S (0.02–20%).

As a satisfactory correlation between these two values was established, we concluded that we had identified the HSC in the mouse (van Bekkum *et al.* 1971).

It is also likely that an HSC exists in primates, since the general properties of the haemopoietic system do not differ essentially from those of rodents. Strong support for this concept would be the finding of cells with similar morphological aspects to those of the HSC in the mouse. The frequency of this cell population in the bone marrow of primates is likely to be less than 1% if the concentrations are comparable to those in mouse bone marrow, so that it would be virtually impossible to detect them without first concentrating them.

In the present study, suspensions of both monkey and human bone marrow were fractionated by the discontinuous albumin density gradient technique. For highly enriched stem cell fractions to be isolated, we had to modify the gradient method previously developed for separating immunocompetent cells from HSC in primate bone marrow (Dicke *et al.* 1969). For this modification a quantitative test for HSC was needed as a control system.

Obviously, in the primate such an assay for HSC has to be an *in vitro* method and extensive earlier studies in mice showed that the CFU–C** in the thin layer agar culture method which we developed specifically for this purpose provides a quantitative measure of the HSC population (Dicke 1970, 1971a; Dicke & van Bekkum 1972a). In this paper, additional support for this concept will be provided by the demonstration of a strict parallel, in the monkey, between the numbers of CFU–C in highly enriched fractions and the capacity of such fractions to restore haemopoiesis in lethally irradiated recipients.

Finally, it will be shown that in CFU–C-enriched bone marrow fractions from the monkey and man there are high concentrations of cells morphologically similar to the mouse HSC. In such purified fractions, quantitative morpho-

---

*   Colony-forming cells–spleen: cells capable of forming colonies in the spleen of a lethally irradiated mouse recipient. Only a few of the injected CFC–S actually give rise to colonies and these cells are referred to as colony-forming units–spleen: CFU–S.

** Colony-forming units–culture: cells that actually form colonies in agar. These cells are a subclass of the CFC–C (colony-forming cells–culture): cells capable of forming colonies in agar.

logical studies with both the light and the electron microscope revealed a strict correlation between the 'Mouse Stem Cell-Like Cell' (MSCLC) and the number of CFU–C.

THE CFU–C ASSAY: THE THIN LAYER AGAR COLONY TECHNIQUE

Techniques

The thin layer agar technique described extensively elsewhere (Dicke 1971*a*; Dicke & van Bekkum 1972*b*; Dicke & Schaefer 1972) is based on agar colony formation methods developed by Pluznik & Sachs (1966) and Bradley & Metcalf (1966). Briefly, bone marrow cells are cultured in plastic Falcon Petri dishes in which 0.5×10^6 embryonic fibroblasts are layered as a monolayer when mouse marrow suspensions are cultured. When monkey and human marrow cells are cultured, embryonic chimpanzee fibroblasts are used as the feeder system. (Previously we also used kidney tubules and human embryo fibroblasts and although some of these feeders were similarly effective, we prefer chimpanzee fibroblasts since they are highly consistent in feeding the cells.) On top of the feeder, 4.5 ml of a mixture of agar (final concentration 0.5%), Dulbecco's modified Eagle's medium and horse serum is added. After 24 hours, the top layer of 0.25% agar medium (agar + Dulbecco + horse serum) in which the bone marrow cells are suspended is put on top of the 0.5% agar medium. The total volume of the top layer is 0.2 ml. The dishes are kept in 7–10% CO_2 in a gas-controlled incubator at 37°C, in a 100% humidified atmosphere, for 7–10 days, after which distinct colonies are visible. The numbers of colonies containing more than 50 cells were counted by using an inverted microscope (magnification 80 ×).

Evidence for CFU–C being an HSC

Much of the exploratory work on whether the CFU–C belongs to the HSC compartment has been done in the mouse, using mouse haemopoietic cells, since comparison with the results of an established *in vivo* haemopoietic stem cell assay, the CFU–S assay, is possible only in that species. Only when a parallel between CFU–S and CFU–C can be demonstrated under various conditions in different haemopoietic suspensions is the use of the *in vitro* CFU–C assay as a quantitative HSC assay justified. The experimental results may be summarized as follows:

(1) *In vivo* colonies derived from HSC concentrates prepared from bone marrow of mice pretreated with mustine vinblastine contain CFU–S. This was demonstrated by injecting the cells from five-day-old *in vitro* colonies into lethally irradiated mouse recipients and counting the spleen colonies. The number of CFC–S per colony was calculated to be up to five, indicating that HSC replicate *in vitro* (Dicke *et al.* 1971; Dicke & van Bekkum 1972*a*) and strongly suggesting that these colonies must originate from a stem cell.

(2) The CFU–C has the capacity of self-replication *in vitro*, as demonstrated by the fact that replating five-day-old *in vitro* colonies derived from stem cell concentrates produces an eightfold increase in the number of colonies of the same size as those in the primary cultures (Table 1). However, since the colonies

TABLE 1

Results of replating colonies[a] obtained from mouse stem cell cultures

No. of primary colonies harvested	No. of cells replated	No. of colonies in secondary cultures	Multiplication factor
100[b]	(7.5×10^4)	800[c]	8
300[b]	Fr. 1 (2×10^4) Fr. 2 (4×10^4) Fr. 3 (2×10^4) Fr. 4 (2×10^4)	1200 2800 3800 416 } 8200[c]	27

[a]   From 5-day old cultures.
[b]   The colonies were collected using a fine Pasteur pipette, after which they were pooled and dispersed to yield cell suspensions.
[c]   Colonies were counted 7 days after culture in the secondary dishes. Clones containing more than 50 cells were scored as colonies. The total cellularity of the secondary cultures was not estimated.

on the plates were not extensively mapped, the possibility cannot be excluded that the more differentiated descendants of the original CFU–C were also triggered to colony formation. The self-replicating ability is much more pronounced when the cells constituting these colonies are fractionated before being plated in secondary dishes. The increased capacity for self-replication after gradient centrifugation might be due to the removal of mature myeloid cells, a population which inhibits colony formation (Dicke & van Bekkum 1972*a*).

(3) As well as myeloid cells, megakaryocytes have been shown to proliferate in these *in vitro* colonies, demonstrating the pluripotency of these colony-forming cells in certain conditions (Nakeff & Dicke 1972).

(4) Separation of CFU–S and CFU–C on the basis of differences in density

or in volume has not been possible (Dicke 1971*b*; Dicke & van Bekkum 1972*a*; Bradley 1972). The separation profiles of CFU–C and CFU–S were identical in the discontinuous albumin density gradient when suspensions of spleen cells and bone marrow cells from untreated mice and mice treated with mustine vinblastine were used (Dicke *et al.* 1971).

In the velocity sedimentation chamber designed by Miller & Phillips (1969) the sedimentation rates of CFU–S and CFU–C, which depend mainly on the volume of the cell, were found to be similar (4.4 mm/h). The results of such a velocity sedimentation are shown in Fig. 1.

(5) Using the *in vivo* [³H]thymidine suicide technique, we saw no differences in the status of the cell cycle of the CFU–S and CFU–C (Dicke & van Bekkum

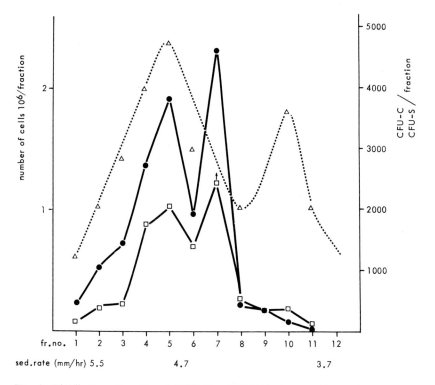

FIG. 1. Distribution of profiles of CFU–C and CFU–S of mouse bone marrow after velocity sedimentation (5 h).

The numbers of CFU–C and CFU–S per fraction have been obtained by plating and injecting appropriate numbers of cells. The arrow in the figure indicates that the number of CFU–S is higher than shown, because spleen colonies were confluent.

□ = CFU–S
● = CFU–C
△ = number of nucleated cells per fraction

1972*a*). In addition preliminary results from *in vitro* [³H]thymidine suicide experiments designed by Iscove *et al.* (1970) and Iscove (1972) have confirmed the findings of the *in vivo* experiments with [³H]thymidine.

Although the above results obtained with mouse haemopoietic cells justify the use in primates of the thin agar layer technique developed as an HSC assay in the mouse, direct experimental evidence in primates concerning the identity of the *in vitro* colony-forming cell and the HSC was still essential. Such evidence is derived from the following observations:

(1) *The similarity of the in vitro data available for mouse, monkey and human bone marrow cells.* The number of colonies per 10^5 plated cells in the three species is strikingly similar, namely 80–120 colonies. The morphology of the colonies is not essentially different: colonies of marrow cells from the three species are mainly granulocytic during the first 7–10 days, after which period of incubation macrophages predominate in the cultures. In human marrow cultures the macrophages may appear somewhat later, between 10 and 14 days after incubation. Moreover in this species the colony growth is slightly less than in monkey and mouse haemopoietic colonies, namely 100–300 cells per colony after 7–10 days of incubation, compared to 300–1000 cells per colony in the monkey and 500–2000 cells per colony in the mouse.

(2) *In vivo transplantation of monkey CFU–C concentrates.* In the routine procedure for bone marrow transplantation in the monkey model, recipients weighing 2–3 kg received 4×10^8 unmodified bone marrow cells/kg body weight from allogeneic donors 24 hours after supralethal whole-body irradiation (850 rads), or $4 - 8 \times 10^7$ cells/kg if autologous bone marrow was used (van Bekkum & de Vries 1967). These cell suspensions contained sufficient HSC to repopulate the haemopoietic organs of 95% of the recipients. In order to investigate whether a parallel exists between the CFU–C content of a haemopoietic suspension and the ability of the suspension to 'take' *in vivo*, equivalent numbers of CFU–C to those present in 4×10^8 unfractionated allogeneic cells or in $4 - 8 \times 10^7$ autologous bone marrow cells from various haemopoietic cell fractions have to be grafted. In other words, in CFU–C concentrates, the numbers of cells being grafted were reduced by the same factor as the CFU-C were concentrated, in comparison with unfractionated marrow. For that purpose, the exact CFU–C content of such fractions had to be determined *before* transplantation. Since the CFU–C assay takes 7–10 days, preservation of the fraction without loss of HSC viability is essential, and the recently developed storage technique of Schaefer *et al.* (1972) makes this possible. The results of grafting equivalent numbers of CFU–C from concentrated suspensions (Table

TABLE 2

Haemopoietic restoration of lethally irradiated monkeys grafted with stem cell concentrates as determined by CFU–C assays

Unfractionated marrow			Stem cell graft			
Monkey no.	Donor type	CFU–C per 10^5 cells	No. CFU–C[a] injected/kg body wt	No. of cells injected/kg body wt $\times$ 10^6	Conc.[b] factor CFU–C	Take[c]
2281	Auto[d]	23	15 000	1.2	52	+
2302	Auto	50	25 000	1.4	35	+
2207	Auto	50	40 000	2.8	38	+
2279	Allo[d]	100	400 000	14	28	+
2280	Allo	100	400 000	14	28	+

[a] Number of CFU–C grafted/kg body weight in autologous situations was equivalent to the number of CFU–C present in 40 – 80 $\times$ 10^6 unfractionated bone marrow cells, the latter values depending on the degree of contamination by peripheral blood. Number of CFU–C grafted/kg body weight in allogeneic combinations was equivalent to the number of CFU–C present in 400 $\times$ 10^6 unfractionated bone marrow cells.
[b] Concentration factor of the number of CFU–C of unfractionated marrow = 1.
[c] The take is scored by the rise of leucocytes (above 1000/μl), reticulocytes (10 % or more) and thrombocytes (above 20 000/μl) in the peripheral blood within 14 days after transplantation.
[d] Auto = autologous; allo = allogeneic.

2) clearly demonstrate that low cell numbers containing the same absolute quantity of CFU–C as unfractionated marrow took as quickly as those observed after grafting of unmodified suspensions of bone marrow. The number of CFU–C grafted differs from experiment to experiment, especially in the autologous transplants. This is mainly because the plating efficiency *in vitro* differs from experiment to experiment and because the numbers of peripheral nucleated blood cells contaminating the different initial punctates vary.

CONCENTRATION OF MONKEY MARROW CFU–C: TECHNIQUE AND RESULTS

The gradient technique used to concentrate the CFU–C in the monkey marrow suspensions is shown in Fig. 2A. The preparation of the albumin (bovine serum albumin: BSA) stock solution and of the different albumin concentrations, as well as of the gradient, have already been described (Dicke *et al.* 1969), so that only the modifications will be mentioned here. These modifications were necessary since the aim of the present studies, namely to achieve a maximum concentration of HSC, differed from that in previous studies. With the standard procedure, an eight- to tenfold concentration of CFU–C had been consistently

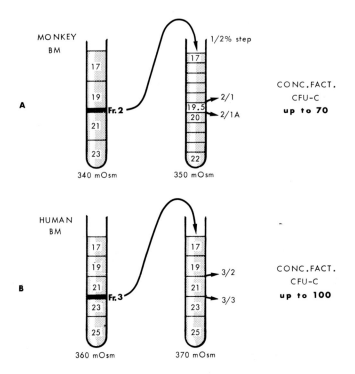

FIG. 2. Schematic representation of bone marrow cell refractionation. The figures in the tubes represent the BSA percentages in the different solutions. The osmolarity represents the tonicity of 35 % BSA stock solutions from which the BSA solutions in the gradients are prepared. The pH of the 35 % BSA stock solutions is 5.2.

(A)   Monkey bone marrow fractionation: fraction 2 from the first gradient is refractionated on a gradient consisting of 0.5 % steps of different BSA solutions.

(B)   Human bone marrow fractionation: fraction 3 from the first gradient is refractionated on a gradient consisting of 2 % steps but of higher osmolarity.

found in fraction 2, the cell band between the 19% and 21% BSA solutions. In the present studies, the fraction 2 which yielded 2–4% of the total amount of cells and 40–60% of stem cells has been refractionated, using gradient steps of 0.5% in the range of 23–18% BSA (density: 1.0682–1.0550) in order to achieve a high enrichment of HSC. The osmolarity of the 35% BSA stock solution from which the refractionation gradient is prepared was 350 mosmol, in contrast with 340 mosmol for the stock solution employed for the first gradient.

Table 3 gives the results of a refractionation experiment representative of seven experiments. The highest concentration is found in fractions 1 and 1A of the refractionation gradient.

TABLE 3

Concentration of CFU–C in monkey bone marrow by the discontinuous albumin gradient technique[a]

	CFU–C assay	
	Numbers of colonies[b] per 10^5 cells	Concentration factor
Unfractionated suspension	99	1
Fractionation Fr. 2 (5.5 %)[c]	1200	12
Re-fractionation		
Fr. 2/1 (0.3 %)	2736	27
Fr. 2/1A(0.3 %)	5600	56
Fr. 2/1B(0.3 %)	2000	20
Fr. 2/1C(0.5 %)	1000	10
Fr. 2/2 (2 %)	500	5
Fr. 2/3 (3 %)	300	3

[a] Values of one experiment, representative of 7 experiments.
[b] The numbers of cells plated per dish are adapted to the number of CFU–C expected. The values are obtained by counting at least 100 colonies or half the surface of a dish. At least 2 dishes per fraction were used.
[c] The figures in parentheses represent the cell yield of the fraction expressed as a percentage of the total unfractionated material.

CONCENTRATION OF HUMAN MARROW CFU–C: TECHNIQUE AND RESULTS

The scheme of the gradient technique used for human marrow suspensions is shown in Fig. 2B. In humans, up to 50% of the total number of CFU–C appear in fraction 3, whereas the number of nucleated cells is 4–8% of the original suspension. In humans most CFU–C are collected in fraction 3 and not in fraction 2 as happens in monkeys; this is due to the high osmolarity of the stock solution (360 mosmol) from which the human gradient has been prepared. Fraction 3 was refractionated on a gradient consisting of albumin solutions of 25, 23, 21 and 19%. The osmolarity of the stock solution is 370 mosmol. Note that for refractionation of human bone marrow a 2% gradient step has been used instead of the 0.5% steps used in the monkey. The reason is that with human bone marrow this type of refractionation for preparative purposes (Dicke & van Bekkum 1972b) yields fractions R2 and R3 (Fig. 2B) which contain most of the CFU–C present in the original fraction 3. As can be seen from

TABLE 4

Concentration of CFU–C in human bone marrow by the discontinuous albumin gradient technique[a]

	CFU–C assay	
	Number of colonies[b] per 10^5 cells	Concentration factor
Unfractionated suspension	83	1
First fractionation Fr. 3 (5%)[c]	700	8.5
Re-fractionation Fr. 3/2 (0.5%)	4100	50
Fr. 3/3 (2.3 %)	1500	18
Fr. 3/4 (2 %)	87	1

[a] Values of one experiment, representative of 7 experiments.
[b] The numbers of cells plated per dish are adapted to the number of CFU–C expected. The values are obtained by counting at least 100 colonies or half the surface of a dish. At least 2 dishes per fraction were used.
[c] The figures in parentheses represent the cell yield of the fraction expressed as a percentage of the total unfractionated material.

the results in Table 4, the concentration of CFU–C in these fractions is 50-fold higher than that in the unfractionated marrow suspensions, whereas in certain other experiments an enrichment factor of 100 has been obtained.

MORPHOLOGICAL STUDIES

Staining procedure for light microscope examination

Standard smears could not be used because a substantial number of cells disintegrate in the smearing procedure. Various methods of avoiding this loss, which would jeopardize the qualitative analysis of the preparations, were investigated and finally the precipitation method described by Sayk (1960) was adopted. A modified staining procedure using the May-Grünwald stain was carried out, as described in detail by van Bekkum *et al.* (1971).

Electron microscopy, technical procedure

Small numbers of fractionated cells from mouse bone marrow were fixed in a mixture of glutaraldehyde and osmium tetroxide, then immersed in uranyl acetate (Hirsch & Fedorko 1968). After fixation, the cells were pelleted with a microcentrifuge, as described by Malamed (1963). After dehydration in a graded ethanol series and treatment with propylene oxide, the material was embedded in Epon (Luft 1961). Thin sections were cut with a diamond knife and collected on uncoated copper grids. Sections were stained with uranyl acetate and lead

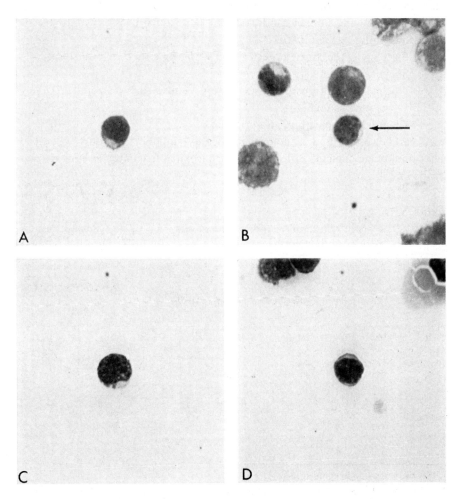

FIG. 3 May-Grünwald-stained HSC of (A) human, (B) monkey and (C) mouse marrow, with (D) a stained preparation of a small lymphocyte for comparison. × 875.

citrate (Venable & Coggeshall 1965) and examined in a Philips 300 electron microscope. Electron microscope sections were quantitatively analysed at a magnification of 3000, which allows about 20 cells to be examined in one field.

Light-microscope results

The morphological entity determined for HSC in the mouse (van Bekkum *et al.* 1971) was easily observed in CFU–C-rich marrow fractions in both monkey and man. May-Grünwald-Giemsa-stained cells representative of the mouse, monkey and human candidate HSC are shown in Fig. 3 and have the following similar characteristics:

Size: the diameter, estimated with a micrometer, was 8 μm.

Shape: round.

Nucleus: light-purple, rather homogeneous structure, round or kidney-shaped.

Cytoplasm: pale blue, no granules.

As can be seen in Fig. 3, the resemblance to lymphocytes is only superficial. The lymphocyte depicted in Fig. 3 has been isolated from human bone marrow (fraction 3/4).

TABLE 5

% MSCLC[a] estimated by light microscopy compared with the % CFU-C in monkey marrow suspensions

Morphological evaluation				CFU–C assay[b]		Ratio
Fraction	Total cell counts	MSCLC counts	% MSCLC	No. of colonies/ 10^5 cells plated	% CFU–C	% MSCLC: % CFU–C
2/1B	1169	107	9	3700	3.7	2.4
1 + 2[c]	395	8	2	1000	1	2
1 + 2/1A	512	59	11	5600	5.6	2
2/1A	594	64	11	4000	4	2.7
2/1	457	42	10	4700	4.7	2.1
1/C	651	52	8	2700	2.7	3
1 + 2/1B	626	32	5	2000	2	2.5
2	630	27	4	1200	1.2	3.3
Unfract.	1100	8	0.7	100	0.1	7
						Mean 3

[a]   MSCLC = mouse stem cell-like cell.

[b] $0.5 - 1 \times 10^5$ cells per dish plated. At least 500 colonies per dish were counted or half of the surface of the dish. Duplicate cultures were used.

[c]   Fractions 1 and 2 were pooled.

Using the criteria listed above, May-Grünwald-stained preparations from CFU–C concentrates of monkey and human bone marrow were inspected for the presence of mouse stem-cell-like cells (MSCLC). Table 5 lists the quantitative counts of MSCLC in CFU–C-enriched monkey marrow fractions and these counts were compared with the number of CFU–C determined per 10^5 cells in these fractions. As can be seen, the ratios of the percentage of MSCLC and the percentage of CFU–C per fraction are highly constant. The mean ratio of % MSCLC/% CFU–C is 3.0 ($n = 9$). In Table 6 the quantitative morphological counts of MSCLC are compared with the numbers of CFU–C in highly concentrated CFU–C fractions obtained from human bone marrow. Again a very consistent ratio can be noted. The mean ratio for six different fractions is 3.1.

TABLE 6

% MSCLC estimated by light microscopy compared with the % CFU–C in human marrow suspensions

Morphological evaluation				CFU–C assay[a]		Ratio
Fraction no.	Total cell counts	MSCLC counts	MSCLC	No. of colonies/ 10^5 cells plated	% CFU–C	% MSCLC: % CFU–C
3/2	615	46	8	4000	4	2
3/3	615	28	5	2000	2	2.5
3/4	701	7	1	120	0.12	8
3/2	1474	28	6	4000	4	1.5
3/3	732	32	4	1100	1.1	3.6
3/3	456	24	5	2400	2.4	2
					Mean	3.1

[a] 0.5 – 1 × 10^5 cells per dish plated. At least 500 colonies per dish were counted or half of the surface of the dish. Duplicate cultures were used.

Electron microscope results

MSCLC from CFU–C-rich monkey and human marrow fractions were identified in electron micrographs of the ultra-thin sections (magnification × 17 000). No differences in cell structure were noted between the mouse HSC and the MSCLC scored in the primate marrow fractions. Representative MSCLC from primate and mouse marrow fractions are shown in Fig. 4, in which the detailed ultrastructural characteristics of the MSCLC can be seen, as well as the strict morphological identity between cells from the different species.

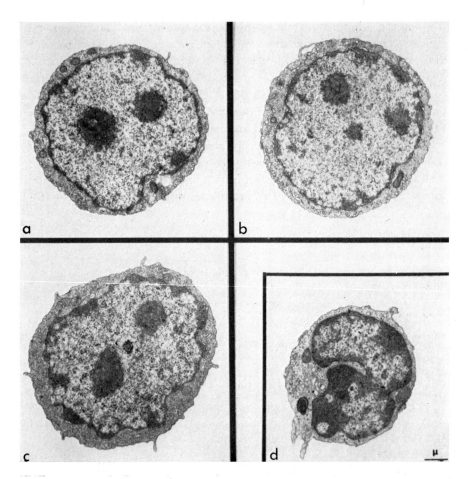

Fɪɢ. 4. Electron microscope sections of the candidate stem cell of (*a*) human, (*b*) monkey, and (*c*) mouse. Nucleus is round with indentations. The subcellular structure is described in detail in Table 7. × 17 000. Note the resemblance of the stem cells in the different species. (*d*) A small lymphocyte from human marrow. The nucleus shows large areas of densely aggregated granular chromatin and smaller light regions. Nucleoli often present in lymphocytes are inconspicuous in this cell. The cytoplasm contains dense bodies and many vesicles of different sizes. Golgi apparatus is present but poorly developed. Many ribosomes are clustered. Mitochondria are large.

Various structures in the nucleus and cytoplasm which are apparent in the more differentiated cells are obviously not present in the MSCLC. The ultrastructural characteristics of the MSCLC are listed in Table 7.

Lymphocytes are generally smaller, have more densely clumped nuclear chromatin, and frequently display in their cytoplasm a Golgi apparatus, a centriole, profiles of endoplasmic reticulum, dense bodies, multivesicular bodies

TABLE 7

Ultrastructural characteristics of the candidate haemopoietic stem cell in the rodent and the primate

Cell	Size	7 – 10 μm[a]
	Shape	Irregular, round
Nucleus	Shape	Round with indentations
	Nucleoli	One or two, large
	Chromatin pattern	Finely dispersed/flocculent with small aggregates at nuclear margins
Cytoplasm	Shape	Narrow
	Golgi apparatus	Not observed
	Endoplasmic reticulum	Not observed
	Lysosomes	Not observed
	Free ribosomes	Abundant
	Clustered ribosomes	Few or absent
	Mitochondria	Several small
	Small vesicles	Present
	Multivesicular bodies	Not observed

[a] Obtained by direct measurements of electron micrographs.

and lysosomes—organelles that have not been observed in our candidate stem cell. It should be remembered that lymphocytes (functionally determined by their response to phytohaemagglutinin *in vitro*) are absent from our stem cell fractions.

After the MSCLC had been identified in the ultra-thin sections at a magnification of × 17 000, the quantitative morphology of the CFU–C concentrates from primates was studied at a magnification of × 3000. Table 8 gives the results from eight CFU–C-rich fractions from the monkey. A striking parallel between the number of MSCLC and CFU–C per fraction is again evident. Table 9 presents counts of MSCLC and numbers of CFU–C in CFU–C-concentrated fractions from human marrow suspensions. These results resemble those in the monkey with regard to the parallel between the morphological entity of the MSCLC and the *in vitro* assay. Note that in the monkey as well as in the human studies the mean ratio % MSCLC: % CFU–C is 2.8 (Tables 8, 9).

K. A. DICKE *et al.*

TABLE 8

% MSCLC estimated by electron microscopy compared with the % CFU-C in monkey marrow suspensions

Morphological evaluation				CFU–C assay[a]		Ratio
Fraction no.	Total cell counts	MSCLC counts	% MSCLC	No. of colonies/ 10^5 cells plated	% CFU–C	% MSCLC: % CFU–C
2/1A	395	60	16	5700	5.7	2.8
2/1	347	57	16	5500	5.5	2.9
2/1	224	16	7	4700	4.7	1.5
2/1	140	16	11	5000	5	2.2
2/1A	267	50	18	5600	5.6	3.2
2/3	319	13	4	1000	1	4
2/1C	300	7	2.4	1000	1	2.4
2/1C	305	15	5	1440	1.4	3.6
					Mean	2.8

[a] $0.5 - 1 \times 10^5$ cells per dish plated. At least 500 colonies per dish were counted or half of the surface of the dish. Duplicate cultures were used.

TABLE 9

% MSCLC estimated by electron microscopy compared with the % CFU–C in human marrow suspensions

Morphological evaluation				CFU–C assay[a]		Ratio
Fraction no.	Total cell counts	MSCLC counts	% MSCLC	No. of colonies/ 10^5 cells plated	% CFU–C	% MSCLC: % CFU–C
3/3	124	11	9	3000	3	3
3/3	240	19	8	2000	2	4
3/2	181	20	11	4800	4.8	2.3
3/2	180	11	6	2000	2	3
3/3	300	22	7	6000	6	1.1
3/3	250	13	5	2000	2	2.5
3/3	257	17	6	1700	1.7	3.5
					Mean	2.8

[a] $0.5 - 1 \times 10^5$ cells per dish plated. At least 500 colonies per dish were counted or half of the surface of the dish. Duplicate cultures were used.

DISCUSSION

The resemblance between the candidate stem cells in human and monkey marrow and those described in the mouse is striking, as evidenced by the electron microscope pictures in Fig. 4. Moreover, the appearance of the MSCLC in the electron microscope is so characteristic that it can easily be distinguished from cell types belonging to any of the four haemopoietic cell lines, particularly from the myeloid and lymphoid lines. Due to its clear morphology, quantitative analysis of the electron microscope sections is a reliable measure of the number of MSCLC in a haemopoietic suspension. The present studies underline our previous statement (van Bekkum *et al.* 1971) that the differences between the mouse HSC on the one hand and the various lymphocytes on the other are so numerous that the stem cells cannot easily be associated with the small lymphocyte compartment in the bone marrow. Some confusion has been caused in the literature by the introduction of the term 'transitional lymphocytes' by Rosse & Yoffey (1967), which was held to represent a primitive population of haemopoietic precursor cells. However, descriptions of the morphology of these cells suggest that most transitional lymphocytes are larger than MSCLC. Yoffey (1971), summarizing the information about the 'lymphocyte transitional compartment', described cells with a pale and basophilic cytoplasm. Part of the transitional cell population might be capable of transforming into large basophilic blast cells. The term 'transitional lymphocytes' has also been used by others to designate characteristic lymphocyte precursors. Veldman (1970), in a histological and electron microscope study of the immune response, reported the same type of cells in the lymph node of rabbits. Light microscope features of the two types of transitional cells were translated into an electron-dense and an electron-lucent cell. In this detailed study by Veldman, the transformation from marginal zone cells to transitional cells and thereafter to plasmablasts was described. Mori & Unnert (1969) mentioned numerous transitional stages between basophilic stem cells and proplasmacytes. Cells were distinguished by the amount of endoplasmic reticulum. Zucker-Franklin (1969) noted a number of plasmacytoid lymphocytes in human bone marrow and thoracic duct with a fine structure quite similar to the transitional cells in the study by Veldman (1970). They were called intermediate cells and considered as precursors of plasma cells. Moore *et al.* (1972) recently described haemopoietic cells or, to be more precise, *in vitro* colony-forming cells with morphological characteristics which they hold to correspond closely to transitional lymphocytes with basophilic cytoplasm. These authors concentrated this cell type with the aid of continuous albumin gradients. Unfortunately the morphological description of these cells was derived only from Giemsa-stained preparations studied by light microscopy. In our opinion it is difficult to compare the results of Moore *et al.* (1972) with our own or any of the other studies because of the absence of electron microscope data.

Just as in the mouse, light-microscope examination using the May-Grünwald staining revealed a superficial resemblance between the MSCLC and the lymphocyte in human bone marrow, particularly with regard to their size. However, some of the specific characteristics of the ultrastructure of the MSCLC seen in the electron microscope could be 'translated' into light-microscope terms, which was helpful for differentiating the MSCLC from the lymphocyte in Giemsa-stained preparations.

We are now investigating whether other staining procedures, such as the metachrome staining method, mark the differences between MSCLC and lymphocytes more clearly, so that quantitative analysis by light microscopy could be applied routinely. Such a staining procedure should be less time-consuming and much less laborious than the CFU–C assay for determining the number of HSC.

The unique morphological appearance of the pluripotent HSC is a matter of dispute. Although there is no absolute proof that our candidate stem cell is identical with the pluripotent HSC, its appearance as one morphological entity and the way in which its frequency parallels the number of CFU–S in a variety of haemopoietic suspensions in mice is striking (van Bekkum *et al.* 1971). The fact that in the monkey and the human bone marrow MSCLCs are found which again correlate in frequency with the pluripotent capability of a great number of different haemopoietic suspensions strongly supports our hypothesis that the pluripotent HSC is a single morphological entity in these mammalian species.

Now that a detailed description of the morphological properties of the candidate stem cell is available, these cells can be counted in various abnormal states of haemopoiesis. Obviously, such analysis will be facilitated by concentration of these cells, e.g. with the density gradient technique. It is to be expected that the results of such studies in human bone marrow will eventually confirm or contradict the conclusions presented here.

ACKNOWLEDGEMENT

The work described has been supported in part by the Commission of the European Communities (EURATOM), Brussels, Belgium, contract no. 079–69–1 BIAC.

References

BECKER, A. J., McCULLOCH, E. A., SIMINOVITCH, L. & TILL, J. E. (1965) The effect of differing demands for blood cell production on DNA synthesis by haemopoietic colony forming cells of mice. *Blood J. Hematol.* **26**, 296

BENNETT, M. & CUDKOWICZ, G. (1968) Hemopoietic progenitor cells with limited potential for differentiation: Erythropoietic function of mouse marrow 'lymphocytes'. *J. Cell.*

Physiol. **72**, 129

BRADLEY, T. R. (1972) in *In Vitro Culture of Hemopoietic Cells* (Proceedings of a workshop/symposium held in Rijswijk, 1971) (van Bekkum, D. W. & Dicke, K. A., eds.), p. 81, Radiobiological Institute TNO, Rijswijk

BRADLEY, T. R. & METCALF, D. (1966) The growth of bone marrow cells *in vitro. Aust. J. Exp. Biol. Med. Sci.* **44**, 287

DICKE, K. A. (1970) Bone marrow transplantation after separation by discontinuous albumin density gradient centrifugation, thesis, University of Leiden

DICKE, K. A. (1971a) in *The Separation of Haemopoietic Cell Suspensions* (Proceedings of a workshop/symposium held in Rijswijk, 1970) (van Bekkum, D. W. & Dicke, K. A., eds.), p. 167, Radiobiological Institute TNO, Rijswijk

DICKE, K. A. (1971b) in *The Separation of Haemopoietic Cell Suspensions* (Proceedings of a workshop/symposium held in Rijswijk, 1970) (van Bekkum, D. W. & Dicke, K. A., eds.), p. 142, Radiobiological Institute TNO, Rijswijk

DICKE, K. A. & SCHAEFER, U. W. (1972) in *In Vitro Culture of Hemopoietic Cells* (Proceedings of a workshop/symposium held in Rijswijk, 1971) (van Bekkum, D. W. & Dicke, K. A., eds.), p. 221, Radiobiological Institute TNO, Rijswijk

DICKE, K. A. & VAN BEKKUM, D. W. (1972a) in *In Vitro Culture of Hemopoietic Cells* (Proceedings of a workshop/symposium held in Rijswijk, 1971) (van Bekkum, D. W. & Dicke, K. A., eds.), p. 136, Radiobiological Institute TNO, Rijswijk

DICKE, K. A. & VAN BEKKUM, D. W. (1972b) Preparation and use of stem cell concentrates for restoration of immune deficiency disease and bone marrow aplasia. *Rev. Eur. Etud. Clin. Biol.* **17**, 645

DICKE, K. A., TRIDENTE, G. & VAN BEKKUM, D. W. (1969) The selective elimination of immunologically competent cells from bone marrow and lymphocyte cell mixtures. III. In vitro test for detection of immunocompetent cells in fractionated mouse spleen cell suspensions and primate bone marrow suspensions. *Transplantation* **8**, 422

DICKE, K. A., PLATENBURG, M. G. C. & VAN BEKKUM, D. W. (1971) Colony formation in agar: in vitro assay for haemopoietic stem cells. *Cell Tissue Kinet.* **4**, 463

FORD, C. E. & MICKLEM, H. S. (1963) The thymus and lymph-nodes in radiation chimeras. *Lancet* **1**, 359

HAAS, R. J., BOHNE, F. & FLIEDNER, T. M. (1971) Cytokinetic analysis of slowly proliferating bone marrow cells during recovery from radiation injury. *Cell Tissue Kinet.* **4**, 31

HIRSCH, J. G. & FEDORKO, M. A. (1968) Ultrastructure of human leukocytes after simultaneous fixation with glutaraldehyde and osmium tetroxide and 'postfixation' in uranyl acetate. *J. Cell. Physiol.* **38**, 625

ISCOVE, N. N. (1972) in *In Vitro Culture of Hemopoietic Cells* (Proceedings of a workshop/symposium held in Rijswijk, 1971) (van Bekkum, D. W. & Dicke, K. A., eds.), p. 395, Radiobiological Institute TNO, Rijswijk

ISCOVE, N. N., TILL, J. E. & McCULLOCH, E. A. (1970) The proliferative states of mouse granulopoietic progenitor cells. *Proc. Soc. Exp. Biol. Med.* **134**, 33

LUFT, J. H. (1961) Improvements in epoxy resin embedding methods. *J. Biophys. Biochem. Cytol.* **9**, 409

MALAMED, S. (1963) Use of a microcentrifuge for preparation of isolated mitochondria and cell suspensions for electron microscopy. *J. Cell Biol.* **18**, 696

MILLER, R. G. & PHILLIPS, R. A. (1969) Separation of cells by velocity sedimentation. *J. Cell. Physiol.* **73**, 191

MOORE, M. A. S., WILLIAMS, N. & METCALF, D. (1972) Purification and characterisation of the in vitro colony forming cell in monkey hemopoietic tissue. *J. Cell. Physiol.* **79**, 283

MORI, Y. & UNNERT, K. (1969) *Electron Microscopic Atlas of Lymph Node Cytology and Pathology*, p. 9, Springer, Berlin

NAKEFF, A. & DICKE, K. A. (1972) Stem cell differentiation into megakaryocytes from mouse bone marrow cultured with the thin layer agar technique. *Exp. Hematol.* **22**, 58

NIEWISCH, H., VOGEL, H. & MATIOLI, G. (1967) Concentration, quantitations and identifications of hemopoietic cells. *Proc. Natl Acad. Sci. U.S.A.* **58**, 2261

NOWELL, P. C., HIRSCH, B. E., FOX, D. H. & WILSON, D. B. (1970) Evidence for the existence of multipotential lympho-hematopoietic stem cells in the adult rat. *J. Cell. Physiol.* **75**, 151

PLUZNIK, D. H. & SACHS, L. (1966) Induction of clones of normal mast cells by a substance from conditioned medium. *Exp. Cell Res.* **43**, 553

ROSSE, C. & YOFFEY, J. M. (1967) The morphology of the transitional lymphocyte in guinea pig bone marrow. *J. Anat.* **99**, 841

SAYK, J. (1960) *Cytologie der cerebro-spinal Flüssigkeit. Ergebnisse vergleichender Untersuchungen*, Fischer, Jena

SCHAEFER, U. W., DICKE, K. A. & VAN BEKKUM, D. W. (1972) Recovery of haemopoiesis in lethally irradiated monkeys by frozen allogeneic marrow grafts. *Rev. Eur. Etud. Clin. Biol.* **17**, 483

TILL, J. E. & McCULLOCH, E. A. (1961) A direct measurement of the radiation sensitivity of normal mouse bone marrow cells. *Radiat. Res.* **14**, 213

TRENTIN, J. J. & FAHLBERG, W. J. (1963) in *Conceptual Advances in Immunology and Oncology: an experimental model for studies of immunologic competence in irradiated mice repopulated with 'clones' of spleen cells*, p. 66, Hoeber, New York

VAN BEKKUM, D. W. & DE VRIES, M. J. (1967) *Radiation Chimaeras*, Logos/Academic Press, London

VAN BEKKUM, D. W. & DICKE, K. A. (1971) in *The Separation of Haemopoietic Cell Suspensions* (Proceedings of a workshop/symposium held in Rijswijk, 1970) (van Bekkum, D. W. & Dicke, K. A., eds.), p. 147, Radiobiological Institute TNO, Rijswijk

VAN BEKKUM, D. W., VAN NOORD, M. J., MAAT, B. & DICKE, K. A. (1971) Attempts at identification of hemopoietic stem cell in mouse. *Blood J. Hematol.* **38**, 547

VELDMAN, J. E. (1970) Histophysiology and electron microscopy of the immune response, p. 100, thesis, University of Groningen

VENABLE, J. H. & COGGESHALL, R. (1965) A simplified lead citrate stain for use in electron microscopy. *J. Cell Biol.* **25**, 407

YOFFEY, J. M. (1971) Experimental approaches to the stem cell problem in post-natal life. *Isr. J. Med. Sci.* **1**, 927

ZUCKER-FRANKLIN, D. (1969) The ultrastructure of lymphocytes. *Semin. Hematol.* **6**, 4

Discussion

Loutit: Professor Yoffey's main points about morphology, quantification and terminology have been covered here. I think it would be agreed from what Dr Dicke has said that this stem cell is not a small lymphocyte, but is one of Professor Yoffey's lympho-transitional groups.

Yoffey: The cell in Fig. 1 (Yoffey) is full of monoribosomes, no polyribosomes; is that a cell meeting your morphological criteria, Dr Dicke?

Dicke: I doubt it. There seem to be many polyribosomes there and the nuclear chromatin structure is not dispersed enough.

Yoffey: But there are very few polyribosomes, in fact. What perhaps gives the impression of the presence of polyribosomes is the dense staining of some of the monoribosomes. The variable staining of the monoribosomes, some ribo-

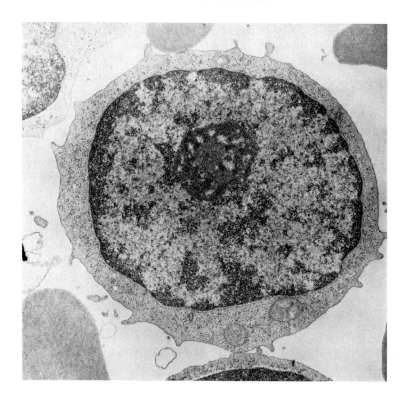

FIG. 1. (Yoffey) A typical medium transitional cell from guinea pig bone marrow. This cell is leptochromatic, the juxta-membranous condensation of chromatin has largely disappeared, and as compared with the pachychromatic small lymphocyte there is an increased ratio of parachromatin to chromatin. The cytoplasm contains mainly monoribosomes. (From Bainton & Yoffey 1970).

somes staining lightly, others quite densely, is a puzzling phenomenon which we have frequently noted.

The comparison with the thoracic duct lymphocytes is a dangerous one, because these are a completely different cell population, not haemopoietic at all and mainly an immunologically conditioned population. The real comparison is with small lymphocytes in bone marrow. Even in bone marrow, as Dr Rosse has shown (1972), about 13% of the marrow small lymphocytes belong to the recirculating group, so that when one considers the morphology or properties of marrow lymphocytes one must bear this distribution in mind.

Dicke: Comparative studies of the CMOMC (cell meeting our morphological criteria, i.e. the haemopoietic stem cell) and lymphocytes derived from the bone marrow have been performed. Cross-sections of cells prepared for electron microscopy revealed a distinct difference in morphology between the CMOMC and the marrow lymphocyte, which latter population could be concentrated also by density gradient centrifugation of the bone marrow.

Yoffey: I would not like to say on morphological grounds that the cells in my Fig. 1 here and your Fig. 4 (p. 60) were two different cells.

Dicke: If your cell (Fig. 1) does not contain many polyribosomes, as you say. I do not see a morphological difference between it and our CMOMC.

Winterhalter: In Table 4 (p. 56) in fractions 3/3 and 3/2 the percentages of CMOMCs seem to be approximately the same. Would that imply that in this step you do not get any purification?

Dicke: In both fractions the recovery of stem cells is about 20%. However, the cell yield per fraction is not the same, so the purification of stem cells in the two fractions is different, namely in fraction 3/2 a factor of 50 and in 3/3 a factor of 18.

Winterhalter: So you are really just cutting the population in half?

Dicke: Yes, but there is a difference in stem cell concentration between the two fractions, as I said.

Astaldi: Some lymphocytes were very responsive to phytohaemagglutinin and others were not responsive. Have you tested the unresponsive cells with pokeweed mitogen, which stimulates both T and B lymphocytes, whereas PHA stimulates only T lymphocytes?

Dicke: In the only two experiments I did the cells were completely negative, but these are preliminary results.

McCulloch: I should like to comment on these morphological papers since in the past I have said repeatedly that a search for a morphological identification of haemopoietic stem cells is a waste of time. I repeat that view now and provide some of the evidence on which it is based.

Dr Dicke said explicitly, and Dr Yoffey implied, that the motivation behind a search for a morphological identification is to use morphology as an assay for stem cells: that is, for Dr Dicke, to monitor suspensions used for transplantation, and for Dr Yoffey, to follow transitions between stem cells and their descendants. Any assay must have at least three characteristics: first, it must specifically identify a discrete class of cells; second, it must be selective so that members of this class are readily identified in a heterogeneous population; third, it must be objective.

The morphological assay lacks all of these three desirable qualities. First, the identifications that we have heard here lack specificity; Dr Yoffey repeatedly emphasized that populations of 'transitional' cells are functionally heterogeneous and hence their identification is not that of cells with functional specificity. His paper also emphasized the immense labour involved in morphological identification, a clear indication that selectivity is absent. Finally, we have just heard Drs Yoffey and Dicke disagree on the interpretation of two pictures of cells, a beautiful demonstration of the subjectivity of morphological methods.

The weakness of morphology is even more apparent when the problem of stem cell identification is examined on the basis of the known physical properties of stem cells. For example, Worton *et al.* (1969) analysed marrow by velocity sedimentation, a technique which allows one to sort cells according to size. In those experiments, the peaks of both CFU–S and CFU–C were quite broad, indicating that these functionally homogeneous populations are heterogeneous in respect to size. Thus, since size is an important part of the morphological identification, it would be unreasonable to expect to identify these cells by their appearance.

Incidentally, the separation that Worton achieved between CFU–S and CFU–C is one of many pieces of evidence that the cells detected by the culture method are not identical with the cells detected by the spleen colony assay.

I regret that these objections tend to deprive morphologists of the aesthetic pleasures they derive from looking at cells. Perhaps a new morphology is emerging however, in which the physical properties of cells can be displayed in a three-dimensional plot similar to a contour map (Moon *et al.* 1972). I submit that such methodology will provide a new way of looking at populations in a quantitative and objective fashion.

Dicke: Concerning the non-identity of the CFU–S and the CFU–C in your culture system, I only want to say that I do not expect that the CFU–C in every culture system being used has properties similar to those of the CFU–S. The CFU–C in the thin-layer method clearly demonstrates an identical behaviour to the CFU–S in many aspects and in particular in the sedimentation chamber in which both cell types show similar sedimentation rate profiles.

References

BAINTON, D. H. & YOFFEY, J. M. (1970) in *Lymphatics, Lymph and the Lymphomyeloid Complex* (Yoffey, J. M. & Courtice, F. C., eds.), Academic Press, London

MOON, R., PHILLIPS, R. A. & MILLER, R. G. (1972) Sedimentation and volume analysis of human bone marrow. *Ser. Haematol.* **5** (2), 163

ROSSE, C. (1972) Migration of long-lived lymphocytes to the bone marrow and to other lymphomyeloid tissues in normal and parabiotic guinea pigs. *Blood J. Hematol.* **40**, 90–97

WORTON, R. G., MCCULLOCH, E. A. & TILL, J. E. (1969) Physical separation of hemopoietic stem cells from cells forming colonies in culture. *J. Cell. Physiol.* **74**, 171

The radiation chimera as an experimental model for the study of haemopoietic stem cell populations

D. BRYNMOR THOMAS

Department of Anatomy, The Medical School, University of Birmingham

Abstract The ability of cells derived from haemopoietic tissues to repopulate the lymphomyeloid complex in lethally irradiated mice has been exploited to provide information about some of the properties of haemopoietic stem cells.

Measured differences in proliferative capacity have been used to assess differences in the stem cell populations of different haemopoietic tissues, and measured changes in proliferative capacity have been used to assess the effects of perturbation on the stem cell population of bone marrow. Changes in the proliferative capacity of transplanted bone marrow cells, which presumably reflect changes in the relative size of the stem cell population of bone marrow, are paralleled by changes in one cell population only—the '*transitional cells*'. A discrepancy between the relative sizes of the transitional cell populations of bone marrow and of foetal liver is not, however, matched by a comparable discrepancy between the proliferative capacities of transplanted cells derived from bone marrow and from foetal liver.

The differentiation of cells derived from different populations, in which contrasting patterns of haemopoietic activity are exhibited, has been analysed after transplantation to various sites. In every instance the transplanted cells have differentiated in a similar fashion in each site. The differentiation of transplanted haemopoietic cells has, however, been shown to be subject to modification under the influence of different local conditions in different microenvironments.

The term radiation chimera was introduced to designate an animal which has been protected against the acute effects of a lethal dose of whole-body X-irradiation by an injection of a haemopoietic cell suspension, when it was demonstrated that such protection can be attributed to repopulation of the damaged haemopoietic and lymphoid tissues by cells derived from the injected suspension (Ford *et al.* 1956; Smith & Congdon 1960; Micklem & Loutit 1966; van Bekkum & de Vries 1967). The population of cells responsible for protection must of necessity maintain itself, while providing a continuous output to the various differentiation compartments of the haemopoietic and lymphoid tissues, throughout the life of the chimera. It is thus by definition a stem cell population, the properties of which will be reflected in the distribution, proliferation and differentiation of donor cells after transplantation and consequently in the patterns of regeneration exhibited by the repopulated tissues. The radiation chimera is therefore a valuable experimental model which can be exploited to provide useful information about haemopoietic stem cell populations (Thomas 1973*a*).

THE PROLIFERATIVE CAPACITY OF HAEMOPOIETIC CELL POPULATIONS

The *proliferative capacity* (PC) of a cell population is a measure of its ability to grow or to undergo renewal without having to import cells. It may be defined as the number of new cells produced under standardized conditions in a sample of given initial size (I) during an arbitrarily defined time interval of adequate convenient duration (T), in which cells capable of proliferation are not lost from the sample. It depends on the number of cells initially present that are capable of proliferating for an indefinite period (stem cells, S), the number capable of proliferating for a limited period (L) and the number of progeny (N_s or N_l) derived from each progenitor during the time selected (T):

$$PC = [(S \times N_s) - S] + [(L \times N_l) - L]$$

As T increases, the number of progeny derived from each progenitor will increase, so that if T is long enough S and L will be insignificant in comparison with $(S \times N_s)$ and $(L \times N_l)$. At the same time N_s will increase relative to N_l until eventually $(L \times N_l)$ becomes insignificant in comparison with $(S \times N_s)$, even though L may be very much larger than S. Hence:

$$PC = (S \times N_s) = (S \times N)$$

The *relative proliferative capacity* (RPC) of a cell population expresses its proliferative capacity (PC_t) in terms of that of a convenient standard population (PC_m). Thus the proliferative capacity of a murine haemopoietic cell population may be expressed in terms of the proliferative capacity of the population of nucleated cells which can be isolated from the femoral diaphysis of a healthy young adult mouse:

$$RPC = \frac{PC_t}{PC_m} = \frac{S_t \times N_t}{S_m \times N_m}$$

The terms proliferative capacity and relative proliferative capacity now proposed are preferable to alternatives such as repopulation ability because the replacement of host cells by donor cells does not necessarily result in detectable regeneration (see p. 83). The term *repopulation index* could be advantageously employed to designate the percentage of donor elements in a particular population and should be used only in this restricted sense.

Any change (C) which occurs in the size of a cell population of initial size I during the interval T will depend on the relationship between its proliferative capacity (PC), the number of cells entering it (E) and the number lost from it (L). If the cells which enter and leave the population are not capable of proliferation:

$$C = PC + E - L$$

When the number of cells lost from the population is proportional to the number of cells in the population (Gilbert & Lajtha 1965), then:

$$L = K (PC + E)$$
$$\therefore C = (PC + E) - K (PC + E) = Ki (PC + E)$$

where $Ki = 1 - K$. When the number of cells entering the population (E) is small in comparison with the number of cells produced in the population (PC), E can be disregarded, so that:

$$C = Ki. PC$$

The RPC of any haemopoietic cell population can thus be estimated by relating the increase in size of a suitable cell population in irradiated mice which have received a given number of cells derived from the population under investigation (C_t), to the increase in irradiated mice which have received an equal number of femoral bone marrow cells from young adult donors (C_m) during a given time, provided that the increase in the size of the population on which the estimate is based is due to donor cell proliferation, that after transplantation Ki is equal for both donor cell populations, and that the proliferative capacities of the two donor cell populations are not differentially modified after transplantation:

$$\frac{C_t}{C_m} = \frac{PC_t}{PC_m} = RPC$$

In order to balance the effects of regulatory mechanisms and of competition for space in the host environment, it is desirable to ensure equal degrees of regeneration in the irradiated recipients of both donor cell populations. At the same time it is advantageous to ensure that the magnitude of the increase in the size of the population on which the assay is based enables it to be measured with maximal accuracy. These requirements can be satisfied by determining the number of cells from each group of donors which is required to produce an increase of convenient, arbitrarily defined magnitude in the cell population under consideration (D_t and D_m) (see Finney 1964). Then:

$$\frac{1/D_t}{1/D_m} = \frac{D_m}{D_t} = \left[\frac{PC_t}{PC_m} = \frac{S_t \times N_t}{S_m \times N_m} \right] = RPC$$

For the validity of this relationship, and of the assumptions made during its derivation, to be tested, it is necessary to determine the values of D_m/D_t (relative proliferative capacity), S_t/S_m (relative proportion of stem cells) and N_t/N_m (relative clone size) for several different populations of haemopoietic cells. In each instance it should then be possible to use any two of these ratios to calculate the third.

Regeneration of the haemopoietic and lymphoid tissues in the mouse radiation chimera has been analysed in an attempt to select the most reliable indices of the proliferative capacity of transplanted haemopoietic cell populations, and the properties of haemopoietic cell clones isolated *in vivo* have been studied in an attempt to assess both the proportion of stem cells and the average number of progeny derived from each stem cell during a given time under standardized conditions.

REGENERATION OF THE HAEMOPOIETIC AND LYMPHOID TISSUES IN MOUSE RADIATION CHIMERAS

The patterns of initial damage and of subsequent regeneration exhibited by the haemopoietic and lymphoid tissues during the eight weeks after exposure to a single lethal dose of whole-body X-irradiation (820 rads, 300 kVp, 5mA, 5.0 mm aluminium + 0.5 mm copper filtration, dose rate 64 rd/min) have been analysed in albino mice (specific pathogen-free females of the CS1 strain, weight 20–25 g, supplied by Scientific Products Farm, Ash, Kent), which received 5×10^6 syngeneic bone marrow cells by intravenous injection within two hours of being irradiated (see Thomas 1971 for technical details).

All six of the parameters represented in Fig. 1 reveal regeneration in the haemopoietic tissues or in the lymphoid tissues and are therefore potentially useful indices of the proliferative capacity of haemopoietic cell populations. In

TABLE 1

Control values (mean ± standard error) for the albino mice (CS1/Ash) used

Blood	
Nucleated cells	5460 ± 380 per mm^3
Neutrophils	270 ± 60 per mm^3
Lymphocytes	2590 ± 150 per mm^3
Neutrophils, 12 hours after intravenous	
endotoxin	1870 ± 220 per mm^3
Bone marrow	
Nucleated cells (per femoral diaphysis)	$13.1 \pm 1.1 \times 10^6$
Thymus	46.4 ± 1.6 mg
Spleen	93.0 ± 3.3 mg
Lymph nodes (pooled inguinal and brachial)	15.4 ± 0.7 mg

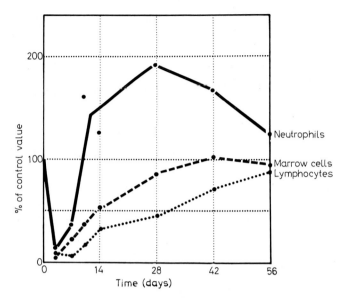

FIG. 1 (*a*) Restoration of the neutrophil content of the blood, the lymphocyte content of the blood and the nucleated cell content of the femoral diaphysis in albino mice which received 5×10^6 syngeneic bone marrow cells after being exposed to 820 rd whole-body X-irradiation. (See also Table 1.)

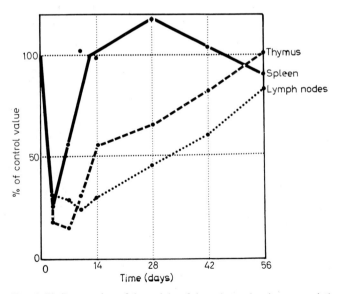

FIG. 1 (*b*) Restoration of the weight of the spleen, the thymus and the lymph nodes (pooled inguinal and brachial nodes).

order to facilitate comparison and graphical representation the value for each parameter is plotted in Fig. 1 as a percentage of the appropriate control value (Table 1).

In order to validate the use of a parameter of haemopoietic or lymphoid tissue regeneration in the radiation chimera as an index of the proliferative capacity of donor cell populations, the following requirements should be satisfied:

(1) The regeneration measured by the parameter must be effected by cells derived from the donor cell population. The haemopoietic and lymphoid tissues of CBA mice are repopulated by proliferating cells carrying marker chromosomes which are derived from suspensions injected shortly after the recipients have been lethally irradiated (Micklem *et al.* 1966). In the absence of differences between host and donor cells, techniques similar to those employed by Micklem and his colleagues are not available for the experimental model on which the present study is based. Allogeneic and xenogeneic cells have however been shown to persist, and CS1 mice which receive 5×10^6 bone marrow cells from CBA donors shortly after exposure to the dose of whole-body X-irradiation used throughout (820 rd) are still unable to reject implants of a CBA mammary adenocarcinoma eight weeks later, whereas similarly irradiated recipients of 5×10^6 CS1 cells reject such tumour implants (Riches & Thomas 1971, and unpublished data). If repopulation had failed to occur, or if reversion had supervened, these CS1 recipients of CBA cells would be expected to reject the tumour allografts in the same way as the CS1 recipients of CS1 cells.

(2) The time required for regeneration of the desired magnitude should be short in order for the assay to be practicable and for survival of the irradiated hosts to be independent of replacement therapy with haemopoietic cells, so that untreated irradiated controls and irradiated mice which receive insufficient numbers of cells from appropriate sources to confer protection can be included. Most CS1 mice survive until the end of the first week after exposure to 820 rd whole-body X-irradiation without receiving replacement therapy, but the majority succumb during the second week after exposure to this dose, which renders the bone marrow virtually acellular and the thymus, spleen and lymph nodes severely atrophic. Even if the irradiated mice are maintained in laminar air-flow cabinets and neomycin is added to the drinking water it is exceptional for more than 50% to survive beyond the end of the second week, but most animals now survive until the 12th day and on the tenth day 95% may be expected to be still surviving instead of 60% in the absence of these precautions (V. Littlewood, A. C. Riches and D. B. Thomas, unpublished data). It is therefore desirable to restrict the period allowed for regeneration to ten days or less.

(3) The regeneration must be large enough to be measured conveniently and

must be shown to be related to replacement therapy with haemopoietic cells. This can be done by comparing the value of the selected parameter in treated animals (V_t) with that in untreated irradiated controls (V_u). The discrepancy between V_t and V_u, on which the usefulness of the parameter depends, can be expressed conveniently in the *regeneration factor* (RF) which measures (V_t-V_u) in relation to V_u:

$$RF = \frac{V_t - V_u}{V_u}$$

On the tenth day after replacement therapy the regeneration factors for the cellularity of the femoral bone marrow, the neutrophil* content of the blood and the mass of the spleen reveal pronounced discrepancies between treated and untreated animals (Fig. 2). The discrepancies are large enough to allow all three of these parameters of regeneration to be used as indices of the proliferative capacity of transplanted haemopoietic cells and to emphasize the dependence of the regeneration measured by each on replacement therapy with haemo-

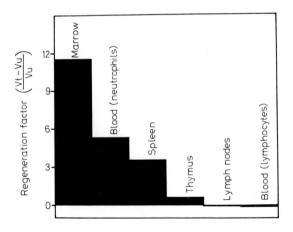

FIG. 2. Regeneration factors in albino mice which received 5×10^6 syngeneic bone marrow cells after being exposed to 820 rd whole-body X-irradiation ten days previously. (V_t: treated; V_u: untreated irradiated controls.)

* There are objections to this designation as these cells do not always exhibit distinct granulation in the mouse. Its use is justified for purposes of comparison, however, as the cells are doubtless analogous to the neutrophils of other animals (Schermer 1967).

poietic cells. In contrast the regeneration factor for the mass of the thymus is small and replacement therapy is not yet reflected in the lymphocyte content of the blood or in the mass of the lymph nodes.

(4) The magnitude of regeneration must be related to the number of donor cells injected, in a manner which allows the dose of donor cells required to effect a convenient, arbitrarily defined degree of regeneration to be estimated reliably· This relationship has been studied in lethally irradiated CS1 mice which had received various doses of bone marrow cells from CS1 donors ten days previously (see p. 74 and Thomas 1971 for technical details).

The *regeneration index* (RI) which is used to compare the recovery patterns revealed by different parameters relates the degree of regeneration which has occurred to the degree of damage sustained—that is to the degree of regeneration required to complete restoration:

$$RI = \frac{V_t - V_u}{V_c - V_u} \times 100$$

where V_c, V_t and V_u represent the values for untreated controls, treated irradiated animals and untreated irradiated animals respectively (Fig. 3). The neutrophil content of the blood, the neutrophil response to endotoxin (TAB vaccine),the nucleated cell content of the femoral bone marrow and the mass of the spleen are all dose-dependent (Fig. 3). A pronounced discrepancy has, however, been revealed between the number of donor cells required to restore the neutrophil content of the blood and the mass of the spleen and the number required to restore the neutrophil response to endotoxin and the nucleated cell content of the femoral diaphysis.

In contrast, the lymphocyte content of the blood, the mass of the thymus and the mass of the lymph nodes are not similarly dependent on the dose of bone marrow cells administered over the range of doses studied. Any assay which required doses in excess of those which have been used would be unsatisfactory, due both to the risk of fatal embolism, which increases with the number of cells injected, and to the difficulty of preparing uncontaminated suspensions of viable cells, which increases with the number of donors required for each recipient.

In the light of these considerations the neutrophil content of the blood, the neutrophil response to endotoxin, the nucleated cell content of the femoral diaphysis and the mass of the spleen emerge as possible indices of proliferative capacity, while the lymphocyte content of the blood, the mass of the thymus and the mass of the lymph nodes fail to do so.

(*a*) *The neutrophil content of the blood* could be used as an index of proliferative capacity only if it could be shown to reflect changes in the total size of the

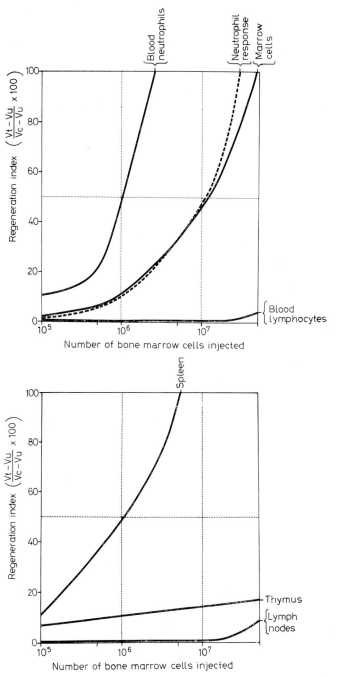

FIG. 3. Regeneration indices in albino mice which received various doses of syngeneic bone marrow cells after being exposed to 820 rd whole-body X-irradiation ten days previously (V_t: treated; V_u: untreated irradiated control; V_c: untreated unirradiated control).

cell populations responsible for neutrophil production. On the tenth day after replacement therapy with haemopoietic cells over 80% of the neutrophils in the blood are of donor origin (Nowell *et al*. 1956), and after the injection of 2.5 × 10^6 bone marrow cells the neutrophil content of unit volume of blood is restored to that in untreated controls. The pattern of restoration of the blood neutrophils does not reflect that of the neutrophil response to endotoxin or that of the bone marrow cells, although it is similar to that of the spleen (Figs. 1, 3). The spleen may therefore provide a supply of blood neutrophils before the bone marrow is able to do so, and this may be supplemented initially by cells derived directly from the neutrophil compartment of the donor cell suspension. An endotoxin-responsive neutrophil reserve comparable in its proportions to that of the bone marrow does not appear to be established in the spleen.

(*b*) *The neutrophil response to endotoxin*. The increase in the neutrophil content of unit volume of blood 12 hours after an intravenous injection of TAB vaccine (0.25 ml) is related to the number of bone marrow cells injected shortly after irradiation ten days previously. Hellman & Grate (1967) have described and exploited a similar relationship between the maximum neutrophil response and the number of cells injected seven days previously but have not demonstrated the relationship which is now evident between the neutrophil response and the nucleated cell content of the femoral diaphysis (Fig. 3).

(*c*) *The nucleated cell content of the femoral diaphysis*. After the seventh day over 90% of the dividing cells in the bone marrow are derived from the donated population (Micklem *et al*. 1966) and the nucleated cell content of the femoral diaphysis on the tenth day is related to the size of this population. In animals which receive 10^5 cells or less, nearly half the cells in the severely hypocellular bone marrow ten days later are lymphocytes and most of the remainder are damaged beyond recognition. After the administration of 5 × 10^5 cells the proportion of lymphocytes decreases and those of granulocytes and erythroblasts increase. As the dose of cells injected is increased above 5 × 10^5 the distribution of haemopoietic cells between the principal morphological categories does not vary significantly (Fig. 4).

Twelve hours after an intravenous injection of TAB vaccine the net loss of neutrophils from the bone marrow (D), in mice exposed to various doses of whole-body X-irradiation ten days previously, is a linear function of the number of neutrophils in the bone marrow (B) before the vaccine was injected (D = 0.85B), and is also related in a linear fashion to the increase in the neutrophil content of unit volume of blood (unpublished data). In the absence of a change in the proportion of neutrophils in the bone marrow as the

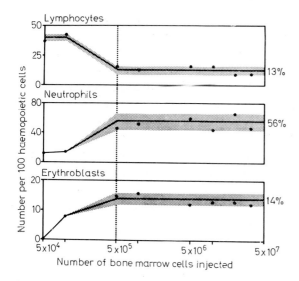

FIG. 4. The distribution of haemopoietic cells between the principal morphological categories in the femoral bone marrow of albino mice which received various doses of syngeneic bone marrow cells after being exposed to 820 rd whole-body X-irradiation ten days previously.

number of cells injected into lethally irradiated recipients is increased, the neutrophil response would thus be expected to reflect the nucleated cell content of the marrow in the way it has been shown to do (Fig. 3). The maximum neutrophil response is determined by examining blood samples at several intervals after an injection of endotoxin, whereas the nucleated cell content of the bone marrow can be estimated using a single suspension, prepared by flushing the contents of the femoral diaphysis into a known volume of suitable fluid, without pretreatment. If the femur is available for examination it is therefore far more convenient to use the nucleated cell content of the diaphysis, without necessarily having to perform a differential count, to assess the size of the marrow neutrophil reserve directly, than it is to use the maximum neutrophil response to do so indirectly.

After injection of 1 μCi of ^{59}Fe, the ^{59}Fe content of the femoral bone marrow and the amount of ^{59}Fe incorporated into haemoglobin are linear functions of the nucleated cell content of the femoral diaphysis in radiation chimeras. The amount of ^{59}Fe incorporated into haemoglobin by a given number of cells is not dependent on the dose of haemopoietic cells in the range from 10^5 to 4×10^7 administered to irradiated recipients ten days previously (Stevens & Thomas 1970), reflecting the absence of a relationship between doses of cells in this range and the proportion of erythroblasts in the bone marrow. Like the neutrophil response, therefore, studies of ^{59}Fe incorporation merely endorse the information provided by measuring the nucleated cell content of the bone marrow, which emerges as a singularly convenient method for measuring a most valuable index of the proliferative capacity of transplanted haemopoietic cells.

On the tenth day the bone marrow of radiation chimeras contains a higher proportion of erythroblasts and a somewhat lower proportion of lymphocytes than the bone marrow of untreated controls, to which it is otherwise very similar with respect to the distribution of cells between the various morphological categories (Fig. 5). The increased relative size of the erythroblast compartment may reflect the increase in the concentration of erythropoietin in the plasma which occurs after the seventh day (O'Grady *et al.* 1966). Subsequently the proportion of erythroblasts decreases and the proportion of lymphocytes increases so that the cellular composition of the bone marrow no longer differs significantly from that in untreated controls.

(*d*) *The weight of the spleen.* Within a week the spleen is repopulated by cells of donor origin (Micklem *et al.* 1966) and on the tenth day the weight of the spleen is related to the number of donor cells injected, as previously noted by Popp *et al.* (1965). Initially enlargement of the damaged spleen does not, however, reflect restoration of the distinctively arranged cell populations of the normal spleen. On the contrary it reflects the establishment of erythroblast and granulocyte populations in the red pulp (Fig. 5), so that the weight of the spleen on the tenth day is a measure of haemopoietic activity rather than of lymphoid tissue recovery. Subsequently the relative sizes of the erythroblast and granulo-

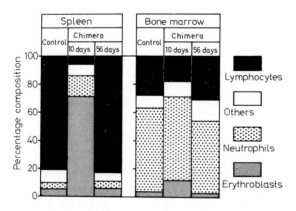

FIG. 5. The composition of the haemopoietic cell populations established in the spleen and in the medullary cavity of the femoral diaphysis 10 and 56 days after the injection of 5×10^6 syngeneic bone marrow cells into albino mice which had been exposed to 820 rd whole-body X-irradiation.

cyte compartments decrease and the white pulp of the spleen regenerates.

The mass of the thymus increases from 7.1 $\pm$ 1.6 mg on the seventh day to 14.4 $\pm$ 3.5 mg on the tenth day and 26.1 $\pm$ 9.4 mg on the 14th day. This increase in the mass of the thymus, which is associated with restoration of its histological organization during the second week, is remarkable because on the 14th day the thymus still contains only a very small proportion of proliferating cells of donor origin (Micklem *et al.* 1966). Presumably therefore the proliferating host cells observed in the thymus by Micklem and his colleagues are responsible for the regeneration which precedes repopulation and parallels the phase of spontaneous thymic regeneration observed in mice exposed to high doses of whole-body X-irradiation without subsequent haemopoietic cell replacement therapy (Thomas 1966; Thomas & Congdon 1967; Sharp & Thomas 1970). The absence of a pronounced difference between the mass of the thymus in treated and in untreated animals on day 10 (Fig. 2) and the absence of a clear relationship between the mass of the thymus and the dose of haemopoietic cells injected ten days previously (Fig. 3) are consistent with this view.

Cells derived from the lymphoid tissues repopulate the lymph nodes but not the bone marrow, the spleen or the thymus, before being replaced by cells derived from the bone marrow (Micklem *et al.* 1966). On the tenth day over 90% of the proliferating cells in the lymph nodes are derived from injected lymphoid cells but the presence of these cells does not appear to be reflected in regeneration. Such *ineffective* repopulation by lymphoid cells contrasts with *effective* repopulation by bone marrow cells. The slow recovery of the lymph nodes is paralleled by slow restoration of the white pulp of the spleen and of the blood lymphocytes. Regeneration of lymphoid tissue is reflected in the recovery of the immune response, which is revealed in restoration of the ability of chimeras to respond to injected sheep erythrocytes (Agarossi & Doria 1968) and to reject tumour allografts (Riches & Thomas 1971).

HAEMOPOIETIC CELL CLONES ISOLATED IN VIVO

After injection of a suitable number of haemopoietic cells into a heavily irradiated mouse, macroscopic nodules form in the spleen (Till & McCulloch 1961). Most of these nodules appear to be clones, each of which is derived from a single progenitor cell of donor origin (Chen & Schooley 1968). Such clones or colonies may be composed of erythroblasts, granulocytes, megakaryocytes or mixtures of cells (Till & McCulloch 1961; McCulloch & Till 1962). A spatial relationship has been demonstrated between a high proportion of surface colonies and discrete zones of iron concentration which are revealed by macroautoradiography (Thomas *et al.* 1970) (Fig. 6). Over 80% of macroscopic surface colonies correspond in position to zones of iron concentration (Thomas 1973*b*). Hyper-transfusion inhibits the formation of these zones (Thomas *et al.* 1972), just as it

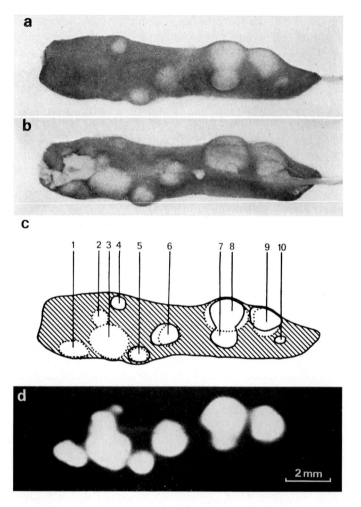

Fig. 6. The spatial relationship between macroscopic surface colonies and zones of iron concentration in the spleen of an albino mouse which received 10^5 syngeneic bone marrow cells by intravenous injection shortly after being exposed to 820 rd whole-body X-irradiation ten days previously. (*a*) Superficial aspect. (*b*) Mirror image of deep aspect. (*c*) *a* and *b* superimposed; colonies visible from the superficial aspect are demarcated by continuous lines and those visible from the deep aspect by dotted lines. (*d*) Macroautoradiogram; colonies 1–9 are represented but the zones representing the adjacent colonies 2–3 and 7–8 are confluent. Colony 10 is not represented and does not appear to have concentrated ^{59}Fe. Macroauto-radiograms prepared from both aspects of the spleen were not appreciably different.

inhibits that of the erythroid colonies which they appear to represent (Schooley 1964; Feldman *et al.* 1966; Curry *et al.* 1967).

Zones of iron concentration enlarge progressively between the fourth day, when they are first clearly demarcated, and the 11th day, when individual zones are obscured by confluence. The time required for zones to double their area can be used to calculate the volume doubling time of the spleen colonies which they represent, and this gives a value that is in good agreement with the cell doubling time in macroscopic colonies estimated in a quite different manner by Schofield & Lajtha (1969).

The number of zones of iron concentration (FeZ) is related to the number of macroscopic surface colonies (SC) in the equation:

$$FeZ = SC - (Co + Cf + Nc) + Dc$$

where Co is the number of surface colonies obscured due to coincidence, Cf is the number obscured by confluence, Nc is the number of surface colonies which do not concentrate iron and Dc is the number of zones which do not correspond in position to surface colonies (Thomas 1973*b*). The errors due to coincidence and confluence can be virtually eliminated by allowing colonies to grow for nine days or less and by adjusting the number of cells injected so as to ensure the formation of not more than ten colonies per spleen.

Neither macroscopic nodules nor zones of iron concentration can be demonstrated in the bone marrow of radiation chimeras but histological examination reveals the presence of scattered discrete collections of cells, which appear during the course of bone marrow regeneration and may be analogous to spleen colonies (Fig. 7). The optimum conditions for the study of these bone marrow colonies are quite different from those for the study of spleen colonies. Whereas spleen colonies must be large enough to be seen macroscopically, bone marrow colonies must be small enough to remain isolated and discrete. Spleen colonies are therefore allowed to grow for nine or ten days to assume considerable dimensions but bone marrow colonies should be allowed to grow for only three or four days. In order to ensure that the large colonies formed in the spleen are not too crowded, a suitably small dose of cells must be injected, but as bone marrow colonies are studied while they are still very small the number of cells injected may be increased in order to increase the number of colonies available for study. Bone marrow colonies, which cannot be enumerated conveniently or accurately,

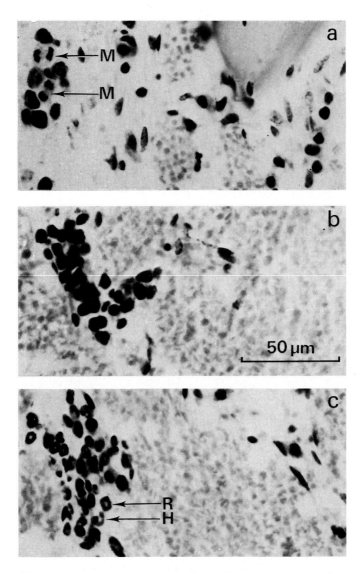

FIG. 7. Collections of haemopoietic cells (colonies) in the medullary cavities of an albino mouse which received 5 × 10⁶ syngeneic bone marrow cells after being exposed to 820 rd four days previously. (*a*) Small, undifferentiated colony in which mitotic figures (M) are conspicuous. (*b*) Erythroid colony. (*c*) Granulocytic colony containing numerous ring (R) and horseshoe (H)-shaped nuclei. (Haematoxylin & eosin.)

can be classified on a cytological basis and are of value in studies of stem cell differentiation rather than of stem cell population size.

The proportion of cells capable of forming colonies or zones of iron concentration should be estimated by determining the number of cells from a population required to establish a convenient number (ten) of colonies or zones in the spleen of an irradiated recipient, rather than by determining the number of colonies or zones established after the injection of a given number of cells (cf. p. 73). If colony-forming cells account for the same proportion of the stem cells in two populations of haemopoietic cells, the relationship between the number of colony-forming cells or units (CFU) in population samples of equal size (st/sm) will be the same as the relationship between the number of stem cells in each sample (S_t/S_m) (*relative stem cell proportion*), provided that colony-forming cells from the two populations are similarly distributed in the irradiated hosts and are not damaged differentially during the preparation and injection of cell suspensions.

The number of cells (H) in a spleen colony is related to the number of progeny (N) derived from its single progenitor (I), the number of cells entering it (E) and the number of cells leaving it (L) during an adequate time interval (T), in the equation:

$$H = N + E - L + I$$

— provided that cells capable of proliferation do not enter or leave the colony. I is equal to one, so if the number of cells lost from the colony bears a constant relationship to the number of cells it contains and if the number of cells entering the colony is small in relation to the number of cells produced in it:

$$H = K . N$$

The relationship between the average number of cells in the colonies derived from two populations (H_t/H_m) will therefore be the same as the relationship between the number of progeny derived from a single stem cell in each case (N_t/N_m), provided that K is the same for both populations.

The number of cells in a colony (H) could be determined directly from serial sections but it would be exceedingly laborious to do so. The volume of spleen colonies can, however, be used as an index of cell content, if it is assumed that the mean volume of the component cells does not vary appreciably. This can be measured in serial sections (Reincke 1970) *or* by using a measuring scale in the eye-piece of a dissecting microscope to measure macroscopic surface colonies, *or* by measuring the surface area of the zones which represent iron concentrating colonies in macroautoradiograms (see p. 83). The relationship between the volume (V_t/V_m) of the colonies is then used to estimate the relationship of N_t to N_m (*relative clone size*).

It has already been seen that under suitable conditions spleen colonies are derived from donor cells and, like the zones which represent iron-concentrating colonies in autoradiograms, achieve adequate dimensions within ten days. As the number of colonies or zones per spleen is a linear function of the number of cells injected over a wide range of doses (Marshall *et al*, 1971), a pronounced discrepancy can be ensured between the number of spleen colonies or zones in radiation chimeras and in irradiated controls (cf. p. 77).

THE RELATIONSHIP BETWEEN INDICES OF PROLIFERATIVE CAPACITY

The ratios s_t/s_m (p. 87) and V_t/V_m (p. 87) may thus be substituted for S_t/S_m and N_t/N_m in the equation on page 73, giving:

$$\frac{D_m}{D_t} = \frac{s_t}{s_m} \times \frac{V_t}{V_m}$$

The indices of proliferative capacity have been determined using lethally irradiated albino mice treated with various doses of cells derived from the femoral bone marrow of untreated donors, foetal liver on the 16th day of gestation, which contains a lower proportion of CFU (McCulloch & Till 1963; Micklem 1966), and the femoral bone marrow of donors treated with mustine hydrochloride four days previously, which contains a higher proportion of CFU (Sharp & Thomas 1971). The estimated values for the three ratios are in reasonably good agreement with the values calculated for each using the other two (Table 2).

The proliferative capacities of haemopoietic cell populations can be compared most completely, conveniently and reliably by determining the number of cells from each required to:

(1) Establish a convenient, arbitrarily defined number of colonies in the spleen (10);

(2) Establish a convenient, arbitrarily defined number of zones of iron concentration in the spleen (10);

(3) Effect a convenient, arbitrarily defined increase in the weight of the spleen (50 mg);

(4) Effect a convenient, arbitrarily defined increase in the cellularity of the femoral bone marrow (5×10^6 cells).

The relative proliferative capacity can then be calculated from (3) or (4) and used together with the relative stem cell proportion, calculated from (1) or (2). The relative clone size, which is tedious to measure, can be estimated using the equation given above and measured directly only when specifically required.

THE MORPHOLOGICAL CHARACTERIZATION OF THE HAEMOPOIETIC STEM CELL

Asynchronous restoration of the CFU content and the nucleated cell content

TABLE 2

The relationship between indices of proliferative capacity

D^1	Number of donor cells required to produce an increase of 50 mg in the weight of the spleen
D^{11}	Number of donor cells required to produce an increase of 5×10^6 in the nucleated cell content of the femoral diaphysis
s	Number of CFU per 10^5 donor cells
V	Mean volume of spleen colonies
m	Femoral bone marrow
t^1, t^2 ...	Test populations

$$\frac{D_m}{D_t} = \frac{s_t}{s_m} \times \frac{V_t}{V_m}$$

(see page 88)

Mouse foetal liver on the 16th day of gestation (unpublished data of D. B. Thomas, C. M. Smith and J. M. Sumpster):

			t/m	
	m	t	Observed	Calculated
D^1	2.2×10^6	3.0×10^6	1.4	1.1
s	10	4	0.4	0.3
V	1.1 mm³	2.5 mm³	2.2	1.8

Mouse bone marrow four days after an injection of mustine hydrochloride (100 µg) (unpublished data of D. B. Thomas, J. G. Sharp and C. V. Briscoe):

			t/m	
	m	t	Observed	Calculated
D^1	2.5×10^6	1.0×10^5	0.04	
			0.06	0.07
D^{11}	1.0×10^7	8.0×10^5	0.08	
s	8	100	13	17
V	1.1 mm³	1.2 mm³	1.1	1.5

of the femoral bone marrow in mice treated with mustine hydrochloride results in an increase in the proportion of CFU on the fourth day (Sharp & Thomas 1971) which is reflected by an increase in proliferative capacity (Table 2). This increase is paralleled by a corresponding increase in only one group of bone marrow cells —the *transitional cells* (see Sharp *et al.* 1971) (Figs. 8, 9). On this basis, therefore, transitional cells are the only candidates for the role of haemopoietic stem cell.

Transitional cells, which may form a complete spectrum of morphological continuity between generalized blast cells and small lymphocytes, have previously

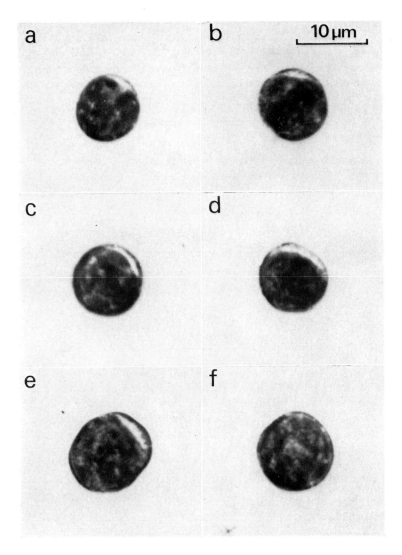

FIG. 8. Transitional cells in murine femoral bone marrow. The basophilic cytoplasm of cell (*f*) surrounds the nucleus almost completely. (Smear: Jenner-Giemsa.)

been observed in rabbit bone marrow (Dominici 1902), guinea pig bone marrow (Yoffey 1957, 1960, 1966) and in human bone marrow during the foetal period (Yoffey & Thomas 1961). The morphology of transitional cells in the guinea pig, which has been described in detail by Yoffey *et al.* (1965), is similar to that of transitional cells in the mouse (Sharp *et al.* 1971) (Figs. 8, 9).

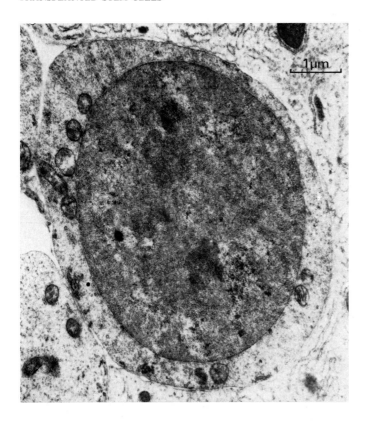

Fɪɢ. 9. Transitional cell in murine foetal liver on the 15th day of gestation. (1 % Caufield's fixative, 1 % phosphotungstic acid, Araldite)

Four days after an injection of mustine hydrochloride (100 μg) the femoral diaphysis of the mouse contains $3.9 \pm 0.3 \times 10^5$ transitional cells ($62 \pm 4\%$ of $6.3 \pm 0.5 \times 10^5$ nucleated cells), compared with only 3.7×10^3 CFU (630 × 1/0.17.) The fraction of the injected CFUs forming colonies in the spleen, 'f', was estimated to be 0.17 by Siminovitch *et al.* (1963). Similar values have been reported by Schooley (1966) and Haskill *et al.* (1970)]. The preliminary results of an investigation currently in progress indicate that 1.2×10^3 (0.3%) of these transitional cells are labelled one hour after an intravenous injection of tritiated thymidine (C. V. Briscoe, V. Littlewood, J. G. Sharp and D. B. Thomas, unpublished data).

According to Covelli *et al.* (1972), 2.2×10^5 cells per hour enter the proerythroblast compartment of a mouse weighing 25 g. The number of haemopoietic cells in the mouse has been estimated to be 2.41×10^7/g body weight (Smith & Clayton 1970), so that a mouse weighing 25 g would be expected to contain

6.0×10^8 haemopoietic cells. This corresponds exactly to the value estimated by Covelli *et al.* (1972). If this population contains between 10 and 20 CFU per 10^5 cells, which represents 0.17 of the cells potentially capable of forming spleen colonies, the mouse will contain $3.5 - 7.0 \times 10^5$ CFU. All the CFU in the animal will therefore be consumed in less than four hours, in order to ensure continued erythrocyte production, if CFU are the cells transferred from the stem cell compartment to the proerythroblast compartment. This estimate does not take into account the entry of stem cells into the other differentiation compartments. In mice treated with phenylhydrazine a sixfold increase in the rate of erythrocyte production has been observed after four days (Stevens & Thomas 1973). This increase may necessitate a similar increase in the rate at which cells enter the proerythroblast compartment—to more than 1×10^6 cells per hour—as has been shown to happen in the rat (Tarbutt 1969). In this case the CFU population, which needs 20–25 hours to double its size while maintaining its output (McCulloch & Till 1964), would be consumed in less than one hour. It is therefore probable that, like the transitional cell population, the population which provides the input to the proerythroblast compartment is very large in comparison with the CFU population.

The proportion of transitional cells is not invariably a guide to the proliferative capacity of a cell population. Thus a tenfold discrepancy between the proportion of transitional cells in suspensions prepared from foetal liver on the 16th day of gestation and from the femoral bone marrow of adult mice is not paralleled by a comparable difference in proliferative capacity or stem cell proportion (Table 2). In foetal liver the interrelationships of different compartments of the stem cell population may be different from those in adult bone marrow and the stem cell population may be related to more generalized cells in a manner such as that envisaged by Thomas & Yoffey (1964).

THE DIFFERENTIATION POTENTIAL OF HAEMOPOIETIC CELL POPULATIONS

The *differentiation potential* of a haemopoietic cell population is a measure of its ability to produce different varieties of cells. It may be assessed by comparing the differentiation of cells derived from the population with that of cells derived from the femoral bone marrow in similar environments under comparable conditions. In lethally irradiated mice the medullary cavity of the femur and the spleen, which are repopulated by cells of donor origin (Micklem *et al.* 1966), provide such environments.

The cell populations established in these two situations have been studied ten days after the injection of various cell suspensions into lethally irradiated recipients. Suspensions of femoral bone marrow cells from untreated donors have been used, together with suspensions of foetal liver cells, bone marrow cells from animals treated with mustine hydrochloride eight days previously, and spleen cells, in which more than four cells out of five are respectively erythroblasts, granulocytes and lymphocytes (Fig. 10). The cell populations established in the medullary cavity are all of similar composition and do not reflect the different patterns of activity exhibited in the donor tissues. A high proportion

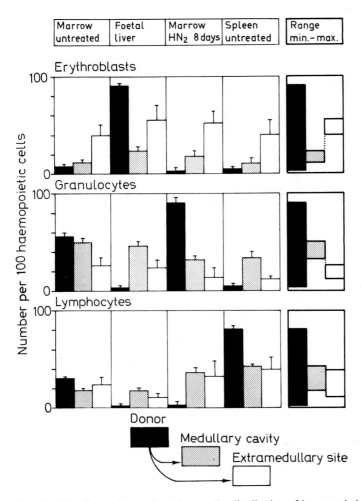

FIG. 10. The effects of transplantation on the distribution of haemopoietic cells between the principal morphological categories (Thomas 1971, and C. V. Briscoe, J. G. Sharp and D. B. Thomas, unpublished data). HN2 8 days – mice which received 100 μg mustine hydrochloride by intravenous injection 8 days before donating bone marrow cells.

of lymphocytes in the bone marrow of a radiation chimera should be interpreted with caution and in relation to the nucleated cell content of the femoral diaphysis, in view of the observation that in irradiated recipients of small doses of donor cells the bone marrow contains a high proportion of lymphocytes (Fig. 4). The cell populations established in the spleen are also all similar in composition and, like those established in the medullary cavity, do not reflect the different patterns of activity exhibited in the donor tissues. The composition of the cell populations established in the spleen is however different from that of the cell populations established in the marrow. Thus in the spleen there are more than two-and-a-half times as many erythroblasts as granulocytes, whereas in the medullary cavity there are less than half as many. For a given number of erythroblasts the medullary cavity contains about six times as many granulocytes as the spleen (Thomas 1970a, 1971). This discrepancy is paralleled in untreated controls and is exaggerated after treatment with mustine hydrochloride, which results in an increase in the granulocyte content of the bone marrow that is most pronounced after eight days, and after treatment with phenylhydrazine, which results in an increase in the erythroblast content of the bone marrow that is maximal after four days (Table 3).

Provided that changes in the kinetic properties of the various differentiation compartments do not balance differences in the output from the stem cell com-

TABLE 3

The effects of phenylhydrazine and of mustine hydrochloride on the proportions of erythroblasts and granulocytes in the medullary cavity of the femur (MC) and in an extramedullary site (EMS) (unpublished data of C. V. Briscoe, J. G. Sharp, R. F. Stevens and D. B. Thomas for CS1 mice)

| Treatment | Granulocytes per 100 erythroblasts (GE) | | GE (MC) / GE (EMS) |
	MC (femur)	EMS (spleen)	
(a) Untreated	800	100	8
(b) 9–12 days after 100 µg mustine hydrochloride	986	14	70
13–16 days after 100 µg mustine hydrochloride	248	14	18
17–20 days after 100 µg mustine hydrochloride	247	56	4
(c) 4 days after 4 mg phenylhydrazine	71	3	24
6 days after 4 mg phenylhydrazine	105	5	21
8 days after 4 mg phenylhydrazine	433	5	86

partment, it may be inferred from the absence of significant differences in the composition of the cell populations which are established in the medullary cavity of the femur or in the spleen by stem cell populations derived from different sources, that these populations do not differ appreciably in their relative abilities to produce erythroblasts, granulocytes or lymphocytes (differentiation potential), although the number of cells from each source required to produce a population of given size (proliferative capacity) does vary. The similarities of differentiation potential suggest that the stem cell populations from each source consist of similar multipotent cells. This is consistent with the observations of Curry *et al.* (1967), Lewis & Trobaugh (1964) and Wu *et al.* (1967, 1968). The alternative interpretation, that the stem cell populations from different sources are mixtures of unipotent stem cells, appears to be highly improbable as it would require the effective proportions of the different varieties of unipotent stem cells in the mixtures to remain balanced in different sites, at different stages of development and during recovery after severe damage.

Different patterns of haemopoietic activity thus appear to reflect the action of different regulatory factors on multipotent stem cells, and different patterns in different situations, which may coexist in the same organism (Thomas *et al.* 1960), appear to reflect the action of different local regulatory factors in different haemopoietic microenvironments. These factors may facilitate or inhibit a particular differentiation pathway, in the way that granulocyte production is inhibited in foetal liver (Thomas 1961).

This interpretation is supported by the discrepancy between the relative proportions of granulocytes and erythroblasts in the cell populations which are established by transplanted haemopoietic cells in the medullary cavity of the femur and in the spleen (Thomas 1970a, 1971) (Fig. 10). A discrepancy of similar magnitude in the relative proportions of the erythroid (Fig. 7b) and granulocytic colonies (Fig. 7c) formed in these two environments, previously reported by Wolf & Trentin (1968), has been observed. In a series of 92 discrete bone marrow colonies which could be classified as granulocytic or erythroid, 66 were granulocytic and 26 were erythroid, whereas in a corresponding series of 86 spleen colonies 17 were granulocytic and 69 were erythroid. The microenvironment provided for haemopoiesis by the medullary cavity of the femur thus appears to be more conducive to the transfer of cells from the stem cell compartment to the granulocyte compartment than to the erythroblast compartment, whereas in that provided by the spleen more cells appear to enter the erythroblast compartment than the granulocyte compartment (Thomas 1971).

It would be quite unjustifiable to extrapolate the generalizations that have been made about the differentiation potential of haemopoietic stem cells in the medullary cavity of the femur and the spleen to the thymus and the lymph nodes, in which effective repopulation is a relatively late event and may depend on a continuing input of cells from other sites. When the mass of the lymph nodes does increase appreciably the magnitude of the increase is not related to the number of donor cells injected over the range from 10^6 to 5×10^7 (D. B. Thomas & C. C. Congdon, unpublished data). This may be because any transplanted stem cell population large enough to confer protection has enough time to amplify its size to a plateau value which may bear a relationship to that in untreated controls.

Hypoplasia of the lymphoid tissues in lethally irradiated recipients of syngeneic foetal liver cells (Barnes *et al.* 1962) may reflect a defect in the differentiation potential of foetal liver cells (Thomas 1963), but it is not an invariable complication of replacement therapy using haemopoietic cells derived from foetal liver, and it does not occur in the albino mice used for the present investigations, which receive protective doses of bone marrow and foetal liver cells of comparable size (Thomas 1970*b*).

SUMMARY

The proliferative capacity and differentiation potential of murine haemopoietic cell populations have been analysed under standardized conditions after transplantation to lethally irradiated recipients.

Changes in proliferative capacity are reflected by comparable changes in the relative size of only one group of cells. The cells which constitute this group have very high nuclear: cytoplasmic ratios and are intermediate in form between generalized blast cells and small lymphocytes.

Haemopoietic stem cells appear to be multipotent and to be directed into different maturation compartments by the action of regulatory mechanisms, the influence of which may be exerted throughout the organism *or* restricted to particular haemopoietic microenvironments.

ACKNOWLEDGEMENTS

This work has been supported by a research grant from the Medical Research Council. It is a pleasure to acknowledge the expert technical assistance of Mrs Cecilie V. Briscoe, Mrs Valerie Littlewood and Mr D. J. F. Steers, together with the help of Miss Margaret Howdle who prepared the line drawings, Mr T. F. Stack who printed the photographs and Miss Anne Greenfield who prepared the manuscript.

References

AGAROSSI, G. & DORIA, G. (1968) Recovery of the hemolysin response in mouse radiation chimeras. *Transplantation* **6**, 419–426

BARNES, D. W. H., LOUTIT, J. F. & MICKLEM, H. S. (1962) Lymphoid aplasia and 'secondary disease'. *Br. J. Haematol.* **8**, 305–306

CHEN, M. G. & SCHOOLEY, J. C. (1968) A study on the clonal nature of spleen colonies using chromosome markers. *Transplantation* **6**, 121–126

COVELLI, V., BRIGANTI, G. & SILINI, G. (1972) An analysis of bone marrow erythropoiesis in the mouse. *Cell Tissue Kinet.* **5**, 41–51

CURRY, J. L., TRENTIN, J. J. & WOLF, N. (1967) Hemopoietic spleen colony studies: II. Erythropoiesis. *J. Exp. Med.* **125**, 703–720

DOMINICI, H. (1902) Polynucléaires et macrophages. *Arch. Med. Exp. Anat. Pathol.* **14**, 1–72

FELDMAN, M., BLEIBERG, I. & LIRON, M. (1966) Regulation of intrasplenic formation of erythroid clones. *Ann. N. Y. Acad. Sci.* **129**, 864–871

FINNEY, D. J. (1964) *Statistical Method in Biological Assay*. Griffin, London

FORD, C. E., HAMERTON, J. L., BARNES, D. W. H. & LOUTIT, J. F. (1956) Cytological identification of radiation-chimaeras. *Nature (Lond.)* **177**, 452–454

GILBERT, C. W. & LAJTHA, L. G. (1965) in *Cellular Radiation Biology* (published for the University of Texas M. D. Anderson Hospital and Tumor Institute), pp. 474–497, Williams & Wilkins, Baltimore

HASKILL, J. S., McNEILL, T. A. & MOORE, M. A. S. (1970) Density distribution analysis of in vivo and in vitro colony forming cells in bone marrow. *J. Cell. Physiol.* **75**, 167–179

HELLMAN, S. & GRATE, H. E. (1967) Production of granulocytic progeny by transplanted bone marrow in irradiated mice. *Blood J. Hematol.* **30**, 103–111

LEWIS, J. P. & TROBAUGH, F. E., JR. (1964) Haematopoietic stem cells. *Nature (Lond.)* **204**, 589–590

MARSHALL, M., RICHES, A. C. & THOMAS, D. B. (1971) The development and frequency of zones of iron concentration in the spleen of the mouse radiation chimera. *J. Anat.* **109**, 350–351

McCULLOCH, E. A. & TILL, J. E. (1962) The sensitivity of cells from normal mouse bone marrow to gamma radiation in vitro and in vivo. *Radiat. Res.* **16**, 822–832

McCULLOCH, E. A. & TILL, J. E. (1963) Repression of colony-forming ability of C57 BL haematopoietic cells transplanted into nonisologous hosts. *J. Cell. Comp. Physiol.* **61**, 301–308

McCULLOCH, E. A. & TILL, J. E. (1964) Proliferation of hemopoietic colony-forming cells transplanted into irradiated mice. *Radiat. Res.* **22**, 383–397

MICKLEM, H. S. (1966) Quoted by Micklem and Loutit (1966), p. 84

MICKLEM, H. S. & LOUTIT, J. F. (1966) *Tissue Grafting and Radiation*, Academic Press, New York

MICKLEM, H. S., FORD, C. E., EVANS, E. P. & GRAY, J. (1966) Interrelationships of myeloid and lymphoid cells: studies with chromosome-marked cells transfused into lethally irradiated mice. *Proc. R. Soc. Lond. B., Biol. Sci.* **165**, 78–102

NOWELL, P. C., COLE, L. J., HABERMEYER, J. G. & ROAN, P. L. (1956) Growth and continued function of rat marrow cells in X-irradiated mice. *Cancer Res.* **16**, 258–261

O'GRADY, L. F., LEWIS, J. P., LANGE, R. & TROBAUGH, F. E., JR. (1966) Factors influencing differentiation of transplanted hematopoietic tissue. *Exp. Hematol.* **9**, 77–80

POPP, R. A., CONGDON, C. C. & GOODMAN, J. W. (1965) Spleen weight as a measure of marrow cell growth in irradiated mice. *Proc. Soc. Exp. Biol. Med.* **120**, 395–398

REINCKE, U. (1970) Methods to determine volumes of hematopoietic nodules in bone-marrow-grafted, irradiated mice. *Exp. Hematol.* **20**, 69–72

RICHES, A. C. & THOMAS, D. B. (1971) in *The Reticuloendothelial System and Immune Pheno-*

mena (Di Luzio, N. R., ed.), pp. 361–372, Plenum , New York

SCHERMER, S. (1967) *The Blood Morphology of Laboratory Animals*, 3rd ed., Davis, Philadelphia

SCHOFIELD, R. & LAJTHA, L. G. (1969) Graft size considerations in the kinetics of spleen colony development. *Cell Tissue Kinet.* **2**, 147–155

SCHOOLEY, J. C. (1964) Studies on the regulation of erythropoiesis in spleen colonies. *Exp. Hematol.* **7**, 79

SCHOOLEY, J. C. (1966) The effect of erythropoietin on the growth and development of spleen colony-forming cells. *J. Cell. Physiol.* **68**, 249–262

SHARP, J. G. & THOMAS, D. B. (1970) Patterns of damage and regeneration in the murine lympho-myeloid complex following single whole-body doses of X-irradiation. *J. Anat.* **106**, 179

SHARP, J. G. & THOMAS, D. B. (1971) The effects of mustine hydrochloride on the colony forming units of murine bone marrow. *Acta Haematol. (Basel)* **46**, 271–274

SHARP, J. G., THOMAS, D. B. & BRISCOE, C. V. (1971) An approach to the morphological characterisation of the haematopoietic stem cell. *J. Anat.* **108**, 597–598

SIMINOVITCH, L., McCULLOCH, E. A. & TILL, J. E. (1963) The distribution of colony-forming cells among spleen colonies. *J. Cell. Comp. Physiol.* **62**, 327–336

SMITH, L. H. & CLAYTON, M. L. (1970) Distribution of injected ^{59}Fe in mice. *Exp. Hematol.* **20**, 82–86

SMITH, L. H. & CONGDON, C. C. (1960) in *Radiation Protection and Recovery*, pp. 242–302, Pergamon Press, Oxford

STEVENS, R. F. & THOMAS, D. B. (1970) Bone marrow regeneration as a measure of the proliferation of transplanted haematopoietic cells. *J. Anat.* **107**, 394

STEVENS, R. F. & THOMAS, D. B. (1973) Quoted by Thomas (1973*a*)

TARBUTT, R. G. (1969) Cell population kinetics of the erythroid system in the rat. The response to protracted anaemia and to continuous γ-irradiation. *Br. J. Haematol.* **16**, 9–24

THOMAS, D. B. (1961) in *Biological Activity of the Leucocyte (Ciba Found. Study Group 10)*, p. 105, Churchill, London

THOMAS, D. B. (1963) Lymphoid hypoplasia complicating foetal hepatic haematopoietic cell transplantation in the irradiated mouse. *Br. J. Haematol.* **9**, 559

THOMAS, D. B. (1966) The effects of whole-body X-irradiation on the thymus. Semiannual Progress Report of the Biology Division of the Oak Ridge National Laboratory, ORNL–3999, 103–105

THOMAS, D. B. (1970*a*) Contrasting patterns of splenic and medullary hematopoiesis. *Exp. Hematol.* **20**, 121–123

THOMAS, D. B. (1970*b*) Lymphoid tissue regeneration in mouse radiation chimeras. *Exp. Hematol.* **20**, 59

THOMAS, D. B. (1971) The differentiation of transplanted haematopoietic cells derived from bone marrow, spleen and fetal liver. *J. Anat.* **110**, 297–306

THOMAS, D. B. (1973*a*) in *The Cell in Medical Science* (Beck, F. & Lloyd, J. B., eds.) Academic Press, London

THOMAS, D. B. (1973*b*) The relationship between zones of iron concentration and macroscopic surface colonies in the spleen of the mouse radiation chimera. *J. Anat.* **114**, 95–100

THOMAS, D. B. & CONGDON, C. C. (1967) Spontaneous recovery in the thymus after supralethal whole-body X-irradiation. *J. Physiol. (Lond.)* **188**, 28P–29P

THOMAS, D. B. & YOFFEY, J. M. (1964) Hepatic haematopoiesis in the human foetus. *Br. J. Haematol.* **10**, 193–197

THOMAS, D. B., RUSSELL, P. M. & YOFFEY, J. M. (1960) Pattern of haematopoiesis in the foetal liver. *Nature (Lond.)* **187**, 876–877

THOMAS, D. B., STEERS, D. J. F. & RICHES, A. C. (1970) A macroautoradiographic method for the demonstration of iron-concentrating spleen colonies. *Transplantation* **10**, 274–275

THOMAS, D. B., MARSHALL, M. & RICHES, A. C. (1972) The effects of hypertransfusion on the formation of zones of iron concentration in the spleen of the mouse radiation chimera.

Acta Haematol. (Basel) **48**, 347–352

TILL, J. E. & McCULLOCH, E. A. (1961) A direct measurement of the radiation sensitivity of normal mouse bone marrow cells. *Radiat. Res.* **14**, 213–222

VAN BEKKUM, D. W. & DE VRIES, M. J. (1967) *Radiation Chimaeras*, Logos/Academic Press, London

WOLF, N. S. & TRENTIN, J. J. (1968) Hemopoietic colony studies. V. Effect of hemopoietic organ stroma on differentiation of pluripotent stem cells. *J. Exp. Med.* **127**, 205–215

WU, A. M., TILL, J. E., SIMINOVITCH, L. & McCULLOCH, E. A. (1967) A cytological study of the capacity for differentiation of normal hemopoietic colony-forming cells. *J. Cell. Physiol.* **69**, 177–184

WU, A. M., TILL, J. E., SIMINOVITCH, L. & McCULLOCH, E. A. (1968) Cytological evidence for a relationship between normal hematopoietic colony-forming cells and cells of the lymphoid system. *J. Exp. Med.* **127**, 455–464

YOFFEY, J. M. (1957) in *Homeostatic Mechanisms (Brookhaven Symp. Biol.* No. 10), 1–25, Brookhaven National Laboratories, Upton, N.Y.

YOFFEY, J. M. (1960) *Quantitative Cellular Hematology*, Thomas, Springfield, Ill.

YOFFEY, J. M. (1966) *Bone Marrow Reactions*, Arnold, London

YOFFEY, J. M. & THOMAS, D. B. (1961) The development of bone-marrow in the human foetus *J. Anat.* **95**, 613

YOFFEY, J. M., HUDSON, G. & OSMOND, D. G. (1965) The lymphocyte in guinea pig bone marrow. *J. Anat.* **99**, 841–860

Discussion

Harris: How long after transfusion do you examine the cellularity of the femoral marrow of the recipient?

Thomas: We routinely examine the bone marrow after ten days. At this time most recognizable haemopoietic cells in the medullary cavity of the femoral diaphysis are lymphocytes in lethally irradiated mice which have received less than 5×10^5 bone marrow cells (Fig. 4, p. 81).

Harris: In some bone marrow transfusion experiments with guinea pigs (Harris & Kugler 1964) we examined some of the recipients' marrows at about the time you mentioned and often had quite a problem trying to get an effective suspension which we could quantitate accurately. There is a lot of mucoid material which we could see in the smears even without a microscope. This material is PAS-positive and we have seen it in the marrow sinusoids and in what appear to be reticulum cells, but that is another story altogether. Have you met this sort of situation?

Thomas: No. We suspend the entire contents of the femoral diaphysis in a measured volume of Isoton (Coulter Electronics) and determine the nucleated cell content of the resultant suspension with a Coulter Counter. This procedure has never presented us with any problems but our experience is restricted to mice.

Rosse: You showed us a cell in the liver which looked like a transitional cell (Fig. 9). I was not aware that they were present there.

Thomas: Transitional cells do occur in murine foetal liver but the proportion is very much smaller in foetal liver than it is in adult bone marrow. These cells are, incidentally, very similar in appearance to the transitional cells in guinea-pig bone marrow.

Rosse: Are lymphocytes present in foetal liver?

Thomas: Yes, but, like transitional cells, lymphocytes account for a very small proportion of the cells in foetal liver, although after the 17th day the proportion of lymphocytes in murine foetal liver is rather larger than it is in human foetal liver between the ninth and 26th weeks of gestation.

Loutit: Time is a great factor here. Is there a particular date at which lymphocytes appear in the foetus?

Thomas: Occasional lymphocytes are already present in smears of cell suspensions prepared from the liver of the mouse foetus on the 13th day of gestation. Subsequently the proportion of lymphocytes increases progressively and concurrently, in the albino mice we usually use, the proportion of CFU in liver cell suspensions falls so that by the end of gestation CFU have virtually disappeared from the liver.

Winterhalter: It seems to me that what Dr McCulloch showed earlier (p. 69) was that the spleen picks up a different size of cell than the CFU–C. But since the spleen may specifically pick up a particular size of cell this finding does not necessarily imply that functionally those cannot be the same cells. What we are really looking for are stem cells.

Yoffey: Human foetal marrow at 20 weeks is full of transitional cells, and there are a lot of them in the blood (Yoffey & Thomas 1961, unpublished). Dr Thomas's preparation is also full of them. As to the size, there cannot be a single size for a stem cell because if, as I think Dr McCulloch has maintained, it has to be a self-proliferating compartment, then smaller cells have to grow large.

McCulloch: They have to be self-maintaining, but in the normal animal they look 95 to 99% non-proliferating. The size heterogeneity is not related to compartment size.

Yoffey: Our data on guinea pigs match yours quite nicely and in normal animals about 10% of cells are transitionals, which are the proliferating members of the compartment. But you have shown that when you stimulate erythropoiesis you greatly increase the proliferating members of those compartments.

McCulloch: That is not what the paper says (Bruce & McCulloch 1964).

Yoffey: Under certain experimental conditions, worked out most fully in guinea-pig marrow, the proliferating members of the lymphocyte-transitional compartment increase greatly. So either new cells are fed in—the old idea was the reticulum cell, which I think nobody now accepts—or the compartment has to be self-maintaining, even if only a small number are dividing. But if a small number are dividing, then there must be a size spectrum as smaller cells grow into larger ones, and these then divide. This may be very simple morphology, but I think it is incontrovertible morphology.

Lajtha: There are many other possibilities. We know that the erythropoietin-responsive cell (ERC) is certainly not identical with the pluripotent colony-forming cell of the spleen. It certainly proliferates much faster than the CFU–S, and we do not know how many times the cells divide during proliferation. Since the ERC is in a proliferative state even in a polycythaemic animal, the cells are either dying at the end of this proliferation chain or turning into something else. Only one or two extra divisions during this transit are needed to double or quadruple the output, without even increasing the feed from the CFU into the ERC. I do not say that increased feed does not occur—in certain conditions of course it occurs—but one has to be very careful how to interpret these end results, because there are several ways these can be produced.

Yoffrey: I agree, but we are discussing the CFU now, not the ERC.

Lajtha: We are discussing morphological entities.

Yoffey: Yes, but we were discussing them in terms of colony formation in the spleen.

Lajtha: Certainly, but a different proportion of these cells may be cycling at any given time. In proliferation tests ($[^3H]$thymidine suicide), operationally the CFU–C and CFU–S are certainly not the same cell. Even the ratio CFU–C: CFU–S, which in absolute numbers per femur is normally around 3.5–4, drops to 1–1.5 during regeneration. So obviously the absolute numbers change considerably.

Yoffey: But if we take the CFU alone, it must be either self-maintaining, in which case there are cells of different sizes, or new cells have to be coming in.

Lajtha: No.

Yoffey: As a simple-minded anatomist, I do not see any alternative. How can you get a compartment to proliferate with all the cells remaining the same size all the time?

McCulloch: I support Dr Lajtha's point that under most conditions the pool of CFU–S is in a state of rest. Other populations of progenitors committed to erythropoiesis and granulopoiesis are in varying states of proliferation in resting marrow. However, to induce proliferation in pluripotent stem cells quite drastic manipulation is necessary. For example, these cells proliferate after transplantation and after stimulation with endotoxins. However, their heterogeneity in respect to size, as displayed in sedimentation velocity profiles, is independent of whether or not they are proliferating (Worton *et al.* 1969; Sutherland *et al.* 1971). I repeat that morphological methods are inappropriate for studying transitions between populations of haemopoietic progenitor cells.

Yoffey: In the endogenous colony technique, when you tested the migration of cells and used the thymidine suicide test, Dr Lajtha, you found that practically 50% of the cells migrating to the spleen took up thymidine (Lajtha *et al.* 1969). You compared that with the exogenous colony test. There you must indeed have been dealing with an extremely actively proliferating population.

Lajtha: Yes; but, as Dr McCulloch says, this experiment only works in the femur-shielded whole-body-irradiated animals, and this is a very efficient way of 'kicking' them into proliferation. It is almost equivalent to grafting. The whole-body dose is 850–900 rads so one would expect the migrating stem cell to cycle.

Yoffey: It is certainly a powerful stimulus, but surely it is only a way of exaggerating a trend which was there previously and was not easily recognizable. You are stimulating here increased proliferation of a group of cells of which previously only a small number were proliferating, but as no foreign cells are being introduced, there does not seem to be anything here comparable to the proliferative stimulus of grafting.

Lajtha: There is a very big difference between 5% of the CFU cycling at any time (in the normal state) and 50% at a time after a whole body dose of 850 rd.

Yoffey: Admittedly, but the cells are in cycle, even at 5%.

Lajtha: Ninety per cent of them are not—this is just the point.

Thomas: While I share many of Dr McCulloch's reservations about morphological correlations, I think that it is very important to emphasize their potential relevance to an understanding of many pathological conditions which are defined and diagnosed on the basis of morphological criteria. In the future it may of course be possible to exploit 'fingerprints' or other characteristics in order to formulate more satisfactory definitions and more useful classifications for these disorders, but meanwhile we are of necessity dependent upon morphological criteria. May I now turn for a moment to numerical correlations or rather to numerical discrepancies? I have referred to the enormous discrepancy between the number of transitional cells and the relatively small number of CFU in the bone marrow and I have suggested that the number of cells in the population which provides the input to the proerythroblast compartment must also be large in relation to the number of CFU (p. 92). Is this suggestion acceptable?

Lajtha: No; it depends on the amplification in the ERC (or other 'committed') population. You do not need to remove more than 1% of the CFU–S population each day, if you allow an amplification of, say, eight divisions in the ERC.

Thomas: Quite so, but it is still necessary to postulate that CFU account for only a small proportion of the cells from which the input to the proerythroblast compartment is derived, unless the duration of the cell cycle is less than one hour in this population!

Lajtha: No. There is a six-hour cell cycle in the ERC.

Thomas: Exactly, and that is wholly consistent with what I am saying.

References

BRUCE, W. R. & McCULLOCH, E. A. (1964) The effect of erythropoietic stimulation on the hemopoietic colony-forming cells of mice. *Blood J. Hematol.* **23**, 216

HARRIS, P. F. & KUGLER, J. H. (1964) The use of regenerating bone marrow to protect guinea pigs against lethal irradiation. *Acta Haematol. (Basel)* **32**, 146–167

LAJTHA, L. G., POZZI, L. V., SCHOFIELD, R. & FOX, M. (1969) Kinetic properties of haemopoietic stem cells. *Cell Tissue Kinet.* **2**, 39–49

SUTHERLAND, D. J. A., TILL, J. E. & McCULLOCH, E. A. (1971) Short term cultures of mouse marrow cells separated by velocity sedimentation. *Cell Tissue Kinet.* **4**, 483

WORTON, R. G., McCULLOCH, E. A. & TILL, J. E. (1969) Physical separation of hemopoietic stem cells from cells forming colonies in culture. *J. Cell. Physiol.* **74**, 171

Precursor cells to erythroblasts and to small lymphocytes of the bone marrow

CORNELIUS ROSSE

Department of Biological Structure, University of Washington School of Medicine, Seattle, Washington

Abstract In an attempt to test, in morphologically and quantitatively definable cell populations, various parameters of stem cell function demonstrated by indirect assay systems, the role of transitional cells in relation to small lymphocyte and erythroblast production was investigated in the bone marrow. Direct observations *in vitro*, as well as autoradiographic studies with [³H]thymidine showed that daughter cells of transitional cell mitoses may either enlarge and divide again to produce transitional cells or condense and become small lymphocytes. Basophilic transitional cells continue to turn over at a rapid rate that is similar in polycythaemic guinea pigs with suppressed erythropoiesis to that seen during restimulation of erythropoiesis and in normal animals. After a large fraction of the basophilic transitional cell pool had been labelled in polycythaemic guinea pigs, the radioactivity in terms of grain count was shown to move into the small lymphocyte compartment when polycythaemia was maintained, but restimulation of erythropoiesis resulted not only in a decrease in the size of the basophilic transitional cell pool but also in a significantly greater loss of radioactivity from this pool, corresponding to the gain in grain count over the newly formed erythroblasts. During the early phase of erythropoietic stimulation basophilic transitional cells incorporated [³H]uridine at a rate similar to proerythroblasts and basophilic erythroblasts. Initial minimum amounts of haemoglobin synthesis were demonstrated by the benzidine reaction and by ^{55}Fe autoradiography in smears and with the electron microscope. Both histochemical techniques indicated that in stimulated animals, in addition to proerythroblasts, haemoglobin synthesis was initiated in cells morphologically indistinguishable from transitional cells. The studies reported identify the transitional cell compartment of bone marrow as containing both the precursor cell to bone marrow small lymphocytes and the erythropoietin-responsive cell.

The increase in small lymphocyte production in the marrow of polycythaemic guinea pigs may represent a mechanism of outflow for controlling the compartment size of the cycling erythroblast precursor population, when erythropoiesis is suppressed.

A number of assay systems developed over the past 20 years demonstrated that precursor cells to formed cellular elements of the blood exist in various degrees of functional differentiation in the haemopoietic tissues, their potential for differentiation and proliferation being definable in terms of the experimental systems used (Lajtha 1970; McCulloch 1970; McCulloch & Till 1971). In addition to furnishing for the first time conclusive and positive evidence for the existence of a pluripotent haemopoietic stem cell, these functional studies provided a wealth of information pertaining to the distribution, migration, physical and cytokinetic properties, and potentialities for differentiation, of this cell and of its progeny. However, most investigators have been reluctant or even opposed to attempting to identify the cells fulfilling the functions documented in the various assay systems which invariably, and of necessity, measured the end-product many steps and several generations removed from the cell or cells of their primary interest. In fact, new concepts and new terms had to be introduced to conform to and express cell function in terms measurable in the specific assay systems. The correlation of the different functional parameters measured in the various assays and the extrapolation of their interpretation to a cellular scale, at present, poses a problem of considerable complexity.

It is desirable to describe the process of haemopoiesis—eventually, and as far as possible—in terms of the cells found in the haemopoietic tissues rather than in terms of the tools used in their study. Therefore, it seems timely to embark on investigations which examine the behaviour of cell populations definable in morphological and quantitative terms in order to test whether they conform in terms of function to the predictions of the functional assays which were germane to establishing the very existence of the cell functions in question. The pitfalls of drawing unwarranted functional conclusions based merely on morphology— examples of which still survive in fair numbers from the age of morphological haematology—can be avoided by combining morphological studies with a battery of modern experimental techniques in testing the function of the cell population investigated.

The work reported here is a summary of experiments based on the foregoing considerations and was designed to test the role of a cell population in the bone marrow—definable in morphological and quantitative terms—primarily in relation to the production of small lymphocytes and of erythroblasts. Some of the experiments have already been reported or will appear in detail elsewhere.

RATIONALE FOR THE CHOICE OF CELL POPULATION TO BE INVESTIGATED

Of all haemopoietic processes probably erythropoiesis lends itself most readily to physiological stimulation through exposure to hypoxia (Moffatt *et al.* 1964*a*)

and also to physiological suppression in a polycythaemic state induced by previous exposure to hypoxia (Moffatt *et al.* 1964*b*). In a series of experiments (Yoffey *et al.* 1961, 1965, 1968; Rosse *et al.* 1970), it became evident that concomitant with alterations in the number of erythroblasts during erythropoietic stimulation and suppression, bone marrow lymphocytes also exhibited significant quantitative changes suggesting an inverse relationship between erythroblast and small lymphocyte production, possibly through demands imposed on a common precursor pool. Furthermore, in polycythaemic guinea pigs whose suppressed erythropoiesis was restimulated, quantitation of populations of bone marrow cells indicated that the number of cells which had entered on erythroid differentiation was most probably derived from a pool of cells described previously by Yoffey as 'transitional cells' (Yoffey & Courtice 1956), since in the experiment no other cell population could meet the requirements imposed on the erythroid precursor cell (Rosse *et al.* 1970).

The transitional cell population was therefore chosen for the present investigations, which were aimed at determining not whether transitional cells can fulfil functional requirements imposed on the pluripotent stem cell, but rather whether they can function as precursors to erythroblasts or to small lymphocytes of the bone marrow, or to both.

THE TRANSITIONAL CELL POPULATION OF BONE MARROW

Morphology

Although transitional cells were originally described by Yoffey as a group of cells in the bone marrow representing intermediate transformation stages of small lymphocytes into blast cells (Yoffey 1957), such a functional connotation is not implied here by the use of the term. The name is used to designate a group of cells with defined morphological characteristics in the fixed and living state (Rosse & Yoffey 1967; Rosse 1969). It still remains to be determined whether the term 'transitional' also applies in the functional sense originally implied. Their morphology at higher levels of resolution conforms to descriptions with the light microscope (Fig. 1).

Transitional cells are morphologically distinct from medium and large lymphocytes (cf. Figs. 1, 2), are usually not seen in lymph and lymph node, but occur in the spleen of the guinea pig. They resemble some cells in the thymus and appear similar to some of the 'activated' lymphocytes after phytohaemagglutinin stimulation and in mixed lymphocyte reaction cultures. Transitional cells represent around 2–4% of nucleated cells in the bone marrow of rodents

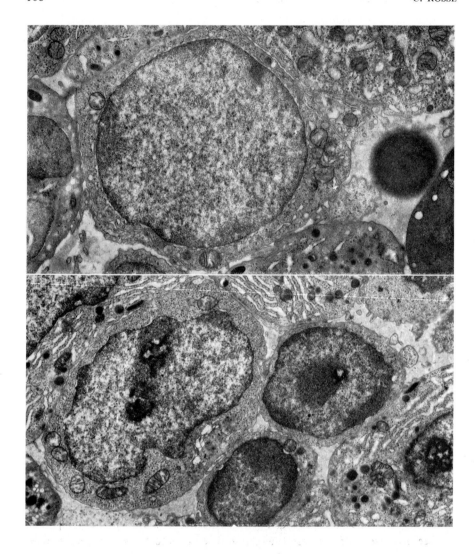

FIG. 1. Two transitional cells from guinea pig bone marrow, fixed in osmium-glutaraldehyde and stained with uranyl acetate and lead citrate ($\times \sim 8000$ and ~ 6600). The nuclear: cytoplasmic ratio is high, as in the small lymphocyte on the right in the lower photograph, but the chromatin is fine and loose. Two nucleoli are present in the lower cell, which contains more polyribosomes and monoribosomes in its cytoplasm than the upper cell.

(Hudson et al. 1963; Ramsell & Yoffey 1961; Turner et al. 1967) and also of the human foetus (Yoffey et al. 1961).

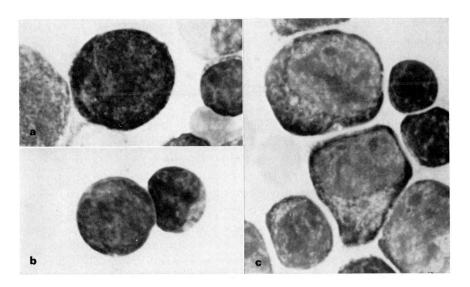

FIG. 2. A basophilic and a pale transitional cell (*a* and *b*, respectively) from a bone marrow smear and lymphocytes from a spleen smear (*c*) of a guinea pig after polychrome staining ($\times \sim 2000$). In medium and large lymphocytes the nuclear chromatin is coarse and the cytoplasm is more extensive than in transitional cells.

Cell kinetics

In the normal guinea pig after a pulse label with [³H]thymidine, 50% of transitional cells incorporated the label, and labelled mitotic counts indicated that cycling cells in this population have a cell cycle of 15 hours with the S phase occupying seven to eight hours (Rosse 1972*a*).

During repeated administration of [³H]thymidine at four-hour intervals it became apparent, however, that transitional cells with basophilic cytoplasm turned over much more rapidly than similar cells with pale cytoplasm (Rosse 1970). The results were interpreted as being suggestive of a continuously cycling basophilic population, while some of the pale cells were considered to remain in G0 for periods up to four days. The cell cycle of cycling pale cells, however, was found to be identical to that of basophilic transitional cells as determined by labelled mitotic counts (Rosse 1970).

Direct observations in tissue culture showed that transitional cells give rise to transitional cells by cell division (Rosse 1972*a*), confirming similar conclusions based on grain counts over mitoses of successive cell generations after pulse label with [³H]thymidine (Rosse 1970, 1972*a*). The tissue culture studies also established that transitional cells are able to enlarge considerably between two successive cell divisions (Rosse 1972*a*).

TRANSITIONAL CELLS AS PRECURSORS TO SMALL LYMPHOCYTES OF THE BONE MARROW

After the *in vivo* autoradiographic studies of Osmond & Everett (1964) which suggested the transitional cell as the *in situ* precursor to bone marrow small lymphocytes, Yoshida & Osmond (1971) presented conclusive evidence that transitional cells sedimenting on density gradients with the lymphocyte-rich fraction of bone marrow give rise to small lymphocytes by division *in vitro*. These findings were confirmed by direct observations of transitional cells in tissue culture (Rosse 1972*a*) which indicated that daughter cells of some transitional cell mitoses, instead of enlarging, after a period of several hours begin to condense and assume the morphology and motility pattern of small lymphocytes. This mode of small lymphocyte production in the bone marrow was also correlated with *in vivo* [^{3}H]thymidine-labelling characteristics of transitional cells.

These studies provide incontrovertible evidence identifying the transitional cell as the precursor to those small lymphocytes of the marrow which turn over rapidly and are produced at a rapid rate. The precursor cell to a minor population of marrow small lymphocytes which represent part of the recirculating pool and turn over more slowly (Rosse 1971, 1972*b*) still awaits identification.

TRANSITIONAL CELLS AS PRECURSORS TO ERYTHROBLASTS

The experimental system used for investigating the possible role of transitional cells as erythroblast precursors was similar to that described previously (Rosse *et al.* 1970). Guinea pigs were made polycythaemic by being exposed to hypoxia in a hypobaric chamber (0.5 atmosphere—5066 N/m) and on the seventh day after their return to an ambient atmosphere (rebound) erythropoiesis was restimulated by reducing the packed cell volume to the normal range by bleeding them and returning them to the hypobaric chamber. The erythroid response under these conditions is illustrated in Fig. 3.

Polycythaemic guinea pigs maintained in normal atmosphere without being bled were used as controls, as well as normal animals.

The following types of studies were performed:

(1) [^{3}H]thymidine labelling before stimulation; (2) Estimation of cell turnover during stimulation and suppression of erythropoiesis; (3) Incorporation of [^{3}H]uridine; (4) Identification of the earliest erythroblasts.

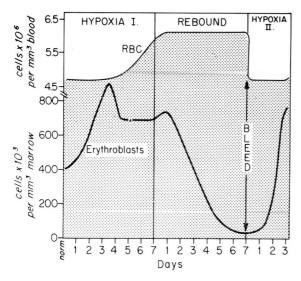

FIG. 3. Changes in the numbers of erythroblasts/mm³ bone marrow and in the red cell count (RBC) of guinea pigs during exposure to hypoxia in a hypobaric chamber (Hypoxia I), after return to normal atmosphere (Rebound) and during stimulation by bleeding and re-exposure to hypoxia (Hypoxia II).

(1) [³H]thymidine labelling before stimulation

Normal guinea pigs and polycythaemic animals received three injections of [³H]thymidine (1 μCi/g body weight) at four-hour intervals on the seventh day of rebound. Thirty minutes after the last injection, bone marrow was obtained from a tibia amputated aseptically (0 hour). Some of the polycythaemic animals were bled and exposed to hypoxia (stimulated animals). A further bone marrow sample was obtained from the right humerus 48 hours after the last [³H]thymidine injection and also at 72 hours, when the animals were killed. The absolute number of various bone marrow cells was determined by the quantitative haemocytometric method of Yoffey (1960).

On autoradiographs of bone marrow smears the number of grains was counted in 100 cells of each of the following cell categories: pale transitional cells, basophilic transitional cells, erythroblasts and small lymphocytes. Thus, the amount of radioactivity could be expressed in absolute terms of grains per cell population in 1 mm³ of marrow. DNA-bound radioactivity/mg of bone marrow was also measured in a liquid scintillation counter.

While the absolute number of erythroblasts per mm³ of marrow was not affected by the experimental operative procedure in normal and polycythaemic

guinea pigs, there was a more than 20-fold increase in the number of morphologically recognizable erythroblasts 72 hours after stimulation in the marrow
of animals bled and subjected to hypoxia (Fig. 4).

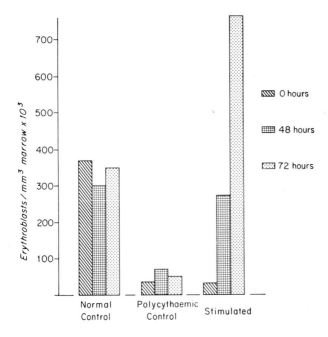

FIG. 4. Changes in the absolute numbers of erythroblasts in the bone marrow of normal,
polycythaemic and stimulated guinea pigs, during 72 h. The values were obtained at 0, 48 and
72 h by serial biopsy in the same animals.

Eighty to ninety per cent of these newly formed erythroid cells were labelled
(grain count: 8–15) and quantitation of the grain count in erythroblasts over the
72 hours convincingly demonstrated that these cells could not have arisen by the
proliferation of the few erythroblasts present in the marrow at 0 hours (Fig. 5).
They must have been derived from a labelled precursor pool. The dramatic increase of radioactivity in the erythroid compartment of stimulated animals
markedly contrasted with the decrease seen in the normal control. Although
there was no significant increase in the number of erythroblasts in polycythaemic
controls (Fig. 4), the low level of erythropoiesis in these animals was also maintained, apparently by an influx of labelled precursors on a much smaller scale
than after stimulation of erythropoiesis.

The similar decrease in overall radioactivity/mg bone marrow in all three
groups of animals (Fig. 6) provides good evidence that the labelled erythroblast

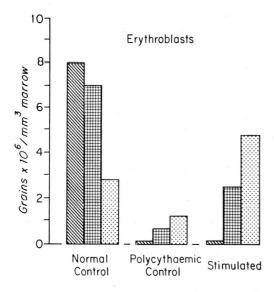

FIG. 5. Changes in radioactivity found in erythroblasts/mm³ of marrow in normal, poly-cythaemic and stimulated guinea pigs. In each group the values were obtained at 0, 48 and 72 h by serial biopsy from the same animals (key: Fig. 4).

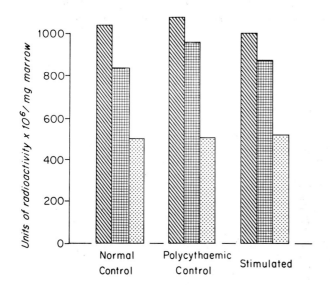

FIG. 6. Changes in DNA-bound radioactivity/mg bone marrow as measured by scintillation counting in normal, polycythaemic and stimulated animals, at 0, 48 and 72 h (key: Fig. 4) on samples obtained by serial biopsy from the same animals.

precursors in stimulated animals were derived from the bone marrow itself and were not immigrant. Therefore, one should be able to detect a disproportionate decrease in radioactivity in the cell population of stimulated animals from which the labelled erythroblast precursors were derived.

Could they have been derived from transitional cells?

The three injections of [³H]thymidine at four-hour intervals labelled 80–90% of basophilic transitional cells in all three groups of animals (cf. Fig. 8) with grain counts in the range of 50–100 per cell. Since these cells were present in greater numbers in the marrow of polycythaemic animals than in the normal, more than three times as much radioactivity was contained in this cell population before stimulation than in the normal control (Fig. 7).

While the high percentage of labelling was maintained in all three groups of animals over the next 72 hours, in stimulated animals the amount of radioactivity in the basophilic transitional cell pool fell by more than 20-fold, contrasting significantly with the pattern in non-stimulated polycythaemic and normal animals. The difference in the loss of radioactivity was marked already at 48 hours (Fig. 7) and was considerably greater than the gain in grain count over the newly formed erythroblasts (cf. Figs. 5, 7) in the stimulated marrow.

These differences in the three groups of animals were also reflected in the absolute number of basophilic transitional cells. In stimulated animals the number of these cells/mm³ marrow decreased fivefold during the first 48 hours of the stimulus, whereas their numbers remained essentially unaltered in both groups of controls.

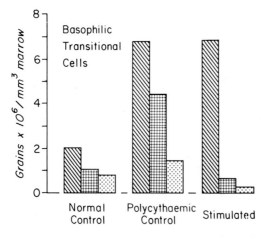

FIG. 7. Changes in radioactivity found in basophilic transitional cells/mm³ bone marrow in normal, polycythaemic and stimulated guinea pigs. In each group the values were obtained at 0, 48 and 72 h by serial biopsy from the same animals (key: Fig. 4).

The quantitative changes in the pale transitional cell population were on a smaller scale and exhibited a different pattern from basophilic cells. Their number had fallen only slightly in stimulated animals, without significant change in the control, while the percentage of labelling increased over the 72 hours in all three groups. Total radioactivity in this population of cells increased in poly-cythaemic animals but decreased in stimulated guinea pigs.

It is not possible to rule out other cell types from functioning as precursors to erythroblasts without including them in these quantitative autoradiographic studies. Such an endeavour does not seem to be warranted, however, since—short of the direct observation of cell transformation—it is difficult to interpret the data any other way than as providing a positive answer to the question posed at the outset of these studies, namely whether transitional cells can function as precursors to erythroblasts. Under the experimental conditions described, the pool of basophilic transitional cells fully meets all the requirements imposed on the erythroid precursor cell by the measured erythroid response.

(2) Cell turnover in the transitional cell population during stimulation and suppression of erythropoiesis

The correlation of the marked quantitative changes in the transitional cell population with cell turnover has considerable importance in regard to their role as precursors to erythroblasts. Turnover was measured by repeated injections of [^{3}H]thymidine at four-hour intervals in the three groups of experimental animals described above. While the rate at which cells acquired label was quite distinct for the basophilic and pale populations, for each population the values in stimulated, polycythaemic and normal animals fell within the same range (Fig. 8). Turnover in the basophilic population was rapid, with nearly 100% of cells being labelled at 24 hours. The differences in the three groups of animals were minimal. It is significant, however, that in stimulated and polycythaemic animals after the initial rapid increase, the labelling remained around 93–96%, suggesting a small but continuous input from a non-labelled precursor pool, since all cells entering DNA synthesis acquired label, as indicated by the absence of non-labelled mitotic figures in the marrow beyond the time of the second [^{3}H]thymidine injection (8 h).

The following conclusions may be drawn from the data:

Basophilic transitional cells turn over at a rapid rate which is comparable

(a) in polycythaemic animals with markedly suppressed erythropoiesis where the compartment size of the transitional cell population is considerably increased;

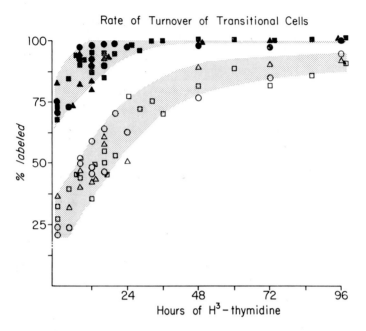

FIG. 8. The rate of turnover of basophilic transitional cells in normal (■), polycythaemic (▲) and stimulated (●) guinea pigs, and of pale transitional cells in the same groups of animals (□, △, ○ respectively) as measured by the percentage of labelling during repeated administration of [³H]thymidine at 4 h intervals. The values represent individual animals. In stimulated animals, the first injection of [³H]thymidine (1 μCi/g body wt) was given 12 h after bleeding and re-exposure to hypoxia, and in non-stimulated polycythaemic controls at a corresponding time.

(b) in animals in which erythropoiesis is undergoing rapid expansion by the large-scale recruitment of cells from the basophilic transitional cell pool, as suggested by the experiment described above, and

(c) in normal animals whose haemopoietic processes are in equilibrium.

(3) Incorporation of [³H]uridine

Since globin synthesis precedes and accompanies the assembly of haemoglobin, it is likely that an increased rate of [³H]uridine incorporation into RNA would be revealed in the precursor cells to erythroblasts during restimulation of erythropoiesis. Bone marrow obtained from the three groups of experimental animals described above was cultured with [³H]uridine for 30 minutes and on autoradiographs the pattern of labelling of transitional cells was compared in the three groups. The most heavily labelled cells (100+ grains) were pro-

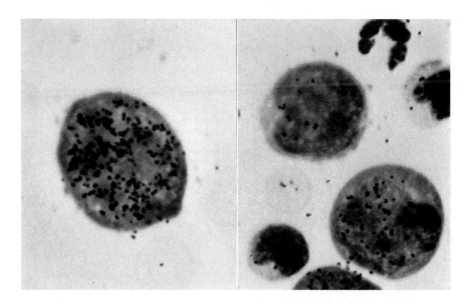

FIG. 9. [³H]Uridine labelling in pale and basophilic transitional cells obtained from the bone marrow 24 h after stimulation ($\times \sim$ 2400). The cells were incubated for 30 min *in vitro* with [³H]uridine. (1 μCi/1 $\times$ 10⁶ cells ml).

erythroblasts and basophilic erythroblasts. Basophilic transitional cells had similar grain density in stimulated animals, in contrast to the weakly labelled pale transitional cells and small lymphocytes (Fig. 9). The findings, although non-specific, are in full agreement with the quantitative autoradiographic studies and support the conclusions drawn therefrom.

(4) Identification of the earliest eythroblasts

The identification of erythroblasts in functional terms depends on the presence of haemoglobin. Therefore, the only cell population in which less than 100% of morphologically similar cells should contain haemoglobin is the cell population which furnishes the precursor to erythroblasts, i.e. in which haemoglobin synthesis is turned on. To detect the initial minimum amount of haemoglobin synthesized, methods more sensitive and critical than conventional morphology are required, be it at the level of resolution of the light or of the electron microscope.

Two methods were used for this purpose: the benzidine reaction (Lepehne 1919; Graham & Karnovsky 1966) and ⁵⁵Fe autoradiography on smears of bone

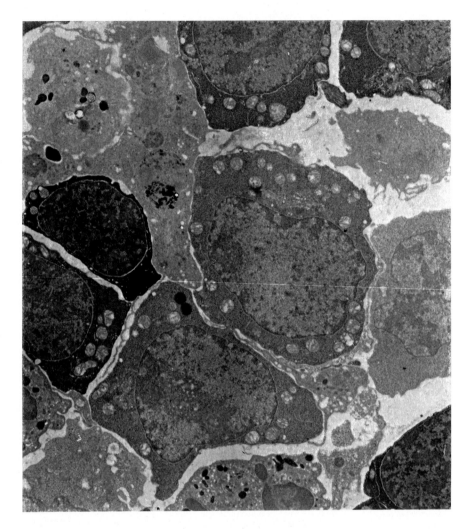

FIG. 10. Bone marrow obtained 60 h after stimulation, fixed with glutaraldehyde, incubated in 3,3'-diaminobenzidine, postfixed with osmium but otherwise unstained ($\times \sim 5700$). Haemoglobin-containing cells, distributed around processes of a reticular cell that contain some phagocytosed material, are identified by various degrees of positivity revealed by different degrees of density. The two cells with darkest cytoplasm on the left are late erythroblasts with marked nuclear clumping, while those on the upper right are young erythroblasts. The two large cells in the centre show cytoplasmic density significantly above that of the reticular cell and of the cell on the right, falling definitely in the 'positive range' when measured with the photographic analyser (see text). They are therefore identified as containing haemoglobin, which would not be possible without the reaction. Their morphology more closely resembles that of the cells shown in the lower parts of Fig. 1 and Fig. 12 than that of the cell shown in Fig. 11.

marrow examined with the light microscope and on sections examined in the electron microscope.

Bone marrow was obtained 40–60 hours after stimulation of polycythaemic animals. Classic proerythroblasts did not give a positive benzidine reaction on smears, but in the electron microscope a proportion of them showed cytoplasmic density significantly greater than morphologically identical cells on sections of tissue not treated with the reagent. The densities were recorded after standardization on the negatives with a Weston Photographic Analyzer. A few transitional cells gave, on smears, a positive reaction comparable in degree to that in basophilic erythroblasts and the presence of haemoglobin in the cytoplasm of these cells was confirmed by extinction of monochromatic light falling in the absorption spectrum of haemoglobin (404.6 nm). Likewise a few cells with morphological features similar to transitional cells were also demonstrated to be positive in the electron microscope (Fig. 10, and cf. Fig. 1).

The majority, but not all, 'proerythroblasts' labelled heavily with ^{55}Fe on smears, while a much smaller proportion contained silver grains on sections examined in the electron microscope (Fig. 11). On smears a small proportion of cells indistinguishable from basophilic transitional cells were found to be labelled heavily with ^{55}Fe. In the electron microscope cells were also seen which incorporated ^{55}Fe but were otherwise indistinguishable from transitional cells on the basis of morphological criteria (Fig. 12, cf. Fig. 1).

These findings convincingly identify two cell populations with distinct morphological features in which haemoglobin synthesis is initiated for the first time: proerythroblasts and transitional cells. It is likely that under the erythropoietic stimulus used, erythroid precursor cells begin to synthesize haemoglobin at a maturation stage earlier in morphological terms than in normal circumstances. Though this occurs very infrequently, the demonstration of haemoglobin synthesis by two independent cytochemical methods in cells indistinguishable from transitional cells provides decisive evidence that at least some erythroid precursor cells are contained in this cell population.

TRANSITIONAL CELLS AS COMMON PRECURSORS TO ERYTHROBLASTS AND BONE MARROW SMALL LYMPHOCYTES

It is questionable whether experimental means will ever be available that are suitable for determining whether a single cell can 'decide' to differentiate in one direction or another. The experiments described indicate, however, that the precursors to both erythroblasts and bone marrow small lymphocytes belong to a pool of cells with identical morphological characteristics. The examination of lymphocyte turnover and production under conditions of erythropoietic

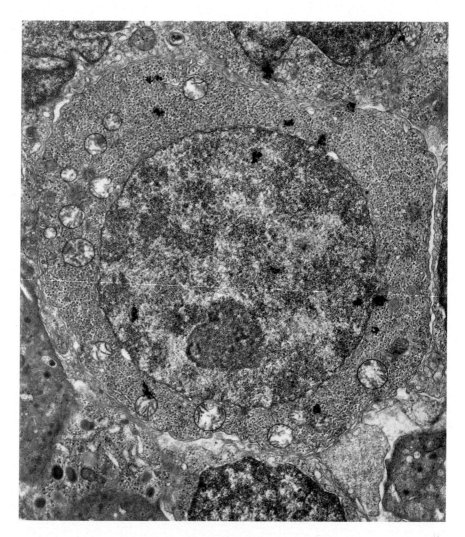

FIG. 11. A proerythroblast obtained from the bone marrow 60 h after stimulation. ^{55}Fe was administered (1 μCi/g body wt, intraperitoneally) in the form of ferrous citrate (New England Nuclear) 4 and 2 h before the animal was killed. The autoradiograph was exposed for 9 weeks. Fixed in osmium–glutaraldehyde, stained with uranyl acetate and lead citrate ($\times \sim 11\ 300$).

suppression and stimulation throws further light on this finding.

Small lymphocytes continued to turn over in the bone marrow of polycy-thaemic and stimulated animals at a rate comparable to that of normal guinea pigs (Fig. 13). Yet the comparison of grain counts over small lymphocyte popu-lations in the three groups of animals, 48 and 72 hours after the precursor pool

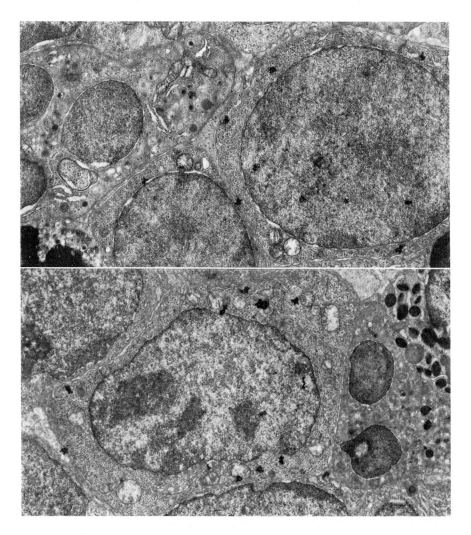

FIG. 12. Transitional cells obtained from the same animal as described in Fig. 11. The cells are labelled with a comparable number of grains due to incorporation of ^{55}Fe as the proerythroblast in Fig. 11, although morphologically they are distinct from it and belong to the same class of cells as those illustrated in Fig. 1. The autoradiograph was exposed for 9 weeks. Fixed in osmium–glutaraldehyde, stained with uranyl acetate and lead citrate ($\times \sim 8000$).

was labelled (three injections of [^{3}H]thymidine at four-hour intervals), revealed marked quantitative differences in lymphocyte production. In all groups the highest radioactivity in these cells was reached at 48 hours, with comparable grain counts per cell. The total activity was, however, twice as much in poly-

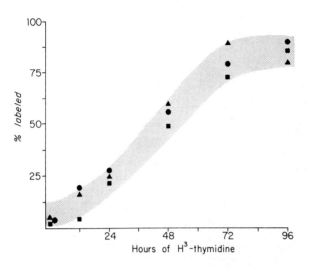

FIG. 13. The rate of turnover of small lymphocytes in the bone marrow of normal (■), polycythaemic (▲) and stimulated (●) guinea pigs as measured by the percentage of labelling during repeated administration of [³H]thymidine at 4 h intervals. The values were obtained from the same groups of animals as described in Fig. 8.

cythaemic animals as in stimulated guinea pigs, the value for the normal being intermediate.

Since the size of the transitional cell compartment was similar in both polycythaemic and stimulated animals at the time of labelling, it must be assumed that fewer transitional cells were available for lymphocyte production in the animals where a demand for erythroblasts was created, than where erythropoiesis remained suppressed. In fact, the sum of the gains in radioactivity over small lymphocytes and erythroblasts at 48 and 72 hours after labelling was quantitatively in fair agreement with the loss of radioactivity from the basophilic transitional cell pool.

INTERPRETATION AND SIGNIFICANCE OF THE OBSERVATIONS

The studies presented were designed to answer the question of whether transitional cells can function as precursors to erythroblasts, or in other words whether the erythropoietin-responsive cell, or the committed erythroid stem cell, belongs to this cell population. In addition, it was found that small lymphocyte precursors in the marrow were also contained in this cell category. Experiments have not yet been performed to investigate the relation of these cells to granulocytopoiesis, or, in other words, to the committed granulocytic stem cell as demonstrated in the *in vitro* haemopoietic colony assay, for instance. Nor were any experiments carried out to test whether erythroblast and small lymphocyte production can continue if transitional cells are eliminated or if their proliferation is blocked. The possibility of the pluripotent stem cell being contained among this class of cells was not tested either, although some experiments might suggest this possibility (Morrison & Toepfer 1967; Osmond 1973) whereas others assigned the pluripotent cell to a different morphological category (Tyler & Everett 1966; Tyler *et al.* 1972). The evidence for the distinct nature of the pluripotent and committed stem cells was reviewed recently (Lajtha 1970; McCulloch & Till 1971), and the present series of experiments demonstrated that transitional cells, as a population—in conformity to the 'minimal model of myelopoiesis' described by McCulloch & Till (1971)—possessed the functional characteristics of the 'committed stem cell' demonstrated by the indirect assay systems.

Evidence was presented for the movement of cells from this population into the erythroid and lymphocytic lines, and it was also shown that basophilic transitional cells are present and continue to turn over rapidly in polycythaemic animals with suppressed erythropoiesis, the findings conforming to those of Hodgson (1967), Stohlman *et al.* (1968), Morse *et al.* (1968) and Lajtha *et al.* (1969). These cells give rise to their own kind and thus maintain the cell compartment during erythropoietic stimulation as well as during the state of erythroid suppression, as indicated by the constancy of the percentage remaining labelled after initial marking of a large fraction of the population with [^{3}H]thymidine. A slow rate of input may occur, however, into this cell compartment from a nonproliferating or slowly proliferating precursor pool which has not been identified.

No increase in the rate of triggering by the stimulus of pale transitional cells postulated to be in G0 could be detected. The increasing proportion of labelling of pale transitional cells after initial administration of [^{3}H]thymidine suggested that non-labelled cells were either selectively removed or morphologically transformed, or both, or that there was an input from a population that initially incorporated the label.

Data are not yet available on whether the cell cycle shortens in basophilic transitional cells in response to the erythropoietic stimulus, as suggested for the erythroblast precursor by Morse *et al.* (1970).

The studies reported provide information about the fate of cells produced by the continuously proliferating erythroid precursor pool in the polycythaemic animal, a consideration previous models neglected to take into account. If these cells continue to turn over, an outflow from the compartment must exist when erythroid differentiation is shut off, unless the compartment is to expand continuously or unless it is limited by cell death. While evidence for the latter possibility has not yet been shown to exist, the data presented suggest the alternative of an increased rate of small lymphocyte production during the suppressed erythropoietic state. Since small lymphocytes produced in the marrow are discharged into the blood (Everett & Caffrey 1967; Brahim & Osmond, 1970), have a finite and short lifespan (Everett & Tyler 1967), and a number are phagocytosed within the marrow (Osmond & Everett 1962), this process of what might be termed 'ineffective lymphocyte production' offers itself as an attractive possible mechanism of providing a variable outflow tract from the erythroblast precursor compartment in differing states of haemopoietic activity, in order to ensure the continuous cycling of the pool of 'committed' stem cells which is under the influence of physiological 'long-range' regulators. It is not irrelevant to note that no function has yet been demonstrated for most lymphocytes found and produced in the marrow.

The significance of these studies is that they tested a number of functional parameters in a morphologically defined cell population in the bone marrow and attempted to correlate morphological and quantitative changes with cell function. Such an approach, while succeeding in describing the process of haemopoiesis in terms of cells rather than in terms of concepts, becomes increasingly difficult and inaccurate the smaller the cell population under investigation and the fewer its distinguishing characteristics. The results are, however, sufficiently encouraging for the author, at least, not to abandon the cell in attempts to investigate the complex process of haemopoiesis.

ACKNOWLEDGEMENTS

The electron microscope studies were performed in collaboration with John A. Trotter and the electron micrographs are published with due acknowledgements to him. Acknowledgement is also made to Charé Vathanaprida for technical assistance.

The work was supported by USPHS Grant AM-13145 from the National Institutes of Health.

References

BRAHIM, F. & OSMOND, D. G. (1970) Migration of bone marrow lymphocytes demonstrated by selective bone marrow labeling with thymidine-H³. *Anat. Rec.* **168**, 139–159

EVERETT, N. B. & CAFFREY, R. W. (1967) Radioautographic studies of bone marrow small lymphocytes, in *The Lymphocyte in Immunology and Haemopoiesis* (Yoffey, J. M., ed.), pp. 108–119, Arnold, London

EVERETT, N. B. & TYLER, R. W. (1967) Lymphopoiesis in the thymus and other tissues: functional implications. *Int. Rev. Cytol.* **22**, 205–237

GRAHAM, R. C. & KARNOVSKY, M. J. (1966) The early stages of absorption of injected horse-radish peroxidase in the proximal tubules of mouse kidney: ultrastructural cytochemistry by a new technique. *J. Histochem. Cytochem.* **14**, 291–302

HODGSON, G. S. (1967) Effect of vinblastin and 4-amino-N^{10} methyl pteroyl-glutamic acid on the erythropoietin responsive cell. *Proc. Soc. Exp. Biol. Med.* **125**, 1206–1209

HUDSON, G., OSMOND, D. G. & ROYLANCE, P. J. (1963) Cell-populations in the bone marrow of the normal guinea pig. *Acta Anat.* **52**, 234–239

LAJTHA, L. G. (1970) Stem cell kinetics, in *Regulation of Hematopoiesis* (Gordon, A. S., ed.), vol. 1, pp. 111–131, Appleton-Century-Crofts, New York

LAJTHA, L. G., POZZI, L. V., SCHOFIELD, R. & FOX, M. (1969) Kinetic properties of haemopoietic stem cells. *Cell Tissue Kinet.* **2**, 39–49

LEPEHNE, G. (1919) Zerfall der roten Blutkörperchen beim Ikterus infectiosus (Weil). *Beitr. Pathol. Anat. Allg. Pathol.* **65**, 163-226

McCULLOCH, E. A. (1970) Control of hemopoiesis at the cellular level, in *Regulation of Hematopoiesis* (Gordon, A. S., ed.), vol. 1, pp. 133–159, Appleton-Century-Crofts, New York

McCULLOCH, E. A. & TILL, J. E. (1971) Regulatory mechanisms acting on hemopoietic stem cells: some clinical implications. *Am. J. Pathol.* **65**, 601–619

MOFFATT, D. F., ROSSE, C., SUTHERLAND, I. H. & YOFFEY, J. M. (1964a) Studies on hypoxia I. The response of the bone marrow to primary hypoxia. *Acta Anat.* **58**, 26–36

MOFFATT, D. J., ROSSE, C., SUTHERLAND, I. H. & YOFFEY, J. M. (1964b) Studies on hypoxia II. A quantitative study of changes in the bone marrow of the guinea pig during post-hypoxic polycythaemia (rebound). *Acta Anat.* **59**, 188–197

MORRISON, J. H. & TOEPFER, J. R. (1967) Survival of lethally X-irradiated rats after treatment with isogenic marrow lymphocytes. *Am. J. Physiol.* **213**, 923–927

MORSE, B., RENCRICCA, N. & STOHLMAN, F., JR. (1968) The effect of hydroxyurea on differentiated marrow erythroid precursors. *Proc. Soc. Exp. Biol. Med.* **130**, 986–989

MORSE, B., RENCRICCA, N., HOWARD, D. & STOHLMAN, F., JR. (1970) The mechanism of action of erythropoietin in relationship to cell cycle kinetics, in *Hemopoietic Cellular Proliferation* (Stohlman, F., Jr., ed.), pp. 160–170, Grune & Stratton, New York, London

OSMOND, D. G. (1973) Kinetic and haemopoietic properties of lymphoid cells in the bone marrow. This volume, pp. 131–152

OSMOND, D. G. & EVERETT, N. B. (1962) Nucleophagocytosis in bone marrow. *Nature (Lond.)* **196**, 488–489

OSMOND, D. G. & EVERETT, N. B. (1964) Radioautographic studies of bone marrow lymphocytes *in vivo* and in diffusion chamber cultures. *Blood J. Hematol.* **23**, 1–17

RAMSELL, T. G. & YOFFEY, J. M. (1961) The bone of the adult male rat. *Acta Anat.* **47**, 55–65

ROSSE, C. (1969) The use of the supravital method in a study of cells susceptible to damage in smears of normal and regenerating bone marrow. *Blood J. Hematol.* **34**, 72–84

ROSSE, C. (1970) Two morphologically and kinetically distinct populations of lymphoid cells in the bone marrow. *Nature (Lond.)* **227**, 73–75

ROSSE, C. (1971) Lymphocyte production and life-span in the bone marrow of the guinea pig. *Blood J. Hematol.* **38**, 372–377

ROSSE, C. (1972a) Lymphocyte production in the bone marrow, in *Proc. Sixth Leucocyte Culture Conference* (Schwarz, M. R., ed.), pp. 55–70, Academic Press, New York

ROSSE, C. (1972b) Migration of long lived lymphocytes to the bone marrow and to other lymphomyeloid tissues in normal parabiotic guinea pigs. *Blood J. Hematol.* **40**, 90–97

ROSSE, C. & YOFFEY, J. M. (1967) The morphology of the transitional lymphocyte in guinea pig bone marrow. *J. Anat.* **102**, 113–124

ROSSE, C., GRIFFITHS, D. A., EDWARDS, A. E., GACHES, C. G. C., LONG, A. L. H., WRIGHT, J. L. W. & YOFFEY, J. M. (1970) Identity of erythroblast precursors in bone marrow.

Acta Haematol. (Basel) **43**, 80–88

STOHLMAN, F., JR., EBBE, S., MORSE, B., HOWARD, D. & DONOVAN, J. (1968) Regulation of erythropoiesis: XX. Kinetics of red cell production. *Ann. N.Y. Acad. Sci.* **149**, 156–172

TURNER, M. S., HURST, J. M. & YOFFEY, J. M. (1967) Studies on hypoxia. VIII. Effect of hypoxia and post-hypoxic polycythaemia (rebound) on mouse marrow and spleen. *Br. J. Haematol.* **13**, 942–948

TYLER, R. W. & EVERETT, N. B. (1966) A radioautographic study of hemopoietic repopulation using irradiated parabiotic rats. *Blood J. Hematol.* **28**, 873–890

TYLER, R. W., ROSSE, C. & EVERETT, N. B. (1972) The hemopoietic repopulating potential of inflammatory exudate cells. *J. Reticuloendothel. Soc.* **11**, 617–626

YOFFEY, J. M. (1957) Cellular equilibria in blood forming tissues, in *Homeostatic Mechanisms (Brookhaven Symp. Biol.* No. 10*)*, pp. 1–30, Brookhaven National Laboratories, Upton, N.Y.

YOFFEY, J. M. (1960) *Quantitative Cellular Haematology*, Thomas, Springfield, Ill.

YOFFEY, J. M. & COURTICE, F. C. (1956) *Lymphatics, Lymph and Lymphoid Tissue*, Arnold, London

YOFFEY, J. M., THOMAS, D. B., MOFFATT, D. J., SUTHERLAND, I. H. & ROSSE, C. (1961) Non-immunological functions of the lymphocyte, in *Biological Activity of the Leucocyte (Ciba Found. Study Group 10)*, pp. 45–54, Little Brown, Boston; Churchill, London

YOFFEY, J. M., ROSSE, C., MOFFATT, D. J. & SUTHERLAND, O. H. (1965) Studies on hypoxia III. The differential response of the bone marrow to primary and secondary hypoxia. *Acta Anat.* **62**, 476–488

YOFFEY, J. M., JEFFREYS, R. V., OSMOND, D. G., TURNER, M. S., TASHIN, S. C. & NIVEN, P. A. R. (1968) Studies on hypoxia VI. Changes in lymphocytes and transitional cells in the marrow during the intensification of primary hypoxia and rebound. *Ann. N.Y. Acad. Sci.* **149**, 179–192

YOSHIDA, Y. & OSMOND, D. G. (1971) Identity and proliferation of small lymphocyte precursors in cultures of lymphocyte-rich fractions of guinea pig bone marrow. *Blood J. Hematol.* **37**, 73–86

Discussion

Thomas: The cell which you called a transitional cell (Figs. 1 and 12) has a much lower nuclear:cytoplasmic ratio and far more numerous mitochondria than I would have expected in a transitional cell.

Rosse: The cells in Fig. 1 and 12, I believe, belong to the population of cells we designate as transitional cells. I don't think there is any discrepancy between the appearance of these cells as seen in the electron microscope and those we call transitional cells on smears, except perhaps for the presence of nucleolar material, particularly in those cells which have numerous polyribosomes in their cytoplasm. As for the cells in Fig. 10 which contain haemoglobin, obviously, by definition, they cannot be called transitional cells. They are different, however, from cells we regard as proerythroblasts.

There are these two groups of cells in which both [55]Fe incorporation and benzidine positivity appear for the first time: one which conforms to what we picture as a proerythroblast, with a round nucleus, a number of prominent nucleoli and fairly extensive cytoplasm, packed full with polyribosomes; and another type of cell in which the nucleus has a more irregular outline—it is leptochromatic, shows some nucleolar material and less cytoplasm than we commonly see in proerythroblasts.

Thomas: I find it extremely difficult to match this cell with the transitional cells which Yoffey *et al.* (1965) have described in electron micrographs of guinea-pig bone marrow or with the similar cells which I regard as transitional cells in murine bone marrow and foetal liver (see Fig. 9, p. 91). I don't know how this particular cell, which appears to contain haemoglobin, is related to the cells which we have all called transitional cells in electron micrographs.

Rosse: This involves looking at two cells side by side and discussing individual characteristics. I wish we could arrive at reliable terminology and parameters by which we could definitely identify these cells. I prefer to think of them as groups of cells. They have a number of features in common but one runs into difficulties on either side of these features.

Yoffey: On this question of the nuclear: cytoplasmic ratio, following up the previous discussion, one has constantly to bear in mind that there is a whole spectrum of cells, and that as they are growing before division the cytoplasm will increase in amount relative to the nucleus.

We have looked for phagocytosis of small lymphocytes very carefully in all our electron microscope studies, but surprisingly, even in severe hypoxia, where one expects stress and lymphocyte death, we do not see any sign of lymphocyte death. We came to the conclusion that Dr Osmond's earlier work on nuclear phagocytosis must have involved essentially extruded red cell nuclei. In the course of many ultrastructural studies we have only twice seen a lymphocyte inside a phagocytic central reticular cell. I do not know whether it was dead or not. Morphologically it looked quite healthy. Of course, we know from the early studies of Humble *et al.* (1956), confirmed by later workers (e.g. Ioachim 1965), that this business of what has been termed 'emperipolesis', namely lymphocytes getting into and out of cells, apparently occurs even if the lymphocytes are quite alive and active.

Metcalf: Coming from an immunological institute, I feel impelled to say that many lymphocytes have functions other than being ancestors of haemopoietic populations! The vast majority of cells with the morphology of lymphocytes are of course engaged in immunological reactions. The lymphocyte-like cells so characteristic of the rat and mouse bone marrow (10–20% of all cells) present a particular problem as the total frequency of haemopoietic stem and progenitor cells in the bone marrow is likely to be only about 2% of all marrow cells. Are the other lymphocyte-like cells in the bone marrow various maturation stages of B lymphocytes—bone-marrow-derived lymphocytes capable of antibody formation? B lymphocytes can be identified by their specific capacity to bind antigen–antibody complexes and I wonder, Dr Rosse, whether you have applied this functional test to any of your marrow lymphocyte populations to determine what proportion are B lymphocytes?

Harris: I was very interested in your evidence that some transitional cells change into erythroid precursors, Dr Rosse. We all know that Dr Thomas and Professor Yoffey have described the very high content of transitional cells in human foetal marrow. In our laboratory we recently found that transitional cells stain positively both with peroxidase and Sudan Black B (P. F. Harris & A. E. Caxton-Martins, unpublished findings, 1972). We feel that this is pretty strong evidence that they are differentiating along both granulocytic and monocytic lines, as well as having erythropoietic potentiality.

Rosse: Granulocyte production needs a different experimental approach.

Lajtha: The chromosome evidence in chronic granulocytic leukaemia would be very strongly against the possibility that, in man, the same cell that gives rise to erythrocytes can give rise to small lymphocytes as well.

Yoffey: I think it is correct to say that the Philadelphia chromosome is found in members of both the erythroid and the granulocytic series (Whang *et al.* 1963; Rastrick *et al.* 1968), but never—as far as I can recall—in lymphocytes of the peripheral blood. For its bearing on the existence of a common stem cell for erythrocytes and granulocytes, the significance of these shared chromosomal abnormalities, whether in disease or experimentally induced, is obvious.

Dicke: I understand now that some of the transitional cells are diamino-benzidine-tetrahydrochloride (DAB)-positive.

Rosse: Yes. Without the benzidine or DAB reaction, you could not tell whether the cell had haemoglobin in it or not, and you could not distinguish it from other cells in the population. These positive cells constitute only about 3% of the overall transitional cell population. One needs to look at a fair sample of marrow to find cells of this morphology labelled with [55]Fe or reacting with benzidine. They are about ten times less numerous than proerythroblasts in similar reactions.

Dicke: Dr. Thomas, was your transitional cell DAB-positive? Ours is negative.

Thomas: The cells I looked at were DAB-negative.

Rosse: If the precursors for marrow small lymphocytes and for erythroblasts are different cell populations, it is impossible to tell the difference morphologic-ally. It is very difficult even to think of an experiment to determine whether a single cell can decide to turn towards erythrocytic or lymphocytic differentiation. From the evidence already presented on the pluripotent functions of the stem cell, it seems that there is a pool in which cells with potentials for different functions may reside. Another possibility should also be considered—that cells with different morphological features may have the same function.

We recently described (Tyler *et al.* 1972) how we obtained cells looking much like monocytes from skin window preparations in mice. These exudates have extremely few lymphocytes and practically no transitional cells in them. Many of these cells belong to the monocytic line and they give good repopulation of erythropoietic activity in the spleens of mice ten days after transfusion.

References

HUMBLE, J. G., JAYNE, W. H. V. & PULVERTAFT, C. N. (1956) Biological interaction between lymphocytes and other cells. *Br. J. Haematol.* **2**, 283–294

IOACHIM, H. L. (1965) Emperipolesis of lymphoid cells in mixed cultures. *Lab. Invest.* **14**, 1784–1794

RASTRICK, J. M., FITZGERALD, P. H. & GUNZ, W. F. (1968) Direct evidence for the presence of Ph' chromosome in erythroid cells. *Br. Med. J.* **1**, 96–98

TYLER, R. W., ROSSE, C. & EVERETT, N. B. (1972) The hemopoietic repopulating potential of inflammatory exudate cells. *J. Reticuloendothel. Soc.* **11**, 617

WHANG, J., FREI, E., TJIO, J. H., CARBONE, P. P. & BRECHER, G. (1963) The distribution of the Philadelphia chromosome in patients with chronic myelogenous leukaemia. *Blood J. Hematol.* **22**, 664–673

YOFFEY, J. M., HUDSON, G. & OSMOND, D. G. (1965) The lymphocyte in guinea pig bone marrow. *J. Anat.* **99**, 851–860

Kinetic and haemopoietic properties of lymphoid cells in the bone marrow

D. G. OSMOND, S. C. MILLER and Y. YOSHIDA

Department of Anatomy, McGill University, Montreal, Quebec

Abstract A series of studies was designed to define the kinetic and morphological properties of lymphoid cell populations in guinea-pig bone marrow and to quantitate their role in the production of small lymphocytes and of non-lymphoid cells. (1) Marrow lymphoid cell populations were analysed by cell size and proliferative activity. (2) Most non-dividing small lymphocytes in the marrow showed a rapid renewal by newly-formed cells, as measured autoradiographically during continuous infusion of [^{3}H]thymidine. (3) The precursors of marrow small lymphocytes were identified among dividing large lymphoid cells by autoradiographic studies and direct microscopic observation of cultures of isolated suspensions of marrow lymphoid cells. (4) The use of two isotopic DNA labels to determine the rates at which large lymphoid cells entered and left DNA synthesis showed these cells to be kinetically heterogeneous. The duration of DNA synthesis was inversely related to cell size. The incidence of DNA-synthesizing cells increased with increasing cell size, cytoplasmic basophilia and nuclear leptochromasia. (5) The overall cell production by large lymphoid cells exceeded the renewal rate of marrow small lymphocytes. (6) When transfused into lethally X-irradiated animals marrow fractions containing highly concentrated lymphoid cells were considerably more effective than unfractionated marrow or lymphocyte-depleted marrow fractions in repopulating the marrow and spleen of recipients. The results indicate that some large lymphoid cells in the marrow are precursors of small lymphocytes and some are self-replicating, while others are progenitors of non-lymphoid cells. The kinetic and morphological properties of subpopulations of large lymphoid cells in the marrow are discussed in relation to the properties ascribed to primitive haemopoietic progenitor cells.

Evidence has accumulated in recent years that the bone marrow is a major site of continuous small lymphocyte production and dissemination (Osmond & Everett 1964; Harris & Kugler 1965; Osmond 1967a, 1972; Everett & Tyler 1967; Brahim & Osmond 1970; Yoffey & Courtice 1970; Rosse 1972). Approximately a quarter of all nucleated cells in the bone marrow of laboratory mammals and the human foetus and infant may be classified morphologically as lymphoid cells (Yoffey & Courtice 1970; Metcalf & Moore 1971). As a group they are clearly distinguishable from the other marrow cell populations by the absence of specific cytoplasmic differentiation and the sharing of certain common features, notably a minimal quantity of cytoplasm and a spherical or slightly indented nucleus (Yoffey *et al.* 1965; Rosse & Yoffey 1967). This broad definition covers a range of cells (Fig. 1) including typical small lymphocytes, morphologically similar to those in other tissues, and a series of larger cells, not identical with the large or medium-sized lymphocytes usually seen elsewhere. Although some of these larger cells have been unequivocally implicated as proliferative precursors of marrow small lymphocytes (Yoshida & Osmond 1971a; Rosse 1972), the definition and kinetic properties of the subpopulations of progenitors and non-dividing progeny remain less well understood in marrow lymphocyto-poiesis than in the parallel processes of erythrocytopoiesis and granulocyto-poiesis. Moreover, the marrow lymphoid cells are functionally heterogeneous. Decisive evidence is required to quantitate the role of the larger lymphoid cells in small lymphocyte production and to determine to what extent they may also include progenitors or stem cells for non-lymphoid cell lines (Yoffey 1960; Harris & Kugler 1964; Kurnick & Nokay 1965; Niewisch *et al.* 1967; Morrison & Toepfer 1967; Bennett & Cudkowicz 1968; Yoffey & Courtice 1970; Metcalf & Moore 1971; Murphy *et al.* 1971; van Bekkum *et al.* 1971; Moore *et al.* 1972).

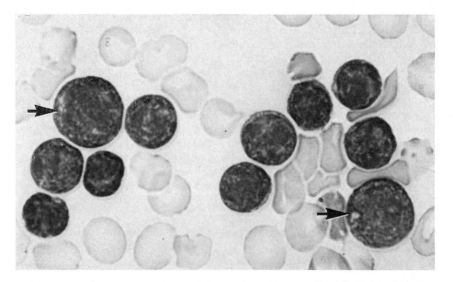

FIG. 1. Smear of lymphoid cells separated from guinea pig bone marrow by brief centrifugation in linear sucrose–serum gradients. Note small lymphocytes, large lymphoid cells (arrows) and numerous erythrocytes. MacNeal tetrachrome stain ($\times$ 1740).

In the present series of studies objective criteria have been developed to characterize the marrow lymphoid cell population. Kinetic and morphological subpopulations of proliferating lymphoid cells have been defined and the immediate progenitors of marrow small lymphocytes have been formally identified. The kinetics of the production of marrow lymphoid cells and the renewal rate of marrow small lymphocytes have been measured and compared. The stem cell potential of marrow lymphoid cells has been assayed by their capacity to repopulate irradiated haemopoietic tissues.

Hartley guinea pigs weighing approximately 400 g were used in all experiments. The work was facilitated by the development of a simple technique for separating lymphoid cells in high concentrations from suspensions of marrow cells (Fig. 1) (Osmond 1967*b*, *c*; Yoshida & Osmond 1971*a*, *b*, *c*).

CHARACTERIZATION OF POPULATIONS OF MARROW LYMPHOID CELLS

Cell size and proliferative capacity were used as basic criteria in analysing the population of marrow lymphoid cells.

Fig. 2 shows the size distribution of lymphoid cells in marrow, based on their mean nuclear diameter in serum smears of marrow suspensions. Representative sampling of all cell sizes was ensured by preparing the smears under standard conditions and measuring cells along the entire length of each smear. The results, in good agreement with other studies in guinea pigs, show that the size distribution profile is highly reproducible under standard conditions and is sensitive to subtle shifts in the composition of the population (Osmond 1967*a*, *c*; Yoshida & Osmond 1971*a*).

Autoradiographs of marrow lymphoid cells sampled one hour after intracardiac administration of [^{3}H]thymidine (1 μCi/g body weight; 6.7 Ci/mmol) revealed that the cells which initially incorporated the isotope and were therefore in DNA synthesis constituted $14.2 \pm 0.8\%$ of the entire lymphoid cell population and were confined to the larger size groups (Fig. 2). Two main lymphoid cell subgroups could be defined in smears on the basis of size and proliferative capacity: small lymphocytes (nuclear diameters < 8.0 μm) and large lymphoid cells (nuclear diameters $\geqslant 8.0$ μm).

Since only $2.2 \pm 0.1\%$ of small lymphocytes incorporated [^{3}H]thymidine they could be regarded essentially as a non-proliferative cell compartment. They constituted $54.3 \pm 1.7\%$ of the entire population of marrow lymphoid cells, including the peak incidence of cells at 7.0–7.9 μm nuclear diameter. The large lymphoid cells included most of the proliferating cells, $28.3 \pm 1.1\%$ being in DNA synthesis at any given time. Morphologically, they were more hetero-

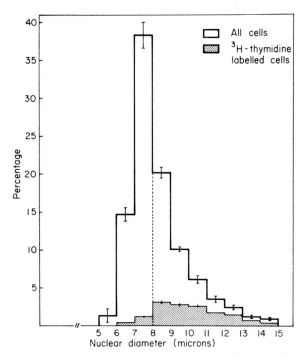

FIG. 2. Size distribution of lymphoid cells in smears of guinea pig bone marrow sampled 40–104 min after intracardiac administration of [³H]thymidine (1 μCi/g). Approximately 1500 lymphoid cells were measured in each of 16 experiments (mean ± standard error).

geneous than small lymphocytes. While most of them had a relatively leptochromatic nucleus and corresponded with previous descriptions of transitional cells (Yoffey *et al.* 1965; Rosse & Yoffey 1967), some pachychromatic cells and an overlap with some non-proliferating cells were also included (see p. 142).

RENEWAL OF SMALL LYMPHOCYTES IN BONE MARROW

Autoradiographic studies after a single pulse of [³H]thymidine in guinea pigs established that, although not themselves proliferating, most marrow small lymphocytes were rapidly replaced by newly formed cells (Osmond & Everett 1964; Osmond 1967a). Lymphocyte turnover in guinea pigs was subsequently examined after repeated injections of [³H]thymidine (Rosse 1972). The rate of small lymphocyte renewal in guinea pig marrow has now been determined by continuous infusion of [³H]thymidine to label the DNA of all newly formed cells, while the small lymphocytes have been classified by accurate measurements of nuclear size to confine observations to non-proliferating cells.

After an initial 20-hour intraperitoneal infusion of isotonic saline and anti-biotics (penicillin and streptomycin, 2500 units each/ml), [³H]thymidine was added for periods up to five days (1.5 μCi/g body weight daily; 6.7 Ci/mmol). The guinea pigs were allowed to move freely while the infusion was given through fine polythene tubing from a syringe pump (1.0 ml/day). Daily blood smears and terminal smears from femoral marrow were examined autoradiographically in eight animals killed at intervals from two to five days after the start of [³H]thy-midine infusion. There were no significant changes in either total cellularity or differential counts of 1000–4000 nucleated cells in blood and bone marrow throughout the experimental period. In each autoradiograph the grain count over 1000 measured small lymphocytes was recorded.

In the blood, labelled small lymphocytes increased progressively in numbers from seven hours onwards. Approximately one-third of blood small lymphocytes were labelled by five days (Fig. 3). In sharp contrast, the mean labelling index of marrow small lymphocytes reached 90.0% by four days (Fig. 3). The effectiveness

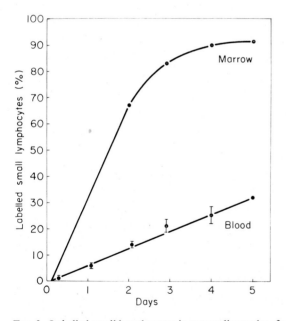

Fig. 3. Labelled small lymphocytes in autoradiographs of guinea pig blood and bone marrow during intraperitoneal infusion of [³H]thymidine (1.5 μCi/g daily). Exposure time: 28 days. Labelled cells had more than three overlying grains. (Background grains over marrow ery-throcytes: mean, 0.02–0.37; range, 0–3 grains. Grain counts of labelled marrow lymphocytes: at 48 h: 44 % > 20 grains, 78 % > 10 grains, 97 % > 5 grains; at 120 h: 64 % > 20 grains, 94 % > 10 grains, 99 % > 5 grains).

of the labelling procedure was indicated by the complete labelling by five days of all identifiable erythroid and granulocytic cells in the marrow and of the granulocytes in the blood. Labelling of blood granulocytes was seen first at two days ($4.0 \pm 2.9\%$), increased rapidly thereafter ($49.5 \pm 15.7\%$ at 3 days; $88.9 \pm 2.9\%$ at 4 days), and was complete (99.0%) by five days.

The disappearance of unlabelled small lymphocytes from the marrow could be represented as an exponential function of time for the first four days (Fig. 4), 50% replacement of the population occurring in 28.0 ± 1.5 hours. The renewal rate of marrow small lymphocytes was thus ($\ln 2/28$ hour) $\times 100$ or 2.4% per hour. This value is appreciably higher than that reported in guinea pigs given repeated injections of [^{3}H]thymidine (Rosse 1972) but compares closely with a half-time renewal of 24 hours in Lewis rats (Everett & Tyler 1967).

ORIGIN OF NEWLY FORMED SMALL LYMPHOCYTES IN MARROW

Several lines of evidence have demonstrated that the appearance of newly formed small lymphocytes in guinea pig marrow is due to local cell production rather than a haematogenous immigration. When [^{3}H]thymidine was administered to guinea pigs, but excluded from one hindlimb by temporary circulatory arrest, normal numbers of labelled small lymphocytes appeared in the marrow having direct access to the [^{3}H]thymidine but very few appeared in the marrow of the initially occluded limb (Osmond & Everett 1964; Osmond 1967a). Bone marrow continued to show the production of labelled small lymphocytes when isolated from the circulation in intraperitoneal diffusion chambers (Osmond & Everett 1964). Marrow lymphocyte production has been demonstrated by [^{3}H]thymidine labelling in the shielded limbs of otherwise lethally irradiated guinea pigs (Harris & Kugler 1965). Direct injection of [^{3}H]thymidine into the medullary cavity of guinea pig limb bones resulted in the local labelling of marrow small lymphocytes, and their subsequent migration to blood, spleen and lymph nodes, in the absence of labelling of precursor cells in extramyeloid tissues (Brahim & Osmond 1970).

These findings, together with the observed rapidity of small lymphocyte renewal, imply the existence of a large and actively proliferating population of small lymphocyte precursors in the marrow.

IDENTITY OF PRECURSORS OF MARROW SMALL LYMPHOCYTES

Lymphocyte production has been studied in cultures of lymphoid cells separated from guinea-pig bone marrow by centrifugation in sucrose–serum

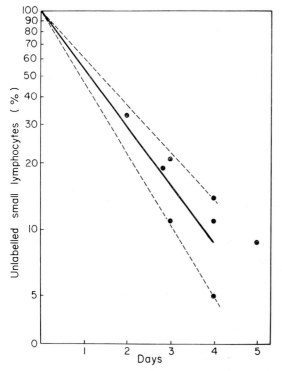

Fig. 4. Disappearance of unlabelled small lymphocytes from autoradiographs of guinea pig bone marrow during intraperitoneal infusion of [³H]thymidine as in Fig. 3. The regression line was calculated by the method of least squares from the individual values for the first four days. Broken lines indicate 100 % limits of experimental values. Half-time renewal: 28 ± 1.5 h (mean ± standard error).

gradients (Osmond 1967*b, c*; Yoshida & Osmond 1971*a, b, c*). Slowly sediment-ing fractions of marrow cells contained high concentrations (96.6 ± 1.9%) of small and large lymphoid cells, the latter being confined mainly to the pre-DNA synthetic (G1) phase and early DNA synthetic (S) phase of the cell cycle (Yoshida & Osmond 1971*a*). During short-term cultures they showed a wave of DNA synthesis and mitosis. When the large lymphoid cells were pulse-labelled with [³H]thymidine during the peak of DNA synthesis, labelled small lympho-cytes subsequently appeared in such large numbers that their immediate pre-cursors could only have been contained within the population of labelled large lymphoid cells (Yoshida & Osmond 1971*a*). The mean grain count of the labelled small lymphocytes was half that of the initially labelled large lymphoid cells. Residual large lymphoid cells in the cultures showed a declining grain count, indicating that they were self-replicating.

Production of marrow lymphocytes *in vitro* has also been observed directly by phase contrast microscopy (E. S. Lou, Y. Yoshida & D. G. Osmond 1968, unpublished). Lymphocyte-rich marrow fractions were dispersed as a monolayer between the dialysis membrane and coverglass of Rose's chambers according to the technique of Pinet *et al.* (1969). During incubation at 37 °C the chambers were perfused continuously with Eagle's minimum essential medium (MEM), saturated with 95% O_2 and 5% CO_2, and supplemented with 25–30% fresh guinea pig serum, 0.2% glucose, penicillin and streptomycin. Mitoses of large lymphoid cells, initially absent, were seen with increasing frequency from 18 to

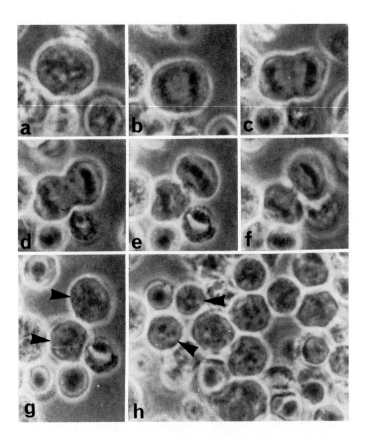

FIG. 5. Mitosis of large lymphoid cell in a lymphocyte-rich fraction of guinea pig bone marrow incubated in a Rose chamber. *(a)* Metaphase (0 min), *(b)* mid-anaphase (5 min), *(c)* early telophase (11 min), *(d)* mid-telophase (12 min), *(e)* & *(f)* late telophase (15–20 min), *(g)* & *(h)* two daughter cells (27–39 min). The lower of the two daughter cells in *(h)* is focused to show its small lymphocyte morphology. Phase contrast (× 1500) (E. S. Lou, Y. Yoshida and D. G. Osmond, 1968), unpublished).

24 hours after the cells had been separated from the bone marrow (Fig. 5), corresponding well with the synchronous behaviour seen in tube cultures (Yoshida & Osmond 1971a). Mitoses of large lymphoid cells were readily located and followed under direct observation at 22–24 hours. Some of the daughter cells were typical small lymphocytes (Fig. 5) while others still showed the morphology of large lymphoid cells. The mitotic duration was approximately 75 minutes from late prophase and 20–25 minutes from mid-anaphase onwards. These correspond well with similar observations by Rosse (1972).

There is thus no doubt that some of the large lymphoid cells are immediate precursors of newly formed small lymphocytes in marrow. To determine whether or not they could account entirely for the observed renewal of small lymphocytes the total proliferative capacity of the lymphoid cell population has been quantitated by measuring the duration of S phase and the incidence of DNA-synthesizing lymphoid cells.

PROLIFERATION OF LARGE LYMPHOID CELLS IN BONE MARROW

The duration of S phase of large lymphoid cells in marrow was determined by the DNA-labelling method using two isotopes, described by Lala et al. (1965). At intervals from 40 to 104 minutes after an intracardiac injection of [^{3}H]thymidine (1 μCi/g, 6.7 Ci/mmol) guinea-pig femoral marrow cells were removed and incubated for 15 min with [^{14}C]thymidine (0.5 Ci/ml, 50 mCi/mM) in Eagle's MEM containing 25% fresh guinea-pig serum. The cells were then washed, smeared, methanol-fixed and examined in thick-emulsion autoradiographs prepared by dipping twice in Kodak NTB$_2$ liquid emulsion, exposing for 28 days, and staining through the processed emulsion with a modified MacNeal's tetrachrome stain. Cells labelled with [^{14}C]thymidine could be readily distinguished in autoradiographs by the characteristically wide spread of grains in contrast with the precise supranuclear localization of grains produced by [^{3}H]thymidine alone. Measurements of 1000 lymphoid cells in each of 17 experiments showed that neither the cell size distribution nor the proportion of cells in DNA synthesis had been altered by the short in vitro incubation. The ratio of the number of cells labelled with [^{3}H]thymidine alone to 1000 measured large lymphoid cells labelled with [^{14}C]thymidine ($\pm$ [^{3}H]thymidine) was determined in each experiment. It indicated the proportion of cells which had been in DNA synthesis at the time of [^{3}H]thymidine administration but had subsequently left S phase (efflux from S phase).

The results, presented in Fig. 6, showed a linear increase in the percentage efflux of cells from S phase with increasing time intervals between the two isotopic

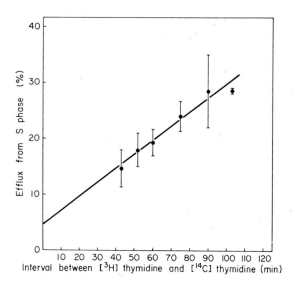

FIG. 6. Percentage efflux of marrow large lymphoid cells from S phase at various intervals between exposure to [³H]thymidine *in vivo* and [¹⁴C]thymidine *in vitro* (mean ± standard error). The regression line was calculated from 17 experimental values by the method of least squares [y = 21.5 + 0.251 (x − 67.4)]. Mean efflux rate: 15.1 %/h.

labels. The slope of the curve indicated an efflux of 15.1% per hour and, thus, a mean duration of S phase for all large lymphoid cells of 6.6 hours. The double isotope method provided an accurate measure of S phase duration. Any tendency to overestimate the efflux from S phase by classifying cells weakly labelled with ¹⁴C as ³H-labelled cells was avoided by using the slope of the efflux curve over a range of time intervals. Such a bias remained the same in each experiment, since the number of sampled ¹⁴C-labelled cells was constant. As a result, the efflux curve intercepted the ordinate above zero (Fig. 6). Relative to this intercept the mean and standard error of all values for the duration of S phase was 6.6 ± 0.5 hours.

From the mean duration of S phase (6.6 h) and the total incidence of DNA-synthesizing cells in the marrow lymphoid cell population (14.2%) the rate of cell production may be calculated as 2.2% of the total population of marrow lymphoid cells per hour, equivalent to a turnover time of 46.5 hours for the entire population of marrow lymphoid cells. Further studies have shown that not all subpopulations of large lymphoid cells contribute equally to this cell production.

HETEROGENEITY OF LARGE LYMPHOID CELLS IN BONE MARROW

Large lymphoid cells showed striking kinetic differences from one another when classified by cell size in smears.

Double-isotope labelling of DNA demonstrated clear differences in the absolute duration of S phase with cell size (Fig. 7). Regression curves for the efflux of cells from S phase with time increased in slope with increasing nuclear diameters. In parallel experiments the rate of movement of cells into S phase was determined by measuring the ratios of large lymphoid cells labelled with [3H] alone to those with [14C] ($\pm$ [3H]) in marrow exposed *in vitro* firstly to [14C]-thymidine and one hour later to [3H]thymidine. The influx into S phase was closely similar to the efflux for each cell size, indicating that proliferating cells of all sizes were mixed randomly with respect to their position in the cell cycle and that the differences in the efflux from S phase represented true differences in duration of S phase. From efflux curves the duration of DNA synthesis was calculated to increase from 3.5 $\pm$ 0.3 hours for the largest cell group ($\geqslant$ 11.0 μm) to 10.9 $\pm$ 0.9 hours for the smallest (8.0–8.9 μm) (Fig. 7).

The proportion of cells in DNA synthesis decreased from 54.9 $\pm$ 2.3% among the largest cell group ($\geqslant$ 11.0 μm) to 14.8 $\pm$ 1.6% (8.0–8.9 μm) (Fig. 7). The lower proportion of DNA-synthesizing cells among the smaller cells could result from several factors, including a size overlap with non-dividing cells, the

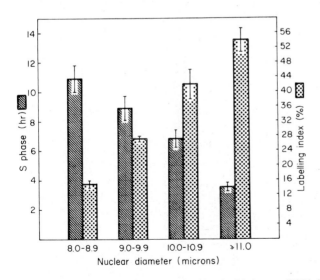

FIG. 7 Duration of S phase, determined by double isotope DNA labelling, and [3H]thymidine labelling index of marrow large lymphoid cells classified by nuclear diameter in smears (mean $\pm$ standard error, 17 experiments).

presence of potentially proliferative cells in a non-cycling or 'resting' (G0) phase, or a predominance of cells in a relatively long post-mitotic (G1) phase of the cell cycle. On the other hand, the combination of a short time for DNA synthesis (3.5 h) and a high proportion of cells in DNA synthesis (54.9%) demonstrates that the largest lymphoid cells must be highly proliferative and have a short mean cycle (maximum 6.4 h).

The nuclear chromatin pattern is commonly used as a criterion of cell maturity, the most mature cells, typified by small lymphocytes, being markedly pachychromatic. Marrow lymphoid cells were classified into three groups according to the degree of chromatin condensation: pachychromatic, intermediate and leptochromatic. Essentially all marrow lymphoid cells larger than 10.0 μm nuclear diameter in smears were leptochromatic, while those less than 8.0 μm nuclear diameter were pachychromatic. In the intermediate size range pachychromatic cells constituted approximately 40% of all cells measuring 8.0–8.9 μm nuclear diameter and approximately 7% of those measuring 9.0–9.9 μm (Fig. 8). Very few pachychromatic cells incorporated [³H]thymidine (Fig. 8). They may thus be considered as non-dividing cells, functionally equivalent to small lymphocytes. Together with those of less than 8.0 μm nuclear diameter, pachychromatic cells constituted approximately 63% of the entire population of marrow lymphoid cells.

Cytoplasmic basophilia has been used to distinguish subpopulations of marrow large lymphoid cells (Rosse & Yoffey 1967; Moffatt et al. 1967;

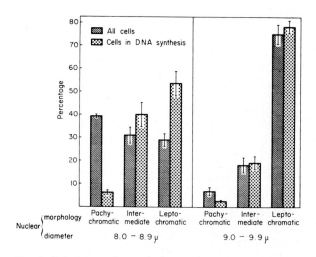

FIG. 8. Relative numbers of marrow large lymphoid cells (all cells and [³H]thymidine-incorporating cells) classified by nuclear morphology and diameter in smears (mean ± standard error); 500 cells and 200 labelled cells, respectively, were examined in each of three experiments.

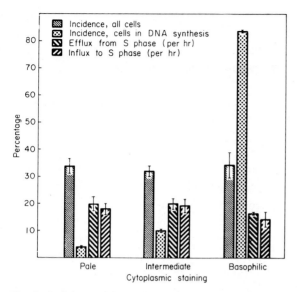

FIG. 9. Relative numbers of marrow large lymphoid cells (all cells and [³H]thymidine-incorporating cells), and rates of movement into and out of S phase of marrow large lymphoid cells classified by cytoplasmic basophilia in smears (mean ± standard error); 2000 cells were measured in each of three experiments.

Rosse 1970). In the present study, large lymphoid cells were classified into three groups according to intensity of cytoplasmic staining: pale, intermediate and basophilic (Fig. 9). Although each group was present in approximately equal numbers most of the DNA-synthesizing cells (86%) were basophilic. Thus, the cell cycle parameters derived from marrow large lymphoid cells, including the duration of S phase relative to cell size, reflect predominantly the characteristics of the basophilic cells. The calculated [³H]thymidine-labelling indices from the data in Fig. 9 were: 69.8% basophilic cells; 8.9% intermediate cells; 3.3% pale cells. Double-isotope labelling of DNA revealed that the rates of movement into and out of S phase were essentially identical for each of the three cell groups, thus confirming that the mean duration of S phase is not related to cytoplasmic basophilia (Rosse 1970).

COMPARISON OF RATE OF CELL PRODUCTION BY MARROW LYMPHOID CELLS AND RENEWAL RATE OF MARROW SMALL LYMPHOCYTES

Marrow small lymphocytes measuring less than 8.0 μm nuclear diameter in smears were renewed at a mean rate of 2.4% per hour, as noted above, and constituted 54.3 ± 1.7% of the entire population of marrow lymphoid cells.

The number of newly formed cells required to enter this population to maintain a steady state would thus be equivalent to 1.3% of the entire population of marrow lymphoid cells per hour. This estimate is maximal since it assumes an exponential replacement of all marrow small lymphocytes, regardless of the small subpopulation of long-lived cells in the marrow (Haas *et al.* 1971; Rosse 1972; Osmond 1972). Even so, the observed rate of cell production by proliferating lymphoid cells, equivalent to 2.2% of the entire population of lymphoid cells per hour, considerably exceeded the requirements for renewal of small lymphocytes.

Several factors may account for this apparent imbalance: (1) as already noted, some non-dividing cells, functionally equivalent to small lymphocytes, are larger than 8.0 μm nuclear diameter in smears and should be included in the renewal figures; (2) some cell death may occur among proliferating cells; (3) some proliferating cells with lymphoid morphology may be the precursors of non-lymphoid cells. The first factor can account only partially for the discrepancy. Non-dividing cells should constitute 90% of the entire lymphoid cell population to balance fully the cell production by dividing lymphoid cells, assuming the renewal rate of all non-dividing cells to be the same (2.4%/h). This is clearly incompatible with experimental findings, since DNA-synthetic cells alone constituted 14.2% of the lymphoid cell population. As yet, there has been no evidence of ineffective production of lymphoid cells and cell death, although this possibility cannot be excluded. On the other hand, the ability of isolated suspensions of marrow lymphoid cells to repopulate the haemopoietic tissues of lethally X-irradiated animals has supported the view that some marrow lymphoid cells can function as precursors of non-lymphoid cell lines.

HAEMOPOIETIC REPOPULATING ABILITY OF MARROW LYMPHOID CELLS

The haemopoietic potential of suspensions of bone marrow cells and separated fractions of marrow lymphoid cells in the guinea pig has been assayed by their capacity to restore the cellularity and proliferative activity of the marrow and spleen when transfused into lethally X-irradiated guinea pigs.

Non-transfused guinea pigs showed a consistent reduction of femoral marrow cellularity and spleen weight eight days after 750 R whole-body X-irradiation (Table 1). The marrow and spleen were always devoid of recognizable erythroid or granulocytic precursors. Intracardiac transfusion of unfractionated bone marrow cells 18–20 hours after irradiation resulted in the repopulation of recipient tissues by haemopoietic progenitor cells, as shown by the presence of erythroid and granulocytic cells in the marrow and an increase in the eight-day

TABLE 1

Effects of transfusion of bone marrow cells on spleen weight and marrow cellularity of lethally irradiated guinea pigs

Cell dose ($\times 10^6$)	Number of experiments	Spleen weight (mg)	Femoral marrow cellularity (nucleated cells: $\times 10^3/mg$)
0	30	349 ± 13[a]	66 ± 3[a]
10	4	357 ± 24	76 ± 11
60	10	447 ± 29	98 ± 14
100	12	476 ± 45	188 ± 28

[a] Mean ± standard error

spleen weight and marrow cellularity (Table 1). These values increased with increasing cell dose, though not in a simple linear fashion.

Table 2 compares the repopulating ability of fractions separated from guinea-pig bone marrow by brief centrifugation in sucrose-serum gradients (Osmond 1967b, c; Yoshida & Osmond 1971a, b, c). Fraction 1, the most slowly sediment-

TABLE 2

Effects of transfusions of cells separated from bone marrow by brief centrifugation in sucrose–serum gradients on the spleen weight, marrow cellularity and [³H]thymidine incorporation of spleen and marrow of lethally irradiated guinea pigs

Marrow cells transfused	Cell dose ($\times 10^6$)	Number of experiments	Spleen		Femoral marrow	
			Weight (mg)	[³H]thymidine incorporation (cpm/spleen)	Number of nucleated cells ($\times 10^3/mg$)	[³H]thymidine incorporation (cpm/mg)
Fraction 1[b]	5	5	370 ± 31[a]	397 ± 115[a]	110 ± 10[a]	558 ± 105[a]
	10	10	421 ± 32	367 ± 57	123 ± 18	740 ± 76
	15	7	526 ± 32	1303 ± 367	211 ± 33	1573 ± 230
Fraction 1[c]	8	11	371 ± 32	361 ± 11	88 ± 9	795 ± 153
Fraction 2[d]	10	12	327 ± 25	190 ± 58	91 ± 9	308 ± 83
	55	5	321 ± 27	188 ± 95	79 ± 18	539 ± 201

[a] Mean ± standard error
[b] Fraction 1 = Slowly-sedimenting, lymphocyte-rich fraction separated from bone marrow cell suspensions by centrifugation in a single sucrose–serum gradient
[c] Fraction 1a = Lymphocyte-rich marrow fraction derived from two successive gradient centrifugations
[d] Fraction 2 = Rapidly sedimenting, lymphocyte-depleted marrow fraction

ing nucleated cell band, consisted predominantly (78.1 ± 10.7%) of lymphoid cells (Figs. 1, 5), together with relatively mature erythroid and granulocytic cells and a small number (2.5 ± 1.4%) of large blast-like cells. Some of the fractions contained as many as 93% lymphoid cells. When fraction 1 was centrifuged in a second similar sucrose–serum gradient, consistently high concentrations of lymphoid cells (96.0 ± 1.9%) with few blast cells (1.9 ± 1.1%) were again recovered from a slowly sedimenting fraction (fraction 1*a*). In contrast, the most rapidly sedimenting cells recovered from the bottom of sucrose–serum gradients (fraction 2) were depleted of lymphoid cells (9.5 ± 2.6%), but contained appreciable numbers (5.8 ± 2.0%) of large blast-like cells and a predominance of granulocyte and erythrocyte precursors, many of which were large proliferative immature cells.

As detailed in Table 2, transfusions of fraction 1 cells showed markedly enhanced repopulating ability compared with unfractionated marrow. The marrow cellularity, spleen weight and total proliferative activity of marrow and spleen measured by liquid scintillation counting of DNA hydrolysates one hour after intracardiac [^{3}H]thymidine (1 μCi/g body weight, 6.7 Ci/mmol), all increased steeply with increasing doses of fraction 1 cells (Table 2). In autoradiographs of host marrow, many of the proliferating cells were erythroid and granulocytic precursors. Fraction 1*a* retained the repopulating ability of fraction 1 (Table 2). In contrast, even large doses of fraction 2 cells had little or no repopulating ability (Table 2). Spleen weight and proliferation were even less than in non-transfused irradiated animals. Such a paradoxical effect is not incompatible with the presence of some haemopoietic stem cells (Lajtha *et al.* 1969). Nevertheless, despite the high proportion of proliferating cells present in the original cell fraction, the recipient marrow showed little or no persisting proliferative activity and erythroid or granulocytic cells could be identified in the marrow of less than a quarter of the animals.

The only cells present in the slowly sedimenting fractions (1 and 1*a*) which could account for the haemopoietic repopulating activity were either lymphoid cells or the small group of large blast-like cells. However, the repopulating ability of unfractionated marrow and the three marrow fractions was inversely related to their content of blast-like cells. These observations, together with the effective repopulation by suspensions containing more than 98% lymphoid cells, indicated that the repopulating cells were contained within the lymphoid cell population. Repopulating ability correlated most closely with the numbers of large lymphoid cells. Dose-response curves for fraction 1 and unfractionated marrow showed the closest similarity in slope when expressed in terms of their large lymphoid cell content but were widely disparate in terms of blast cell number (D. G. Osmond & Y. Yoshida, unpublished).

DISCUSSION

The present series of studies establishes a number of parameters needed to formulate a model of lymphocyte production in guinea-pig bone marrow, including the requirements for lymphoid progenitor cells. An accurate characterization of the population profile of marrow lymphoid cells by cell size and kinetic behaviour allows for the first time a definition and quantitative comparison of kinetic subpopulations in relation to the whole. Of these subpopulations, the small cells, which are not dividing but are rapidly renewed, are regarded as small lymphocytes because of their typical morphology (Yoffey *et al.* 1965; Yoffey & Courtice 1970) and the demonstration that they contribute to the small lymphocyte populations of the blood, spleen and lymph nodes (Brahim & Osmond 1970). The larger cells, which include the dividing forms, may be termed 'large lymphoid cells' because of their lymphocyte-like morphology, and the demonstration that some of them are the immediate precursors of small lymphocytes (Yoshida & Osmond 1971*a*). However, in addition to an overlap of cell size with non-dividing cells the group of large lymphoid cells also embraces several subpopulations which differ from one another markedly with respect to their kinetic properties and haemopoietic potential.

Kinetically, the most active proliferation is seen among the largest lymphoid cells. They have a shorter duration of S phase and a higher incidence of DNA-synthesizing cells than the smaller dividing cells. This proliferation is a property mainly of lymphoid cells with basophilic cytoplasm and a leptochromatic nucleus. Cells with pale-staining cytoplasm and more evident condensation of nuclear chromatin show the lowest incidence of DNA-synthesizing cells and tend to be most numerous among the smaller dividing cells. Possibly they represent a mixture of actively dividing cells either with cells in a 'resting' (G0) phase of the cell cycle (Moffatt *et al.* 1967; Rosse 1970) or with non-dividing cells. Each subpopulation of lymphoid cells shows a range of properties in relation to cell size, nuclear chromatin pattern and cytoplasmic staining. None of these parameters, singly or in combination, provides a clear-cut dividing line between groups of lymphoid cells which are actively dividing, 'resting' in G0, or non-dividing. Thus, the somewhat conflicting values previously reported for the relative incidence of marrow small lymphocytes and of large lymphoid cells or transitional cells (Yoffey & Courtice 1970; Metcalf & Moore 1971) cannot be equated with non-dividing and dividing compartments.

In terms of haemopoietic potential it is clear that not all large lymphoid cells are the immediate precursors of small lymphocytes. Some are self-replicating, though further data are required to determine whether they can divide repeatedly in a self-sustaining manner (Harris & Kugler 1965; Moffatt *et al.* 1967). In addition, the present studies lend strong support to the view that some marrow cells with lymphoid cell morphology act as precursors for non-lymphoid cell lines (Yoffey 1960; Yoffey & Courtice 1970). The apparent overproduction by the dividing lymphoid cells, in the absence of any evidence of selective cell death, can be explained most readily by the acquisition of non-lymphoid morphology in an appreciable proportion of their progeny. The ability of suspensions of purified marrow lymphoid cells to repopulate the marrow and spleen of lethally X-irradiated guinea pigs with erythroid and granulocytic cells as well as lymphocytes indicates the presence of primitive haemopoietic progenitor cells. The effectiveness of transfusions of bone marrow with a high content of lymphoid cells in experiments on post-irradiation protection has been noted previously in the guinea pig (Harris & Kugler 1964), rat (Morrison & Toepfer 1967) and mouse (Kurnick & Nokay 1965; Bennett & Cudkowicz 1968). The present studies, using preparations of marrow lymphoid cells of greater purity and a more comprehensive assay system than those previously used, discount the activities of non-lymphoid cells and suggest that repopulating ability is a property of some of the large lymphoid cells rather than the small lymphocytes. Although the repopulation assay system which was developed for the guinea pig may not reveal all the stem cell potential of the transfused cells (Lajtha *et al.* 1969), it probably does reflect the activities of progenitor cells which are dividing continuously in normal bone marrow. It has been shown by the '[^{3}H]thymidine suicide' technique (Becker *et al.* 1965) that the repopulating progenitor cells are normally in cell cycle; DNA-synthesizing cells constitute approximately 30% of the cells which repopulate rat marrow after transfusion into irradiated hosts (Blackett 1968) and 43% of the cells which repopulate irradiated mice from a shielded femur (Lajtha *et al.* 1969). The demonstration that some marrow lymphoid cells are progenitor cells which can repopulate X-irradiated lymphomyeloid tissues therefore accounts, at least in part, for the apparently excessive cell production by lymphoid cells in normal marrow. It is also consistent with the existence of a common progenitor cell for lymphoid cells and non-lymphoid haemopoietic cells (Nowell *et al.* 1970).

Several other assay systems have correlated primitive haemopoietic progenitor activities with the presence of marrow cells which appear to be morphologically identical or closely similar to subpopulations of large lymphoid cells. The stem cells which form spleen colonies in irradiated mice have been equated, on the basis of a density separation method, with mononuclear cells 8.0 μm diameter that have pale-blue-staining cytoplasm and a nucleus of 'rather homogeneous structure' (van Bekkum *et al.* 1971). Cells in a light density fraction of marrow from polycythaemic mice which repopulated X-irradiated spleens after direct intrasplenic transfusion were large mononuclear cells with predominantly leptochromatic nuclei and nuclear diameters of 8–15 μm in smears (Murphy *et al.* 1971). Similar cells have been separated from mouse spleen (Niewisch *et al.* 1967). The cells which formed granulocytic colonies in agar culture in light density fractions of monkey marrow were basophilic leptochromatic 'transitional lymphocytes', 9–11 μm diameter (Moore *et al.* 1972). Other studies have linked lymphoid cells mainly with erythropoietic progenitor activity (Bennett & Cudkowicz 1968; Yoffey & Courtice 1970).

Separate studies, using sedimentation velocity and '[³H]thymidine suicide' techniques, have shown that haemopoietic cells detected by the various assay systems differ from one another with respect to their size and kinetic properties. In each case, these properties, taken in conjunction with the morphological studies noted above, correlate closely with the size, kinetic properties and morphology of subpopulations of large lymphoid cells elucidated in the present work. Spleen colony-forming cells in mice tend to be somewhat larger than the marrow cells which cause graft-versus-host reactions (Phillips & Miller 1970), i.e. small lymphocytes (Yoshida & Osmond 1971c), though there is a considerable spread and overlap of cell size (Phillips & Miller 1970). Relatively few (< 10%) spleen colony-forming cells are normally in DNA synthesis (Becker *et al.* 1965; Lajtha *et al.* 1969). These properties, and the morphological properties seen by van Bekkum *et al.* (1971), resemble the characteristics determined in the present work for the smaller, pale-staining, dividing marrow lymphoid cells, which overlap with the non-dividing small lymphocytes in size. On the other hand, both the progenitor cells which form granulocytic colonies in agar culture and those which initiate erythropoiesis in response to erythropoietin have a modal size larger than that of the spleen colony-forming cells (Worton *et al.* 1969; Stephenson & Axelrad 1971; Metcalf & Moore 1971) and high proportions of cells in DNA synthesis: 45% and 70%, respectively (Lajtha *et al.* 1969; Metcalf & Moore 1971; Moore *et al.* 1972). These properties, and the morphological description of Moore *et al.* (1972), match closely the characteristics derived in the present work for the larger basophilic dividing lymphoid cells.

CONCLUSIONS

These studies emphasize the magnitude of small lymphocyte production and the functional heterogeneity of lymphoid cells in the bone marrow. Any complete haemopoietic stem cell model must take into account the continuous demands for the production of marrow small lymphocytes as well as erythrocytes, granulocytes and thrombocytes. The group of dividing large lymphoid cells in the marrow includes both precursors of small lymphocytes and primitive progenitor cells which have the ability to repopulate X-irradiated haemopoietic tissues. The marrow large lymphoid cells show gradients of proliferative activity with respect to nuclear diameter, cytoplasmic basophilia and nuclear chromatin condensation. Further studies are required to elucidate the progenitor cell sequences and regulatory mechanisms involved in marrow lymphocytopoiesis.

ACKNOWLEDGEMENTS

This work was supported by grants from the Medical Research Council of Canada and the National Cancer Institute of Canada.

The technical assistance of Mrs E. D. Watson and Mrs O. Graville is gratefully acknowledged.

References

BECKER, A. J., McCULLOCH, E. A., SIMINOVITCH, L. & TILL, J. E. (1965) The effect of differing demands for blood cell production on DNA synthesis by hemopoietic colony-forming cells of mice. *Blood J. Hematol.* **26**, 296–308

BENNETT, M. & CUDKOWICZ, G. (1968) Hemopoietic progenitor cells with limited potential for differentiation: erythropoietic function of mouse marrow 'lymphocytes'. *J. Cell. Physiol.* **72**, 129–140

BLACKETT, N. M. (1968) Investigation of bone-marrow stem cell proliferation in normal, anemic, and irradiated rats, using methotrexate and tritiated thymidine. *J. Natl Cancer Inst.* **41**, 908–918

BRAHIM, F. & OSMOND, D. G. (1970) Migration of bone marrow lymphocytes demonstrated by selective bone marrow labeling with thymidine-H^3. *Anat. Rec.* **168**, 139–160

EVERETT, N. B. & TYLER, R. W. (1967) Lymphopoiesis in the thymus and other tissues: functional implications. *Int. Rev. Cytol.* **22**, 205–237

HAAS, R. J., BOHNE, F. & FLIEDNER, J. M. (1971) Cytokinetic analysis of slowly proliferating bone marrow cells during recovery from radiation injury. *Cell Tissue Kinet.* **4**, 31–45

HARRIS, P. F. & KUGLER, J. H. (1964) The use of regenerating bone marrow to protect guinea pigs against lethal irradiation. *Acta Haematol. (Basel)* **32**, 146–167

HARRIS, P. F. & KUGLER, J. H. (1965) An investigation of lymphocyte production in guinea pig bone marrow. *Acta Haematol. (Basel)* **33**, 351–369

KURNICK, N. B. & NOKAY, N. (1965) Repopulation of bone marrow in mice: number and type of cells required for post-X-irradiation protection. *Radiat. Res.* **25**, 53–67

LAJTHA, L. G., POZZI, L. V., SCHOFIELD, R. & FOX, M. (1969) Kinetic properties of haemopoietic stem cells. *Cell Tissue Kinet.* **2**, 39–49

LALA, P. K., MALONEY, M. A. & PATT, H. M. (1965) Measurement of DNA-synthesis time in myeloid-erythroid precursors. *Exp. Cell. Res.* **38**, 626–634

METCALF, D. & MOORE, M. A. S. (1971) *Haemopoietic Cells*, North-Holland, Amsterdam

MOFFATT, D. J., ROSSE, C. & YOFFEY, J. M. (1967) Identity of the haemopoietic stem cell. *Lancet* **2**, 547–548

MOORE, M. A. S., WILLIAMS, N. & METCALF, D. (1972) Purification and characterisation of the in vitro colony forming cell in monkey hemopoietic tissue. *J. Cell. Physiol.* **79**, 283–292

MORRISON, J. H. & TOEPFER, J. F. (1967) Survival of lethally X-irradiated rats after treatment with isogenic mouse lymphocytes. *Am. J. Physiol.* **213**, 923–927

MURPHY, M. J., BERTLES, J. F. & GORDON, A. S. (1971) Identifying characteristics of the haematopoietic precursor cell. *J. Cell Sci.* **9**, 23–47

NIEWISCH, H., VOGEL, H. & MATIOLI, G. (1967) Concentration, quantitation, and identification of hemopoietic stem cells. *Proc. Natl Acad. Sci. U.S.A.* **58**, 2261–2267

NOWELL, P. C., HIRSCH, B. E., FOX, D. H. & WILSON, D. G. (1970) Evidence for the existence of multipotential lympho-hematopoietic stem cells in the adult rat. *J. Cell. Physiol.* **75**, 151–158

OSMOND, D. G. (1967*a*) Lymphocyte production in the bone marrow: radioautographic studies in polycythaemic guinea pigs, in *The Lymphocyte in Immunology and Haemopoiesis* (Yoffey, J. M., ed.), pp. 120–130, Arnold, London

OSMOND, D. G. (1967*b*) The separation of lymphocytes from bone marrow by centrifugation in a density gradient. *Anat. Rec.* **157**, 295

OSMOND, D. G. (1967*c*) Separation of lymphocytes from bone marrow by centrifugation in density gradients and by filtration through glass bead columns. *Exp. Hematol.* **14**, 37

OSMOND, D. G. (1972) The origins, life spans and circulation of lymphocytes, in *Proc. Sixth Leucocyte Culture Conference* (Schwarz, M. R., ed.), pp. 3–36, Academic Press, New York

OSMOND, D. G. & EVERETT, N. B. (1964) Radioautographic studies of bone marrow lymphocytes in vivo and in diffusion chamber cultures. *Blood J. Hematol.* **23**, 1–17

PHILLIPS, R. A. & MILLER, R. G. (1970) Physical separation of hemopoietic stem cells from cells causing graft-vs-host disease. I. Sedimentation properties of cells causing graft-vs-host disease. *J. Immunol.* **105**, 1168–1174

PINET, J. M., OSMOND, D. G. & LEBLOND, C. P. (1969) In vitro observations of mitosis in unstimulated rat thymic lymphocytes, in *Proc. Third Annual Leucocyte Culture Conference* (Rieke, W. O., ed.), pp. 217–226, Appleton-Century-Crofts, New York

ROSSE, C. (1970) Two morphologically and kinetically distinct populations of lymphoid cells in the bone marrow. *Nature (Lond.)* **227**, 73–75

ROSSE, C. (1972) Lymphocyte production in the bone marrow, in *Proc. Sixth Leucocyte Culture Conference* (Schwarz, M. R., ed.), pp. 55–70, Academic Press, New York

ROSSE, C. & YOFFEY, J. M. (1967) The morphology of the transitional lymphocyte in guinea pig bone marrow. *J. Anat.* **102**, 113–124

STEPHENSON, J. R. & AXELRAD, A. A. (1971) Separation of erythropoietin-sensitive cells from hemopoietic spleen colony-forming stem cells of mouse fetal liver by unit gravity sedimentation. *Blood J. Hematol.* **37**, 417–427

VAN BEKKUM, D. W., VAN NOORD, M. J., MAAT, B. & DICKE, K. A. (1971) Attempts at identification of hemopoietic stem cell in mouse. *Blood J. Hematol.* **38**, 547–558

WORTON, R. G., MCCULLOCH, E. A. & TILL, J. E. (1969) Physical separation of hemopoietic stem cells from cells forming colonies in culture, *J. Cell. Physiol.* **74**, 171–182

YOFFEY, J. M. (1960) The lymphomyeloid complex, in *Haemopoiesis: Cell Production and its Regulation (Ciba Found. Symp.)*, pp. 1–42, Churchill, London

YOFFEY, J. M. & COURTICE, F. C. (1970) *Lymphatics, Lymph and the Lymphomyeloid Complex*, Academic Press, London

YOFFEY, J. M., HUDSON, G. & OSMOND, D. G. (1965) The lymphocyte in guinea pig bone marrow. *J. Anat.* **99**, 841–860

YOSHIDA, Y. & OSMOND, D. G. (1971*a*) Identity and proliferation of small lymphocyte precursors in cultures of lymphocyte-rich fractions of guinea pig bone marrow. *Blood J. Hematol.* **37**, 73–86

YOSHIDA, Y. & OSMOND, D. G. (1971*b*) Blastogenic response of lymphocytes separated from bone marrow to allogeneic lymphoid cells in vitro. *Immunology* **21**, 767–779

YOSHIDA, Y. & OSMOND, D. G. (1971*c*) Graft-versus-host activity of rat bone marrow, marrow fractions, and lymphoid tissues quantitated by a popliteal lymph node weight assay. *Transplantation* **12**, 121–129

Discussion

Metcalf: The kinetics of production of small lymphocytes in the marrow is almost identical with that in the thymus, with total population replacement occurring every three or four days in the adult mouse or rat. Lymphocyte production in the adult thymus appears to be in excess of the body's needs and there is evidence (Metcalf 1966) that relatively few of the lymphocytes produced in the adult thymus ever leave the organ. This implies that most cells die within the thymus only a few days after they are formed. Burnet (1962) has suggested that this large-scale local death of thymic lymphocytes represents the elimination of T cells which are autoreactive against the body's own tissue antigens.

Is it possible that a similar process occurs within the bone marrow? Is the production of B lymphocytes in the adult marrow in excess of requirements and do many of these cells die locally within the marrow? If so, are these B lymphocytes which potentially might have been able to synthesize antibodies directed against host antigens?

Osmond: There is no doubt that many newly formed small lymphocytes are rapidly discharged from the marrow. By using intramyeloid injections of [^{3}H]thymidine *in vivo* we have labelled the cells within the hindlimb bone marrow of guinea pigs without labelling cells elsewhere, and then followed the migration of labelled marrow small lymphocytes from their site of formation (Osmond 1966). Labelled small lymphocytes were discharged from the marrow into the bloodstream and then localized in the spleen and lymph nodes (Brahim & Osmond 1970). They stayed in these organs for several days and then disappeared. Thus, many of the small lymphocytes in the spleen and lymph nodes are cells which, a few hours or days before, circulated from the bone marrow. The majority of them appear to be short-lived, but we are still left with the basic problem of their ultimate fate.

Yoffey: From a purely quantitative point of view the data are very puzzling (Yoffey & Courtice 1970). The numbers continually leaving the marrow are so vast that if they *all* went to the various members of the lymphomyeloid complex to which some of them have been unquestionably traced, they would replace the cells of their recipient organs in a very short time.

Your large lymphoid cells, Dr Osmond—the same as the cells we have been calling and still prefer to call transitionals—have been shown in several ways to have a protective capacity. Harris & Kugler (1963, 1967), following up the pioneer studies of Harris (1956) on changes in guinea-pig marrow after sublethal irradiation, found that 14–16 days after irradiation, when the marrow contained about 80% lymphocyte transitional (LT) cells, it was very effective in conferring protection. Lajtha *et al.* (1964) subjected mice to sublethal irradiation and used the erythropoietin test as an index of stem cell recovery. Their data indicated a stem-cell overshoot about 10–15 days after irradiation, at about the same time as the LT overshoot in guinea pigs. In rats, Morrison & Toepfer (1967) prepared an enriched suspension of LT cells from normal rats and found that they also had a high protective ability. That aspect of the problem can be regarded as very effectively established.

The old problem of whether all the LT cells are protective, or whether, as is more likely, some of them are specialized subgroups which are not stem cells, is another matter. I think it is true to say that all these enriched suspensions of LT cells contain at least a small number of pachychromatic small lymphocytes, and it would be interesting to know whether any of these latter can play a part in conferring protection. You found that 2% of small lymphocytes were labelled one hour after thymidine administration, Dr Osmond, and Dr Rosse had a figure of about 1%. It is only a small number but labelled small lymphocytes one hour after thymidine could not have originated from the division of labelled precursors, could they?

Osmond: Probably there is an overlap in cell diameters between the populations of non-dividing and dividing cells. The very few lymphocytes smaller than 8.0 μm nuclear diameter which we see in DNA synthesis may represent the extreme tail of the size distribution curve of the dividing population. Functionally, they may not be small lymphocytes.

Yoffey: I think you assumed in your calculations that one division of transitional cells was needed to form small lymphocytes. Wouldn't the larger ones take at least two divisions?

Osmond: The calculation was that of the total rate of cell production by dividing lymphoid cells relative to the whole population of marrow lymphoid cells. It was not dependent on any particular number of cell generations in marrow lymphocytopoiesis.

Yoffey: I was preparing to interpret these labelled small lymphocytes as a small population of small lymphocytes which was possibly enlarging to re-enter the transitional compartment in quite a different way from that in which PHA-enlarged cells do. Dr Micklem in his earlier work (1966) administered PHA to mice, and found a fair increase in CFU in the blood 72 hours later. As far as I know, PHA acts only on the pachychromatic small lymphocytes, not on the larger cells. Dr Micklem's observations, as also those of Scaro *et al.* (1971), seem still to leave open the possibility that some small lymphocytes might enlarge to re-enter the stem cell (CFU) compartment. Have you continued that work, Dr Micklem?

Micklem: The number of circulating CFUs was increased 72 hours after intravenous PHA. I don't know whether this represented a release of existing CFUs from the marrow, or a generation of new CFUs. The rise in the CFU content of lymph nodes was small according to our limited data, and I interpreted it in terms of trapping, or settling out, of a few of these circulating cells (Micklem 1966).

Metcalf: If one injects a mouse with a pulse label of tritiated thymidine, a small number of lymphocytes in the thymus incorporate thymidine by direct uptake. These cells are usually heavily labelled and intermediate in size between small and medium lymphocytes (Metcalf & Wiadrowski 1966). Are these stem cells which have recently entered the organ from the marrow?

It should be emphasized that the morphology of stem cells in foetal life is quite different from that of functionally similar cells in adult life (Metcalf & Moore 1971). In foetal life, haemopoietic stem cells entering, for example, the thymus are large basophilic cells (Moore & Owen 1967), whereas studies on adult stem cells indicate that they probably have the morphology of small lymphocytes.

Rosse: In relation to the discharge of lymphocytes from the marrow, I should perhaps mention some studies we did on parabiotic guinea pigs (Rosse 1972) in which we labelled a special population of lymphocytes with [³H]-thymidine—those which turn over slowly and seem to have a longer lifespan than most cells in the bone marrow. After a time, when we could exclude the reutilization of the label and be confident that only the long-lived cells contained label, we united one guinea pig with an unlabelled syngeneic partner. After allowing 14 days for cross-circulation to develop, we examined the various haemopoietic tissues. There was complete equilibration of what we call the recirculating pool of lymphocytes in the thoracic duct, in lymph nodes and, interestingly enough, also within the bone marrow. We had previously shown that the bone marrow, in addition to small lymphocytes that turn over rapidly, has a smaller fraction of small lymphocytes which turns over much more slowly (Rosse 1971). This study clearly showed that there is a population of lymphocytes which migrate into the marrow and these are long-lived. They behave in the same way and equilibrate in the same way as lymphocytes of the thoracic duct. However, we have been unable to show this in quantitative terms within the thymus. The thymus does not seem to participate in equilibration of recirculating long-lived cells.

Astaldi: The enzyme asparaginase inhibits lymphocyte transformation to blast-like cells when stimulated with PHA or antigens (Astaldi *et al.* 1969).

Have you any information on what asparaginase does to bone marrow lymphocytes and their growth, Dr Osmond? That could be a help in distinguishing whether there are differences from a functional point of view. Asparaginase does not inhibit the stem cell lymphocyte, according to Alexander *et al.* (1971).

Osmond: We have studied the stimulation of bone marrow lymphocyte fractions, both with mitogens and with genetically dissimilar cells, *in vitro* (Osmond & Yoshida 1971; Yoshida & Osmond 1971*a*). In both systems some small lymphocytes respond by blastogenic transformation. Moreover, using a weight assay for popliteal lymph nodes *in vivo*, appreciable graft-versus-host activity has been detected amongst a subpopulation of marrow small lymphocytes, which is enhanced in lymphocyte-rich marrow fractions as compared with whole unfractionated marrow (Yoshida & Osmond 1971*b*). However, in these experiments the precise numbers of responding cells remain uncertain. It is possible that the responding marrow small lymphocytes are to be found among the long-lived immigrants rather than the locally produced cells. Current studies with selectively labelled marrow lymphocyte subpopulations are being conducted to investigate this point directly. We have no information on the effects of asparaginase on marrow lymphocytes.

Astaldi: If you can inhibit some lymphocytes in the marrow and not others, you may perhaps get further information.

Micklem: Is there any evidence that the long-lived recirculating population gets into the extravascular part of the marrow?

Rosse: About 1000 times as many long-lived labelled cells are present in a cubic millimetre of marrow sample in these experiments, as in a cubic millimetre of blood. Also, on sections, one can demonstrate labelled long-lived cells in the parenchyma, lying outside the vascular channels.

References

ASTALDI, G., BURGIO, G. R., KRC, J., GENOVA, R. & ASTALDI, A., Jr. (1969) L-Asparaginase and blastogenesis. *Lancet* 1, 423

ALEXANDER, P., DELORME, E. J., CURRIE, G. A. & SIME, G. C. (1971) Inhibition of immunoblast response *in vivo* and *in vitro* by asparaginase from *E. coli* and agouti serum, in L-asparaginase, pp. 189–193, International Symposium No. 197, Centre National de la Recherche Scientifique, Paris

BRAHIM, J. & OSMOND, D. G. (1970) Migration of bone marrow lymphocytes demonstrated by selective bone marrow labelling with thymidine-H^3. *Anat. Rec.* 168, 139–159

BURNET, M. (1962) Role of the thymus and related organs in immunity. *Br. Med. J.* 2, 807–811

HARRIS, P. F. (1956) Quantitative examination of bone marrow in guinea pigs after gamma irradiation. *Br. Med. J.* 2, 1032–1034

HARRIS, P. F. & KUGLER, J. H. (1963) The use of regenerating bone marrow to protect guinea pigs against lethal irradiation. *Acta Haematol. (Basel)* 32, 146–167

HARRIS, P. F. & KUGLER, J. H. (1967) Transfusion of regenerating bone marrow into irradiated guinea pigs, in *The Lymphocyte in Immunology and Haemopoiesis* (Yoffey, J. M., ed.), pp. 133–148, Arnold, London

LAJTHA, L. G., GILBERT, C. W., PORTEOUS, D. D. & ALEXANIAN, R. (1964) Kinetics of a bone marrow stem cell population. *Ann. N. Y. Acad. Sci.* **113**, 742–752

METCALF, D. (1966) The nature and regulation of lymphopoiesis in the normal and neoplastic thymus, in *The Thymus (Ciba Found. Symp.)* pp. 242–263, Churchill, London

METCALF, D. & MOORE, M. A. S. (1971) *Haemopoietic Cells*, North-Holland, Amsterdam

METCALF, D. & WIADROWSKI, M. (1966) Autoradiographic analysis of lymphocyte proliferation in the thymus and thymic lymphoma tissue. *Cancer Res.* **26**, 483–491

MICKLEM, H. S. (1966) Effect of phytohemagglutinin-M (PHA) on the spleen-colony-forming capacity of mouse lymph node and blood cells. *Transplantation* **4**, 732–741

MOORE, M. A. S. & OWEN, J. J. T. (1967) Experimental studies on the development of the thymus. *J. Exp. Med.* **126**, 715–726

MORRISON, J. H. & TOEPFER, J. R. (1967) Survival of lethally X-irradiated rats after treatment with isogenic marrow lymphocytes. *Am. J. Physiol.* **213**, 923–927

OSMOND, D. G. (1966) The origin of peritoneal macrophages from the bone marrow. *Anat. Rec.* **154**, 397

OSMOND, D. G. & YOSHIDA, Y. (1971) Blastogenic transformation in lymphocyte-rich fractions of guinea pig and rat bone marrow, in *Proc. Fourth Annual Leucocyte Culture Conference* (McIntyre, R., ed.), pp. 97–109, Appleton-Century-Crofts, New York

ROSSE, C. (1971) Lymphocyte production and lifespan in the bone marrow of the guinea pig. *Blood J. Hematol.* **38**, 372

ROSSE, C. (1972) Migration of long lived lymphocytes to the bone marrow and to other lymphomyeloid tissues in normal parabiotic guinea pigs. *Blood J. Hematol.* **40**, 90

SCARO, J. L., CARRERA, M. A., TERUEL, J. E. & DE TOMBOLESI, R. A. P. (1971) Phytohemagglutinin and hematopoietic stem cells in the mouse. *Acta Haematol. (Basel)* **46**, 275–281

YOFFEY, J. M. & COURTICE, F. C. (1970) *Lymphatics, Lymph and the Lymphomyeloid Complex*, Academic Press, London

YOSHIDA, Y. & OSMOND, D. G. (1971a) Blastogenic response of lymphocytes separated from bone marrow to allogeneic lymphoid cells *in vitro*. *Immunology* **21**, 767–779

YOSHIDA, Y. & OSMOND, D. G. (1971b) Graft versus host activity of rat bone marrow, marrow fractions and lymphoid tissues quantitated by a popliteal lymph node weight assay. *Transplantation* **12**, 121–129

Regulation of growth and differentiation in haemopoietic colonies growing in agar

D. METCALF and M. A. S. MOORE

Cancer Research Unit, The Walter and Eliza Hall Institute, Melbourne

Abstract The specific progenitor cells of granulocytes and monocytes (*in vitro* colony-forming cells) from all mammals including humans are able to proliferate in semi-solid agar cultures and generate colonies of granulocytes or macrophages, or both. Colony formation is dependent on stimulation by a specific glycoprotein, colony-stimulating factor (CSF), which appears to be a normal regulator of both granulopoiesis and monocyte formation. CSF is active *in vitro* at a concentration of 10^{-11}–10^{-12}M and affects both proliferation and differentiation of colony cells. Analysis of colony growth *in vitro* has proved that granulocytes and monocytes are derived from common ancestral cells and has elucidated some of the factors determining the switch from granulocyte to macrophage differentiation. The availability of highly enriched preparations of *in vitro* colony-forming cells (CFC) and CSF, and the high cloning efficiency of the culture system makes the *in vitro* CFC–CSF system ideal as a model for analysing control of cellular division and differentiation in haemopoietic cells.

Because of the complex nature of haemopoietic populations and of the systems regulating proliferation and differentiation of haemopoietic cells, it is of critical importance to devise simple *in vitro* cloning systems in which individual cell populations can be analysed under controlled conditions.

The independent development by two groups of an agar cloning system capable of supporting the growth of granulocytic or macrophage colonies or both (Bradley & Metcalf 1966; Ichikawa *et al.* 1966) has permitted detailed studies to be made of many aspects of the biology of these two haemopoietic populations in a wide variety of animal species and man.

In this culture system, haemopoietic cells from the bone marrow, spleen or blood are suspended in tissue culture medium made semi-solid by the inclusion of agar or methyl cellulose. Plastic or glass Petri dishes are normally used and cultures are incubated in a fully humidified atmosphere of 10% CO_2 in air without change of medium for 7–21 days (Metcalf 1970). Provided a source of a specific growth regulator—colony-stimulating factor (CSF)—is incorporated in the cultures, certain of the haemopoietic cells begin to proliferate and they generate cell aggregates ranging in size from 2 cells to 10 000. Virtually all aggregates are initially composed of granulocytic cells but on continued incubation macrophages appear in most aggregates and eventually comprise the sole population (Metcalf *et al.* 1967*a*; Metcalf 1969). Aggregates larger than 50–100 cells are referred to as 'colonies' whilst the more numerous, but smaller, aggregates are referred to as 'clusters'. A remarkable feature of the culture system is that differentiation of colony and cluster cells occurs during colony growth with the development of mature polymorphonuclear leucocytes (polymorphs) and macrophages, the latter cells exhibiting a full complement of membrane receptor sites for the Fc fragment of immunoglobulin G (IgG) (Cline *et al.* 1972).

ORIGIN AND NATURE OF IN VITRO COLONY-FORMING CELLS

Colonies arise by the proliferation of single cells known as *in vitro* colony-forming cells (CFC). The clonal nature of such colonies has recently been formally demonstrated in subpopulations of monkey bone marrow cells fractionated by centrifugation in continuous albumin gradients and containing up to 25% of *in vitro* CFC (Moore *et al.* 1972*a*). When individual colony-forming cells from such preparations were transferred by micromanipulation to agar cultures, a high proportion of transferred cells gave rise to typical colonies. This experiment documented the unusually high cloning efficiency of the system (25–100%) and also proved that individual cells could generate colonies which were a mixture of granulocytes and macrophages. This confirmed earlier conclusions, reached with the agar culture system, that granulocytes and monocyte–macrophages were closely related populations sharing a common ancestor, the *in vitro* CFC (Metcalf *et al.* 1967*a*; Metcalf 1969, 1971*a*). Although most monocytes and tissue macrophages were known to be of bone marrow origin (Volkman & Gowans 1965) the present evidence indicates that most are closely related to granulocytes and not lymphocytes as previously proposed (Howard *et al.* 1966). This close ancestral relationship between granulocytes and monocytes would appear to be the reason why leukaemia frequently develops in which both cell populations are involved in the neoplastic process (myelomonocytic leukaemia). Indeed karyotypic and microdensitometry studies on a murine myelomonocytic leukaemia which exhibited colony growth in agar indicated that the leukaemic stem cells in the population generated both granulocytes and monocytes (Warner *et al.* 1969; Metcalf *et al.* 1969; Metcalf & Moore 1970). Work on another murine myeloid leukaemia has also shown that leukaemic granulocytic cells can generate macrophages when cloned in agar (Ichikawa 1969, 1970).

Although cell separation procedures using glass bead adherence columns, albumin gradient centrifugation and velocity sedimentation have enriched mouse, monkey and human bone marrow populations for *in vitro* CFCs, these techniques have not yet succeeded in producing pure populations of these cells (Worton *et al.* 1969; Haskill *et al.* 1970; Janoshwitz *et al.* 1971; Metcalf *et al.* 1971*a*; Moore *et al.* 1972*b*). However a combination of these procedures with autoradiography, using tritiated thymidine, has indicated that in the monkey most *in vitro* CFCs are mononuclear cells, 9–11 μm in diameter, with a slightly basophilic but agranular cytoplasm (Fig. 1) (Moore *et al.* 1972*a*). Indirect evidence indicated that in foetal life *in vitro* CFCs are larger and lighter than corresponding adult *in vitro* CFCs (Moore *et al.* 1970; Haskill & Moore 1970).

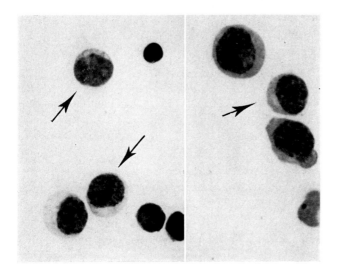

FIG. 1. Fractionated monkey bone marrow cells showing morphology of cells (arrowed) capable of forming granulocytic and macrophage colonies *in vitro*. Remaining cells are myeloblasts and small lymphocytes. Giemsa stain × 800.

Most experimental data so far have suggested that *in vitro* CFCs are equivalent in maturation to erythropoietin-sensitive cells in the erythropoietic series and belong to the progenitor class of haemopoietic cells (Metcalf & Moore 1971). Progenitor cells are the progeny of multipotent haemopoietic stem cells (spleen colony-forming cells, CFU) and differ from CFU in a number of characteristics: (*a*) unlike CFU, most progenitor cells are in active cell cycle, (*b*) most progenitor cells have only a limited capacity for self-generation, and (*c*) progenitor cells have undergone selective genetic derepression so that they are capable only of generating progeny of a single cell class, or, in the special case of *in vitro* CFC, cells of two classes—granulocytes and macrophages.

Work on mouse foetal liver and adult marrow populations has shown that most *in vitro* CFC can be discriminated from CFU on the basis of adherence properties, buoyant density, volume and cell cycle status. However, others have reported that low numbers of CFU are detectable in colonies grown in some types of agar culture (Dicke *et al.* 1971) and it may be that a minor subpopulation of CFU exists with properties intermediate between typical CFU and *in vitro* CFC.

In the mouse, the first demonstrable multipotent stem cells are observed in the eight-day yolk sac. After a vascular system has developed in the embryo, CFU are detectable in the liver. Because assays with the *in vitro* culture system can be done with very small numbers of cells, the first *in vitro* CFC are actually detectable in the yolk sac at day 7 of gestation (Moore & Metcalf 1970). If seven-day embryos are separated from the yolk sacs and cultured for two days as organ cultures, a heart and vascular system develops but the body is devoid of *in vitro* CFC whereas the normal nine-day embryo contains many such cells. Organ-cultured yolk sacs on the other hand develop higher than normal numbers of *in vitro* CFC, suggesting that normally the *in vitro* CFC population of the yolk sac is kept low by migration of these cells into the embryo (Moore & Metcalf 1970).

After CFU and *in vitro* CFC have been seeded to the liver, a rapidly expanding population of these cells develops in this organ, and with the subsequent development of the spleen and bone marrow these latter organs develop populations of both cell types (Metcalf & Moore 1971). After birth, the liver population of haemopoietic cells declines rapidly and the bone marrow and spleen remain as the only organs in which CFU and *in vitro* CFC are detectable, although small numbers of these cells are present also in the blood, peritoneal and pleural cavities. The incidence of *in vitro* CFC in various species is shown in Table 1.

TABLE 1

Incidence of *in vitro* colony-forming cells per 10^5 cells in various species

Tissue	Man	Monkey	Mouse
Bone marrow	20 – 100	200	250
Spleen	< 1	0.5	5
Blood	0.5 – 1	0.5	0.5

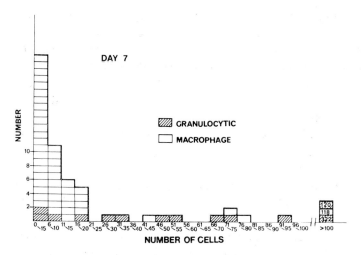

FIG. 2. Frequency of aggregates of various sizes in a 7-day culture of 5000 C57BL bone marrow cells stimulated by endotoxin serum. Aggregates larger than 50 cells scored as colonies.

In all agar cultures of marrow or spleen cells in which colonies have formed there is a pronounced heterogeneity in the size of the aggregates in the culture dish (Fig. 2). Does this heterogeneity arise from intrinsic differences between cells capable of proliferating in agar or from the operation of stochastic processes? It could be postulated that all cells capable of proliferating in the agar culture system are essentially similar *in vitro* colony-forming cells but that because of the asynchronous initiation of proliferation or the operation of random events, leading to premature differentiation to non-dividing cells, the majority of cells never have an opportunity to generate large colonies. In support of this interpretation, most cells generating clusters, i.e. aggregates of subcolony size, have similar adherence properties, buoyant density and cell cycle status to colony-forming cells. Furthermore, clusters at seven days of incubation are usually composed of a mixed granulocytic, mixed granulocytic–macrophage or purely macrophage population, suggesting a more advanced stage of differentiation and population evolution than in some colonies.

The alternative view of the relationship between clusters and colonies is that cluster-forming cells are the immediate progeny of colony-forming cells. This would account for the higher frequency of cluster-forming cells, their more restricted capacity for proliferation and the more highly differentiated state of cluster cells. A number of arguments support this alternative as the most likely explanation of the relationship between cluster- and colony-forming cells: (*a*) Since the progeny of colony-forming cells have no difficulty in proliferating within a developing colony in agar, progeny generated *in vivo* by these same *in vitro* CFC must also be capable of proliferating in agar and must therefore be represented in the culture dish. (*b*) When the incubation period is extended or the culture conditions are made supra-optimal (Bradley *et al.* 1971*b*), then even though clusters may continue to grow in size they always remain relatively smaller than colonies in the same culture dish. (*c*) There are large variations in the ratio of clusters and colonies in cultures from different sources. Cultures of normal mouse spleen cells, particularly from germ-free animals, exhibit very low numbers of clusters in proportion to colony numbers and many cultures of normal mouse blood contain no clusters whatsoever. (*d*) Under conditions of active regeneration, e.g. in the bone marrow after irradiation, or in reactive states, e.g. with spleen cells from antigenically stimulated mice, a large increase is observed in the relative frequency of clusters. (*e*) Although both cluster-forming and colony-forming cells have the same general physical properties, some selective concentration of one type in preference to the other can sometimes be achieved, e.g. by albumin gradient sedimentation (Metcalf *et al.* 1971*a*).

The factors leading to the transformation of colony granulocytes to macrophages have not been fully characterized but appear to involve a complex of lipoproteins present in all normal sera. These lipoproteins are termed 'CSF-inhibitors' since they may be bioassayed because of their capacity to exert a species-specific blocking effect on CSF action *in vitro* (Chan *et al.* 1971). In the presence of CSF-inhibitors, granulocytic colonies transform prematurely to macrophage colonies and for this reason colonies stimulated by undiluted normal serum are typically loose and composed of macrophages. *In vitro* CFC preincubated with inhibitors, then thoroughly washed, also form colonies which transform prematurely to macrophages. Furthermore, bone marrow cells from mouse strains with high levels of serum inhibitor, e.g. BALB/c, usually produce an excessive proportion of macrophage colonies compared with cells from mice with low levels of serum inhibitor, e.g. C57BL (Chan 1971).

The *in vivo* significance of CSF-inhibitors remains to be determined but it is likely that they modulate the stimulating effects of CSF and may in part determine the proportion of proliferating granulocytic cells which enters the alternative monocyte-macrophage pathway.

ACTION OF CSF IN STIMULATING COLONY FORMATION

Bone marrow cells from all species depend absolutely on CSF for colony formation *in vitro*. The apparent ability of cells from many species, including man, to form colonies in the absence of exogenous CSF is due to the endogenous production of CSF by certain 'autostimulating' cells in these populations.

When autostimulating cells are removed by differential centrifugation, the *in vitro* CFC from these species exhibit the same requirement for exogenous CSF as mouse bone marrow cells (Moore & Williams 1972; Moore *et al.* 1972*a*).

CSF has a concentration-dependent influence on the number and growth rate of both granulocytic and macrophage colonies developing in cultures of mouse bone marrow cells (Metcalf 1970). Despite the fact that most *in vitro* CFCs are in cell cycle, analysis of developing bone marrow cultures has shown that there is a marked asynchrony in the lag period before individual cells begin to proliferate. Thus there is a linear increase with time in the number of discrete proliferating aggregates for at least the first five days in cultures of both mouse and human bone marrow cells, and the average lag period before proliferation begins is shortened by increasing the concentration of CSF. Exposure of cells *in vitro* to lethal concentrations of tritiated thymidine (thymidine suiciding) reduces the incidence of *in vitro* CFC in mouse marrow cell populations by 30–45% (Lajtha *et al.* 1969; Iscove *et al.* 1970; Metcalf 1972), suggesting that most cells are in cycle and that cell cycle times are relatively short (less than 12 hours). The nature of the lag period before cells begin to proliferate in agar is obscure and is not related to the status of the *in vitro* CFC in the cell cycle at the beginning of incubation (Metcalf 1972). Since most cells exhibit a lag of 24–48 hours before they begin to proliferate *in vitro*, other factors in agar cultures must operate to block temporarily cells already in cycle.

Culture of cells in the absence of CSF for as little as 24 hours leads to death or permanent loss of proliferative capacity of most *in vitro* CFC (Metcalf 1970). CSF is required continuously in the cultures for progressive colony growth, and transfer of developing colonies to CSF-free medium is followed by cessation of growth or death of colonies (Metcalf & Foster 1967*a*; Paran & Sachs 1968).

In a detailed analysis of the early events in colony formation, 1 ml cultures containing 25 000 C57BL bone marrow cells were stimulated by 0.1 ml of pooled serum from C57BL mice injected three hours previously with 5 μg of endotoxin. This 'endotoxin serum' has a very high concentration of CSF and is an exceptionally good stimulus for granulocytic colony formation (Metcalf 1971*b*). At intervals during the incubation period, sequential aggregates were picked off the culture plates and the cell numbers in individual aggregates were determined. In the first 72–96 hours of incubation, peak incidences of aggregates were observed with 4, 8, 16, 32 and 64 cells (Fig. 3), suggesting strongly that initial cell divisions were symmetrical with respect to the proliferative capacity of the progeny. It is quite common even at day 7 of incubation to observe colonies composed of two or four daughter colonies of roughly equal size and always containing granulocytic cells at an equivalent stage of differentiation. This also implies that a significant degree of symmetry must have been present

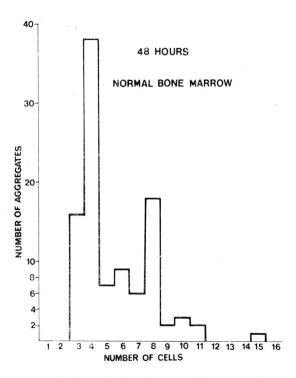

Fig. 3. Histogram showing frequency of aggregates of various sizes at 48 hours of incubation in a culture of 25 000 C57BL bone marrow cells stimulated by endotoxin serum. Note peak incidences of 4- and 8-cell clusters.

early in colony growth.

Because cell death does not occur in the first 72 hours of colony growth and since the above evidence suggested a high degree of symmetry in colony growth during this period, the rate of increase in colony size might be expected to provide an estimate of mean cell cycle times during early colony growth. Analysis of colony growth rates was made by determining the size of the largest 15 colonies in cultures of 25 000 C57BL mouse bone marrow cells stimulated by various concentrations of endotoxin serum. Because of the asynchronous onset of proliferation only the largest colonies are likely to have begun to proliferate early after cultures had been initiated. In fact an average of 15 clusters containing three or more cells was present in these cultures at 24 hours, which determined the choice of 15 for the number of colonies surveyed for the growth curves. The results (Fig. 4) indicated that colony growth was exponential for the first 72 hours and that, in the presence of progressively higher concentrations of CSF colony doubling times (and presumably mean cell cycle times) were progressively

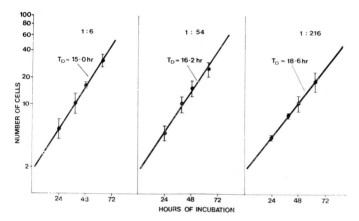

FIG. 4. Influence of varying dilutions of CSF-containing endotoxin serum on population doubling times (T_D) of developing colonies. Mean values from 15 colonies $\pm$ standard deviations at each time point.

shortened. The estimate of a mean cell cycle time of 15 hours for colonies growing in the highest concentrations of CSF is certainly not a minimum cell cycle time. When the number of bone marrow cells per culture dish was increased, e.g. to 75 000/ml, the initial rate of colony growth was much greater and indicated mean cell cycle times of 12 hours or less.

Is CSF involved either in the transformation of granulocytic to macrophage colonies or in the differentiation of colony granulocytes? The evidence on these two questions is not conclusive. With CSF derived from human urine, a relationship can be observed between CSF concentration and the percentage of granulocytic colonies at day 7 of incubation in cultures of mouse bone marrow cells (Table 2). However the percentage of granulocytic colonies is also increased

TABLE 2

Effect of CSF concentration on morphology of mouse bone marrow colonies

Urine CSF dilution	Mean no. colonies[a]	Mean percentage of colonies		
		Granulocytic	Mixed	Macrophage
1:1	45 $\pm$ 7	26	44	30
1:2	31 $\pm$ 5	14	40	46
1:4	15 $\pm$ 3	4	39	57
1:8	3 $\pm$ 1	0	7	93

Each culture contained 50 000 C57BL bone marrow cells and 0.1 ml of a semipurified preparation of human urine CSF. Colonies were analysed at day 7 of incubation.
[a] Mean data from six replicate cultures $\pm$ standard deviations. Thirty sequential colonies typed from each culture.

TABLE 3

Effect of colony crowding on morphology of mouse bone marrow colonies

No. of cells cultured	Mean no. colonies[a]	Mean percentage of colonies		
		Granulocytic	Mixed	Macrophage
2 000	4 ± 2	0	14	86
5 000	7 ± 2	6	29	65
10 000	13 ± 3	11	16	73
25 000	38 ± 7	16	25	59
75 000	114 ± 15	40	16	44

Cultures prepared from C57BL bone marrow cells and stimulated by 0.1 ml of a semipurified preparation of human urine CSF. Colonies analysed on day 7 of incubation.
[a] Mean data from six replicate cultures ± standard deviations. Thirty sequential colonies typed from each culture.

when larger numbers of colonies are present per culture dish (Table 3), a situation which can be achieved by using the same CSF concentration but a higher number of cultured cells. The apparent relationship between CSF concentration and the percentage of granulocytic colonies may therefore be an indirect one, with high CSF concentrations increasing colony crowding and thereby increasing the proportion of granulocytic colonies. Furthermore, this relationship between CSF concentration and colony morphology is not so evident when endotoxin serum or medium conditioned by mouse lung is used as the source of CSF (J. Sheridan and D. Metcalf, unpublished data). The most highly purified preparations of CSF derived from human urine (100 000-fold purified with respect to protein) clearly stimulate the formation of both granulocytic and macrophage colonies and the same CSF molecule would appear to be able to stimulate the proliferation of both types of population.

When cultures are stimulated by endotoxin serum, some colonies are composed entirely of primitive granulocytic cells, exhibiting no differentiation to non-dividing cells (blast colonies). The percentage of blast colonies is lower in cultures containing lower concentrations of endotoxin serum (Table 4). This might suggest that CSF tends to inhibit differentiation and, if so, this could be an important factor in determining the more rapid rates of colony growth observed in cultures containing high concentrations of CSF. However endotoxin serum must contain many factors other than CSF and there is no certainty that the results obtained with unfractionated endotoxin serum were due solely to the action of CSF.

The growth rate of colonies is also increased by adding a variety of viable or non-viable cells to the cultures, e.g. lymphocytes or killed bone marrow cells

TABLE 4

Influence of endotoxin serum concentration on colony morphology

Endotoxin serum dilution	Percentage of Colonies	
	Blast	Other granulocytic
1:2	7	41
1:4	7	34
1:8	0	35
1:16	0	15
1:32	0	21

All cultures contained 75 000 C57BL bone marrow cells and 0.1 ml of endotoxin serum. Colonies sampled at day 7 of incubation. Fifty sequential colonies sampled from each type of culture.

(Metcalf 1968). Autoradiographic studies on colonies growing in cultures containing killed cells labelled with tritiated thymidine indicated that dividing colony cells extensively reutilized nuclear material, and such a process may affect cell cycle times and cellular differentiation.

Plate mapping studies have given no indication that the morphology or differentiation of colony populations is affected by the morphology or differentiation status of adjacent colonies. In cultures of mouse bone marrow at seven days of incubation it is common to find, in close proximity, granulocytic colonies of quite different composition, for example one may be composed entirely of blast cells, the next of mature polymorphs and the next of a mixture of cells at all stages of differentiation. It might be argued that stochastic processes could account for this type of variability. However such colonies can contain 500–2000 cells and if all granulocytic colony cells had a uniform probability of undergoing differentiation at each cell division, the vast majority of large granulocytic colonies should be composed of granulocytes at different stages of differentiation. This in fact is not observed. In an analysis in 7-day cultures of the differentiation patterns of 75 000 C57BL bone marrow cells stimulated by endotoxin serum, 162 sequential granulocytic colonies were classified on the basis of their differentiation. The percentages of various granulocytic colonies were: pure blast cell colonies, 6%; myeloblast and myelocyte colonies with no evident metamyelocytes or polymorphs, 57%; mixed colonies with cells ranging from myeloblasts to polymorphs, 31%; colonies composed solely of polymorphs, 6%. Data of this type clearly give only a restricted view of the potentiality of such colonies since a colony composed of blast cells at day 7 of incubation subsequently may undergo maturation or transformation to a macrophage colony. Furthermore, modification of culture conditions might well have been able to alter the morphology of that colony by day 7 of incubation. Despite these qualifications, the data are more consistent with the hypothesis that there is a significant degree of heterogeneity between granulocytic colony-forming cells, some being capable of generating blast cell colonies only under defined culture conditions, while others are predetermined either by genetic derepression or phenotypic modification to form colonies composed of differentiated poly-morphs under the same conditions. Stochastic processes might well operate to modify this individual heterogeneity or predisposition, as might environmental factors in the culture medium.

This concept of intrinsic heterogeneity amongst colony-forming cells and their progeny is supported by the observations that colony-forming cells are hetero-geneous with respect to size, buoyant density and adherence properties (Worton *et al.* 1969; Haskill *et al.* 1970; Metcalf *et al.* 1971*a*), and intrinsic heterogeneity amongst progenitor cells is a factor which must be taken into account in the interpretation of data on granulopoiesis obtained from kinetic studies using tritiated thymidine *in vivo* (Cronkite 1969).

THE NATURE AND ORIGIN OF COLONY-STIMULATING FACTOR (CSF)

The serum and urine of mice and humans exhibit detectable colony-stimulat-ing activity when assayed in test cultures of mouse bone marrow cells (Robinson *et al.* 1967; Metcalf & Foster, 1967*b*; Metcalf & Stanley 1969; Chan *et al.* 1971). The active factor in serum and urine was given the operational title 'colony-stimulating factor' (CSF). Studies on normal human urine have demonstrated that CSF is a neuraminic acid-containing glycoprotein of molecular weight 45 000 and that it constitutes less than 0.001% of the total urinary protein (Stanley & Metcalf 1969, 1972). Digestion of CSF with neuraminidase reduces the charge of the molecule but does not destroy its biological activity *in vitro*. CSF is active *in vitro* at extremely low concentrations (100 pg/ml or approxi-mately 10^{-11} or 10^{-12}M). This implies strongly that the primary action of CSF may be restricted to specific membrane receptor sites on target CFC and colony cells *in vitro*. It has been shown that CSF can be radioiodinated without loss of biological activity and autoradiographic studies with the electron microscope may reveal some aspects of this interaction. However difficulties can be anti-cipated with this approach because of the known capacity of granulocytic cells to bind many proteins, e.g. labelled bacterial antigens, presumably through relatively non-specific processes.

CSF may be extracted from all tissues in the mouse and the highest amounts per milligram wet weight of tissue are found, in descending order, in: male submaxillary gland, female submaxillary gland, lung, thymus, kidney, spleen, lymph nodes, pancreas and marrow, with the remaining organs containing only low amounts of extractable CSF (Sheridan & Stanley 1971). Large amounts of CSF are also produced and/or released by cells from many tissues or cell lines in culture medium (conditioned medium). Outstanding in this regard are fibroblasts, whole embryo cells, mouse lung cells, peritoneal macrophages and the stromal cells that adhere to the wall of the bone marrow cavity (Pluznik & Sachs 1966; Bradley & Sumner 1968; Austin *et al.* 1971; Bradley *et al.* 1971a; Chan & Metcalf 1972). Until highly specific anti-CSF antibodies are available for fluorescence microscopy, it cannot be determined whether many different cell types can elaborate CSF or whether cells common to all organs, e.g. macrophages, fibroblasts or endothelial cells, are the source of this factor.

Human urine CSF is antigenic in rabbits (Stanley *et al.* 1970). Although the species-specificity of anti-CSF antibodies evoked by this material varies somewhat between different rabbits, in most cases the antibodies inactivate CSF *in vitro* from a variety of human materials but do not inactivate CSF from mouse sources. This indication of minor species differences in the antigenicity and structure of CSF is confirmed by observations on the responsiveness *in vitro* of CFC populations to CSF from various species. In general, mouse CFC *in vitro* responded well to the stimulation by CSF from most mammalian species, e.g. human, monkey, dog, rabbit, guinea pig and rat. *In vitro* CFC from other species tended to respond best to stimulation by homologous CSF and were sometimes quite unresponsive to heterologous CSF. For example, human CFC *in vitro* responded to stimulation by medium conditioned by human and monkey cells but less well to medium conditioned by pig, mouse, guinea pig or rabbit cells (M.A.S. Moore, unpublished data).

A further complication regarding the nature of CSF is the fact that CSF extracted from different tissues can differ considerably in physical properties. All share a comparable pH and heat stability and a resistance to proteolytic enzymes and carbohydrases but differ widely in elution properties from calcium phosphate gels and in electrophoretic mobility (Stanley *et al.* 1971; Sheridan & Stanley 1971; Stanley & Metcalf 1972). While urine and conditioned medium CSF appear to have a molecular weight in the 45 000–60 000 range (Stanley & Metcalf 1969; Austin *et al.* 1971), it has recently been demonstrated that the CSF in medium conditioned by mouse lung tissue has an apparent molecular weight of 15 000 (J. Sheridan and D. Metcalf, unpublished data). This raises the serious possibility that forms of CSF with higher molecular weights may be polymeric forms of a basic subunit, but so far an extensive examination of human CSF has failed to produce evidence of fragments which can be split off the molecule while retaining their biological activity.

The heterogeneity of tissue CSF was emphasized by a study of the response of mice to the injection of endotoxin. Endotoxin, like other bacterial products, e.g. flagellin, induces a 50–100-fold rise in CSF in serum within three hours of injection (Metcalf 1971*b*; McNeill & Killen 1971). This rise was found to be preceded by an extremely rapid rise in CSF in tissue. What was more remarkable was the fact, seen most clearly with salivary gland CSF, that the newly produced or activated CSF was of different molecular form from that extractable from the normal organs (Sheridan & Metcalf 1972). A similar change in properties was noted in the CSF released by mouse embryo cells during culture over a six-day incubation period (Stanley *et al.* 1971). Much of the observed heterogeneity of CSF may be related to a variable content of carbohydrate residues in the molecule, as a similar variability has been documented for other glycoproteins (Gottschalk 1969). However it remains to be determined how the various forms of CSF are related biologically.

Because the target cells of CSF are restricted essentially to the bone marrow and spleen it has been suggested that the only biologically important CSF is that actually produced by cells located within these haemopoietic organs. Specifically, the polymorphonuclear leucocyte has been proposed as the major cellular source of CSF (Robinson & Pike 1970) and the suggestion made that polymorph breakdown, by releasing CSF, stimulates granulopoiesis in a positive feedback system. However cell separation experiments using monkey, mouse and human cells have shown that purified preparations of polymorphs are unable to release CSF in culture (Moore & Williams 1972; M. A. S. Moore, N. Williams and D. Metcalf, unpublished data). The same experiments did suggest that monocytes released CSF and parallel studies using mouse perito-neal macrophages have shown that they can release significant amounts of CSF *in vitro* (J. Sheridan, unpublished data).

Since monocytes and macrophages are also products of the *in vitro* CFC, the suggestion of a positive feedback system might still be valid, with the monocytes and macrophages—not the polymorphs—priming new cell production.

There is now other evidence to support the concept that local production of CSF within the marrow may be of special importance in regulating granulo-poiesis. In the mouse cells firmly adhering to the wall of the bone marrow can produce large amounts of CSF, and this capacity fluctuates during regeneration of *in vitro* CFC after injury (Chan & Metcalf 1972). After whole-body irradia-tion of C57BL and BALB/c mice, there was a significant rise in the capacity of bone-adherent cells for producing CSF immediately before the onset of regenera-tion of CFC *in vitro*, and this rise was not paralleled by any corresponding rise either in the capacity of marrow haemopoietic cells for producing CSF or in CSF in serum. In larger mammals, including man, the distribution of CSF-producing cells may be more uniform throughout the marrow cavity and certainly bone marrow and peripheral blood cells from the monkey or man are an excellent source of CSF.

Despite this evidence for the importance of local CSF production in haemopoietic tissue, the concept of specific positive and negative feedback regulation of granulopoiesis by breakdown products of the haemopoietic cell as the major regulatory system remains purely speculative. By far the most potent method for elevating serum and tissue levels of CSF is the injection of endotoxin or other bacterial products (Metcalf 1971*b*; McNeill & Killen 1971). This, together with the unusually low levels of CSF in germ-free mice (Metcalf *et al.* 1967*b*), suggests that the level of exposure to bacterial and other microbial products may be a major factor in determining both local and systemic CSF production.

SPECIFICITY OF ACTION OF CSF

Although pure preparations of CSF have not yet been obtained, a number of studies have been made on the specificity of action of semipurified preparations of human urine CSF. No stimulating action *in vitro* was observed in a number of different types of culture systems using various normal or neoplastic mouse cells (Table 5). Similarly the injection of such preparations into mice did not induce an observable change in erythropoiesis or lymphopoiesis. Conversely, neither erythropoietin nor a wide variety of foreign proteins and bacterial products stimulates granulocyte or macrophage colony formation *in vitro* (Bradley *et al.* 1969; Stephenson *et al.* 1971; McNeill 1970; Metcalf 1971*c*).

CLINICAL APPLICATIONS OF THE AGAR CULTURE TECHNIQUE

Because the agar culture system enumerates granulocytic and monocytic progenitor cells with a high cloning efficiency and can assay CSF and CSF-inhibitor levels, this technique has an obvious clinical application in the investigation of any disease state involving granulopoiesis or monocyte formation.

A full discussion of recent applications of the agar culture technique to the analysis of granulocytic leukaemia in humans cannot be given here. In brief, however, CSF levels are increased in many serum and urine specimens from leukaemic patients (Metcalf *et al.* 1971*b*; Robinson & Pike 1970), leukaemic colony-forming cells form colonies of differentiating cells in agar (Pike & Robinson 1970; Paran *et al.* 1970; Iscove *et al.* 1971; Greenberg *et al.* 1971)

TABLE 5

Cell populations failing to respond to stimulation by CSF

		Cells	Parameters measured
In vitro	Agar culture	NZB plasma cell tumour	Colony numbers
		BALB/c plasma cell tumours	Colony growth rates
		DBA mastocytoma	
		Normal pleural fibroblast colonies	
In vitro	Liquid culture (dialysis chamber)	Normal mouse lymphocytes – thymus – lymph nodes – spleen – bone marrow	[³H]thymidine uptake
		Normal fibroblasts	
		Antibody-forming precursor cells	Ab titration
		[SRBC (flagellin)]	PFC enumeration
In vivo		Lymphopoiesis in thymus, spleen, lymph nodes	Organ wt, histology, WBC levels, [³H]thymidine kinetics
		Erythropoiesis	Reticulocytes, ^{59}Fe uptake
		Liver, kidney	Mitotic indices

WBC: white blood cell

but are physically separable from normal colony-forming cells (Moore *et al.* 1972*a*), and all leukaemic colony-forming cells examined so far from patients with acute or chronic granulocytic leukaemia have responded to CSF (D. Metcalf and M. A. S. Moore, unpublished data). These findings are providing some exciting new insights into the nature of leukaemia and they further support the conclusion that CSF is important as a regulator of granulopoiesis.

ACKNOWLEDGEMENTS

This work was supported by the Carden Fellowship Fund of the Anti-Cancer Council of Victoria and the Australian Research Grants Committee.

References

AUSTIN, P. E., McCULLOCH, E. A. & TILL, J. E. (1971) Characterisation of the factor in L-cell conditioned medium capable of stimulating colony formation by mouse bone marrow cells in culture. *J. Cell. Physiol.* **77**, 121–134

BRADLEY, T. R. & METCALF, D. (1966) The growth of bone marrow cells *in vitro. Aust. J. Exp. Biol. Med. Sci*, **44**, 287–300

BRADLEY, T. R. & SUMNER, M. A. (1968) Stimulation of mouse bone marrow colony growth *in vitro* by conditioned medium. *Aust. J. Exp. Biol. Med. Sci.* **46**, 607–618

BRADLEY, T. R., METCALF, D., SUMNER, M. & STANLEY, R. (1969) Characteristics of *in vitro* colony formation by cells from haemopoietic tissues, in *Hemic Cells in Vitro* 4 (Farnes, P. ed.), pp. 22–35, Williams & Wilkins, Baltimore

BRADLEY, T. R., STANLEY, E. R. & SUMNER, M. A. (1971a) Factors from mouse tissues stimulating colony growth of mouse bone marrow cells *in vitro. Aust. J. Exp. Biol. Med. Sci.* **49**, 595–603

BRADLEY, T. R., TELFER, P. A. & FRY, P. (1971b) The effect of erythrocytes on mouse bone marrow colony development. *Blood J. Hematol.* **38**, 353–359

CHAN, S. H. (1971) Influence of serum inhibitors on colony development *in vitro* by bone marrow cells. *Aust. J. Exp. Biol. Med. Sci.* **49**, 533–564

CHAN, S. H. & METCALF, D. (1972) Local production of colony stimulating factor within the bone marrow. Role of non-hematopoietic cells. *Blood J. Hematol.* **40**, 646–653

CHAN, S. H., METCALF, D. & STANLEY, E. R. (1971) Stimulation and inhibition by normal human serum of colony formation *in vitro* by bone marrow cells. *Br. J. Haematol.* **20**, 329–341

CLINE, M. J., WARNER, M. L. & METCALF, D. (1972) Identification of the bone marrow colony mononuclear phagocyte as a macrophage. *Blood J. Hematol.* **39**, 326–330

CRONKITE, E. P. (1969) Kinetics of granulocytopoiesis. *J. Natl Cancer Inst.* **30**, 51–62

DICKE, K. A., PLATENBURG, M. G. C. & VAN BEKKUM, D. W. (1971) Colony formation in agar: *in vitro* assay for haemopoietic stem cells. *Cell Tissue Kinet.* **4**, 463–477

GOTTSCHALK, A. (1969) Biosynthesis of glycoproteins and its relationship to heterogeneity. *Nature (Lond.)* **222**, 452–454

GREENBERG, P. L., NICHOLS, W. L. & SCHRIER, S. L. (1971) Granulopoiesis in acute myeloid leukemia and preleukemia. *N. Engl. J. Med.* **284**, 1225–1232

HASKILL, J. S. & MOORE, M. A. S. (1970) Two dimensional separation: comparison of embryonic and adult haemopoietic stem cells. *Nature (Lond.)* **226**, 853–854

HASKILL, J. S., McNEILL, T. A. & MOORE, M. A. S. (1970) Density distribution analysis of *in vivo* and *in vitro* colony-forming cells in bone marrow. *J. Cell. Physiol.* **75**, 167–180

HOWARD, J. G., BOAK, J. L. & CHRISTIE, G. H. (1966) Further studies on the transformation of thoracic duct cells into liver macrophages. *Ann. N.Y. Acad. Sci.* **129**, 327–339

ICHIKAWA, Y. (1969) Differentiation of a cell line of myeloid leukemia. *J. Cell. Physiol.* **74**, 223–234

ICHIKAWA, Y. (1970) Further studies on the differentiation of a cell line of myeloid leukemia. *J. Cell. Physiol.* **76**, 175–184

ICHIKAWA, Y., PLUZNIK, D. H. & SACHS, L. (1966) *In vitro* control of the development of macrophage and granulocyte colonies. *Proc. Natl Acad. Sci. U.S.A.* **56**, 488–495

ISCOVE, N. N., TILL, J. E. & McCULLOCH, E. A. (1970) The proliferative states of mouse granulopoietic progenitor cells. *Proc. Soc. Exp. Biol. Med.* **134**, 33–36

ISCOVE, N. N., SENN, J. S., TILL, J. E. & McCULLOCH, E. A. (1971) Colony formation by normal and leukemic marrow cells in culture. Effect of conditioned medium from human leukocytes. *Blood J. Hematol.* **37**, 1–5

JANOSHWITZ, H., MOORE, M. A. S. & METCALF, D. (1971) Density gradient segregation of bone marrow cells with the capacity to form granulocytic and macrophage colonies in vitro. *Exp. Cell Res.* **68**, 220–224

LAJTHA, L. G., POZZI, L. V., SCHOFIELD, R. & FOX, M. (1969) Kinetic properties of haemopoietic stem cells. *Cell Tissue Kinet.* **2**, 39–49

MCNEILL, T. A. (1970) Antigenic stimulation of bone marrow colony forming cells. I. Effect of antigens on normal bone marrow cells *in vitro*. *Immunology* **18**, 39–47

MCNEILL, T. A. & KILLEN, M. (1971) The effect of synthetic double-stranded polyribonucleotides on haemopoietic colony-forming cells *in vivo*. *Immunology* **21**, 751–759

METCALF, D. (1968) Potentiation of bone marrow colony growth *in vitro* by the addition of lymphoid or bone marrow cells. *J. Cell. Physiol.* **72**, 9–20

METCALF, D. (1969) Studies on colony formation *in vitro* by mouse bone marrow cells. I. Continuous cluster formation and relation of clusters to colonies. *J. Cell. Physiol.* **74**, 323–332

METCALF, D. (1970) Studies on colony formation *in vitro* by mouse bone marrow cells. II. Action of colony stimulating factor. *J. Cell. Physiol.* **76**, 89–100

METCALF, D. (1971*a*) Transformation of granulocytes to macrophages in bone marrow colonies in vitro. *J. Cell. Physiol.* **77**, 277–280

METCALF, D. (1971*b*) Acute antigen-induced elevation of serum colony stimulating factor (CSF) levels. *Immunology* **21**, 427–436

METCALF, D. (1971*c*) Antigen-induced proliferation *in vitro* of bone marrow precursors of granulocytes and macrophages. *Immunology* **20**, 727–738

METCALF, D. (1972) Effect of thymidine suiciding on colony formation *in vitro* by mouse hematopoietic cells. *Proc. Soc. Exp. Biol. Med.* **139**, 511–514

METCALF, D. & FOSTER, R. (1967*a*) Behavior on transfer of serum stimulated bone marrow colonies. *Proc. Soc. Exp. Biol. Med.* **126**, 758–762

METCALF, D. & FOSTER, R. (1967*b*) Bone marrow colony-stimulating activity of serum from mice with viral-induced leukemia. *J. Natl Cancer Inst.* **39**, 1235–1245

METCALF, D. & MOORE, M. A. S. (1970) Factors modifying stem cell proliferation of myelomonocytic leukemic cells *in vitro* and *in vivo*. *J. Natl Cancer Inst.* **44**, 801–808

METCALF, D. & MOORE, M. A. S. (1971) *Haemopoietic Cells*, North-Holland, Amsterdam

METCALF, D. & STANLEY, E. R. (1969) Quantitative studies on the stimulation of mouse bone marrow colony growth *in vitro* by normal human urine. *Aust. J. Exp. Biol. Med. Sci.* **47**, 453–466

METCALF, D., BRADLEY, T. R. & ROBINSON, W. (1967*a*) Analysis of colonies developing *in vitro* from mouse bone marrow cells stimulated by kidney feeder layers or leukemic serum. *J. Cell. Physiol.* **69**, 93–108

METCALF, D., FOSTER, R. & POLLARD, M. (1967*b*) Colony stimulating activity of serum from germfree normal and leukemic mice. *J. Cell. Physiol.* **70**, 131–132

METCALF, D., MOORE, M. A. S. & WARNER, N. L. (1969) Colony formation *in vitro* by myelomonocytic leukemic cells. *J. Natl Cancer Inst.* **43**, 983–1001

METCALF, D., MOORE, M. A. S. & SHORTMAN, K. (1971*a*) Adherence column and buoyant density separation of bone marrow stem cells and more differentiated cells. *J. Cell. Physiol.* **78**, 441–450

METCALF, D., CHAN, S. H., GUNZ, F. W., VINCENT, P. & RAVICH, R. B. M. (1971*b*) Colony stimulating factor and inhibitor levels in acute granulocytic leukemia. *Blood J. Hematol.* **38**, 143–152

MOORE, M. A. S. & METCALF, D. (1970) Ontogeny of the haemopoietic system: Yolk sac origin of *in vivo* and *in vitro* colony-forming cells in the developing mouse embryo. *Br. J. Haematol.* **18**, 279–296

MOORE, M. A. S. & WILLIAMS, N. (1972) Physical separation of colony stimulating cells from *in vitro* colony-forming cells in hemopoietic tissue. *J. Cell. Physiol.* **80**, 195–206

MOORE, M. A. S., MCNEILL, T. A. & HASKILL, J. S. (1970) Density distribution analysis of *in vivo* and *in vitro* colony-forming cells in developing fetal liver. *J. Cell. Physiol.* **75**, 181–192

MOORE, M. A. S., WILLIAMS, N. & METCALF, D. (1972*a*) Purification and characterisation of the *in vitro* colony-forming cell in monkey hemopoietic tissue. *J. Cell. Physiol.* **79**, 283–292

MOORE, M. A. S., WILLIAMS, N., METCALF, D., GARSON, O. M. & HURDLE, A. D. F. (1972b) Control of leukemic cell proliferation and differentiation in agar culture, in *Cell Differentiation* (Harris, H. & Viza, D., eds.), pp. 108–114, Munksgaard, Copenhagen

PARAN, M. & SACHS, L. (1968) The continued requirement for inducer for the development of macrophage and granulocyte colonies. *J. Cell. Physiol.* **72**, 247–250

PARAN, M., SACHS, L., BARAK, Y. & RESNITSKY, P. (1970) *In vitro* induction of granulocyte differentiation in hematopoietic cells from leukemic and nonleukemic patients. *Proc. Natl Acad. Sci. U. S. A.* **67**, 1542–1549

PIKE, B. L. & ROBINSON, W. A. (1970) Human bone marrow colony growth in agar gel. *J. Cell. Physiol.* **76**, 77–84

PLUZNIK, D. S. & SACHS, L. (1966) The induction of clones of normal mast cells by a substance from conditioned medium. *Exp. Cell Res.* **43**, 553–563

ROBINSON, W. A. & PIKE, B. L. (1970) Leukopoietic activity in human urine: The granulocytic leukemias. *N. Engl. J. Med.* **282**, 1291–1297

ROBINSON, W., METCALF, D. & BRADLEY, T. R. (1967) Stimulation by normal and leukemic mouse sera of colony formation *in vitro* by mouse bone marrow cells. *J. Cell. Physiol.* **69**, 83–92

SHERIDAN, J. W. & METCALF, D. (1972) Studies on the bone marrow colony stimulating factor (CSF): Relation of tissue CSF to serum CSF. *J. Cell. Physiol.* **80**, 129–140

SHERIDAN, J. W. & STANLEY, E. R. (1971) Tissue sources of bone marrow colony stimulating factor. *J. Cell. Physiol.* **78**, 451–460

STANLEY, E. R. & METCALF, D. (1969) Partial purification and some properties of the factor in normal and leukaemic human urine stimulating mouse bone marrow colony growth in vitro. *Aust. J. Exp. Biol. Med. Sci.* **47**, 467–483

STANLEY, E. R. & METCALF, D. (1972) Purification and properties of human urine colony stimulating factor (CSF), in *Cell Differentiation* (Harris, R. & Viza, D., eds.), pp. 149–153, Munksgaard, Copenhagen

STANLEY, E. R., McNEILL, T. A. & CHAN, S. H. (1970) Antibody production to the factor in human urine stimulating colony formation *in vitro* by bone marrow cells. *Br. J. Haematol.* **18**, 585–590

STANLEY, E. R., BRADLEY, T. R. & SUMNER, M. A. (1971) Properties of the mouse embryo conditioned medium factor(s) stimulating colony formation by mouse bone marrow cells grown *in vitro*. *J. Cell. Physiol.* **78**, 301–318

STEPHENSON, J. R., AXELRAD, A. A., McLEOD, D. L. & SHREEVE, M. M. (1971) Induction of colonies of hemoglobin-synthesising cells by erythropoietin in vitro. *Proc. Natl Acad. Sci. U.S.A.* **68**, 1542–1546

VOLKMAN, A. & GOWANS, J. L. (1965) The origin of macrophages from bone marrow in the rat. *Br. J. Exp. Pathol.* **46**, 62–70

WARNER, N. L., MOORE, M. A. S. & METCALF, D. (1969) A transplantable myelomonocytic leukemia in BALB/c mice: cytology, karyotype and muramidase content. *J. Natl Cancer Inst.* **43**, 963–982

WORTON, R. G., McCULLOCH, E. A. & TILL, J. E. (1969) Physical separation of hemopoietic stem cells from cells forming colonies in culture. *J. Cell. Physiol.* **74**, 171–182

Discussion

Loutit: How does colony-stimulating factor (CSF) relate to the granulocytosis promotion factors previously described by Al Gordon and his colleagues (Katz *et al.* 1966) and by others (e.g. Delmonte *et al.* 1968)?

Metcalf: CSF has no relation to the granulocyte-releasing factor (LIF) described by Gordon *et al.* (1964), although serum levels of both factors can be elevated by similar procedures, e.g. the injection of endotoxin or bacterial antigens. Granulocyte-releasing factors produce an acute rise in blood granulocyte levels, maximal between three and six hours after injection, by releasing preformed cells from the bone marrow and other tissue pools. The injection of partially purified CSF does not release granulocytes from the bone marrow and does not mobilize granulocyte progenitor cells (*in vitro* colony-forming cells) (D. Metcalf, unpublished data). However CSF does stimulate an increased production of granulocytes and monocytes with a consequent slow rise of these cells in blood, maximal at 24–48 hours (Metcalf & Stanley 1971). Bacterial antigens cause a large rise in tissue and serum CSF levels within minutes of injection (Metcalf 1971; Sheridan & Metcalf 1972) and CSF may be the factor mediating the increased production of granulocytes and monocytes induced by such agents.

Harris: You said that the CSF was produced by stromal cells, Dr Metcalf. Do you think the reticulum cell in the marrow is associated with the production of CSF? Could this explain why transfused stem cells seed only in specific sites such as the marrow?

Metcalf: The cell types within the marrow shaft which produce CSF have not been identified (Chan & Metcalf 1972) but could certainly include reticulum cells. Other evidence links monocytes with the production of CSF (Moore & Williams 1972). CSF is extractable from all tissues in the body (Sheridan & Stanley 1971) and some of my people feel that tissue macrophages are the source of this organ CSF. I prefer to keep an open mind on this question as I can imagine that many cell types in the body may have the capacity to synthesize CSF. This question can only be resolved by the use of fluorescein-labelled antisera prepared against highly purified tissue CSF, which should reveal which cells actually synthesize CSF.

It may be, however, that only the CSF produced locally within the marrow is biologically important, as this may be the only CSF having direct access to the target cells which mainly reside in the marrow.

Iscove: What is the source of the inhibitor?

Metcalf: We know nothing yet about the tissue source of the serum inhibitors. The only disease state in which serum inhibitors are uniformly low or absent is acute granulocytic leukaemia.

Kubanek: Are the serum inhibitor levels decreased in chronic granulocytic leukaemia?

Metcalf: Inhibitor levels are normal unless the patient is in blast crisis, in which case the levels are low, as in acute granulocytic leukaemia. Conversely, in acute lymphoid leukaemia, they tend to be normal.

Kubanek: Can you explain this difference in these two diseases?

Metcalf: It is intriguing. I am still suspicious that the serum inhibitors might be some type of *in vitro* artifact. However, the data from irradiated mice in which serum inhibitor levels fall immediately before the rise in CSF production by bone-related cells are impressive and suggest that the inhibitors may somehow regulate local CSF production (Chan & Metcalf 1973).

Yoffey: Your observation on the presence of CSF in bone is very intriguing, because many of us worried for a long time about why marrow settles down to develop inside bone cavities. Blood formation is relatively temporary and transient in the spleen, but the marrow is its permanent home. Most people now believe that the blood supply of the marrow is mainly from the nutrient artery, which not only ramifies in the medulla, but also gives off branches which enter the Haversian canals in the compact bone and then drain back into the marrow. Several workers, starting with Rohlich (1941), have speculated that as the blood flows through the bone it may pick up some substances which influence the development of cells in the marrow, but nobody has ever produced convincing evidence. This, as far as I know, is the first intimation that something may be coming out of the bone.

Metcalf: The production of CSF by bone-related cells can only be part of the story. We know that CSF does not influence the behaviour of stem cells or the formation of granulocyte progenitor cells by stem cells. However, the microenvironmental cells of the bone marrow have a profound influence on stem cell behaviour and this could be mediated by cell contact processes or by other humoral factors.

Lajtha: We are talking about a stem cell system and we tacitly assume that there is a 'pluripotent' stem cell, a 'committed' stem cell population, and then a 'recognizable' one (i.e. the erythron). There is very good evidence for that in erythropoiesis. The transit times during erythropoiesis are measurable, and so are the production rates. The numbers are incompatible with the numbers of CFU, so one must have an intermediate cell population. That this cell population can proliferate without erythropoietin is known from grafting experiments, in which a microcolony of some 10^5 cells is triggered by erythropoietin to more than 10^6 normoblasts two days later.

When we come to granulopoiesis, are we not trying to extrapolate too much from the erythropoietic example? What do we know about granulopoiesis? We do not know the precise transit time in the recognizable granulocyte line itself. It is a notoriously bad system for precise quantitative markers. We do not know the number of divisions during this transit. We know that when we specifically hit stem cells with certain agents like busulphan there is a very long transit time, which even in a mouse can be four to six days, and in a rabbit up to ten to twelve days. We know that the colony-stimulating factor is not a trigger; it is needed all the time in the culture to produce these cells. We know that while the erythropoietin-responsive cell can and does proliferate without erythropoietin, the *in vitro* colony-forming cell, which can and does increase *in vitro*, does not do so without a colony-stimulating factor.

Is it not possible that granulopoiesis is entirely different from erythropoiesis? With CSF we may be dealing with a factor which is specifically dragging cells out from the pluripotent CFU, making the first very early myeloblast, which has a transit time of several days, which is why Dr Metcalf does not see mature granulocytes in the first stages of embryonic life. There are nevertheless good *in vitro* colony formers but time is required for them to 'mature' into the later stages. In other words, there may be no committed stem cell for granulopoiesis, but there is a long series of cell cycles for the differentiation, and for the maintenance of this a specific factor is necessary.

Metcalf: To my knowledge no one has succeeded in getting stem cells to produce granulocytic progenitor cells (*in vitro* colony-forming cells) using purified CSF. In such experiments it is not good enough to use crude preparations of conditioned medium as these may contain many different regulatory factors. There is little evidence that *in vitro* colony-forming cells have an extensive capacity for self-replication. CSF appears to be a factor regulating the production of mature progeny from committed granulocytic stem cells (*in vitro* colony-forming cells).

Lajtha: Why call it a stem cell?

Metcalf: Possibly 'committed stem cell' is a bad expression. It refers to the fact that *in vitro* colony-forming cells have been shown to be the progeny of stem cells (Moore *et al.* 1970) and that the differentiating capacity of *in vitro* colony-forming cells appears to be restricted to the granulocytic and monocytic lines. As I see it, CSF is operating on relatively differentiated granulocytic cells in an essentially similar manner to erythropoietin.

Lajtha: Erythropoietin is not needed to take them through. That is what I am driving at. I am prepared to accept that we need something else to trigger CFU into what then becomes the CSF-dependent cell line. But I still do not see the committed stem cell.

Metcalf: Surely you cannot grow an erythroid colony *in vitro* without adding erythropoietin?

Lajtha: I cannot grow an erythroid colony very well anywhere. In the spleen I can grow an ERC colony without erythropoietin.

Metcalf: But *in vitro*, the clonal growth of erythroid cells is entirely dependent on erythropoietin (Stephenson *et al.* 1971).

Lajtha: We do not see erythroid cells or erythroid colonies without erythropoietin, but we can see proliferation of committed erythroid precursor cells in the spleen without erythropoietin. That is very different.

Metcalf: Provided there is no source of erythropoietin in that slice of spleen.

Lajtha: There is none; the detector methods are very sensitive indeed.

Kubanek: Why is there no granulocyte production in the yolk sac or foetal liver? If there is enough CSF and CFC, these CFC should differentiate and produce granulocytes, unless it is the microenvironment that inhibits them from making granulocytes.

Metcalf: The situation could be highly complex. As far as we can determine from assays of foetal and neonatal serum, inhibitor levels are uniformly low. This would not exclude a local concentration of inhibitors within tissue micro-environments or some other inhibiting influence blocking granulopoiesis.

Stohlman: There is certainly a tendency or temptation to equate CSF with erythropoietin, but in my opinion there is no rigorous proof as yet that it acts in the same fashion. It is convenient to think that the committed myeloid compartment is similar to the erythropoietin-responsive compartment, but again the proof is not rigorous. To take another example, the final ploidy values of the megakaryocyte are almost reached before one recognizes it as a megakaryocyte, which would suggest differences in the regulatory mechanisms. These are considerations that we should be thinking about now, rather than restricting our thinking on granulopoiesis and platelet production to red cell models. Of practical importance is the fact that in the irradiated animal erythropoiesis always recovers before myelopoiesis. Bacteriologically, this presents us with a problem: myelopoiesis should start off before erythropoiesis. Maybe they start off simultaneously, but the control mechanisms are different.

Regarding the size of colonies, if you add haemolysates, you can increase the size of colonies quite strikingly, but it is not directly related to the CSF. Is that correct?

Metcalf: All tissue culture systems have some disabilities and certainly the quality of the media, particularly the foetal calf serum, has a general influence on the growth rate of colonies independent of the concentration of CSF. Bradley *et al.* (1971) showed that red cells had a strong potentiating effect on granulocyte and macrophage colony growth but red cells alone do not stimulate colony growth—CSF is still essential. In recent experiments we have noted that red cells potentiate the growth of plasmacytoma cells in agar but CSF is not required in this system (D. Metcalf, unpublished data).

Cotes: Quantities of CSF have been variously presented as: (*i*) percentage of CSA (colony-stimulating activity), (*ii*) dilutions of CSF, (*iii*) number of colonies produced by CSF.

None of these expressions conveys quantitative information which is directly applicable in another laboratory or applicable to another assay system. The first two relate amounts of CSF to unspecified test preparations and the third is a measure of response which is dependent on the test conditions. Effects attributed to CSF include increase in number of colonies, stimulation of cell differentiation and an effect on the distribution of cell types within colonies and, perhaps, maintenance of certain granulocytes. It is clear that, at this stage of work on the characterization of CSFs, the amount of any preparation can only be estimated by comparative assay in terms of another preparation. Such a comparison will only give a valid estimate of potency if similar materials are compared. For this purpose it is necessary to know to what extent CSF preparations from different species and sources are comparable. And might distribution of some common and stable preparation of CSF (readily available to any investigator) facilitate quantitative comparisons between laboratories?

Metcalf: The first prerequisite is to have available a standard preparation of CSF with which unknown preparations can be compared. Use of the standard CSF in every assay run also allows corrections to be made resulting from fluctuations in the media and incubating conditions. The next requirement is to settle on the type and number of target cells in the assay and we have settled for convenience on 75 000 pooled bone marrow cells/ml from C57BL mice aged two to three months. Colony-stimulating activity for CSF content is determined by counting the number of colonies larger than the agreed minimum size (50 cells) on day 7 of incubation. Since CSF is a glycoprotein, CSF levels are then best expressed as corrected colony counts/mg protein in the preparation used. If other laboratories wish to use cultures containing different numbers of target marrow cells, the results could be expressed as corrected colony counts (10^5 bone marrow cells/mg protein).

Lajtha: One also has to use a standardized medium, because even the same CSF preparation has to be matched with a particular batch of serum.

Cotes: In most bioassays (including those used for erythropoietin) it has been found quite impracticable to set up assay systems which give completely predictable responses. For this reason it is usually inappropriate to emphasize standardization of assay conditions (inevitably bedevilled by the intrinsic variability of biological materials); it is better to base quantitation of an active substance on comparison of responses induced by an unknown preparation with the response induced by a reference preparation or standard. The real issue seems to be, is one reference preparation sufficient or are several different ones needed?

Metcalf: Use of a standard preparation of CSF allows each laboratory to correct for such variables as the tissue culture medium. The colony counts obtained are simply corrected on the basis of the agreed number of colonies the standard CSF should stimulate.

McCulloch: There is a problem about a standard preparation with CSA. That is, a wide variety of different preparations have CSA. A glycoprotein of molecular weight of approximately 45 000 can be isolated from mouse L cells (Austin *et al.* 1971) and stimulate colony formation by mouse marrow cells but not by human cells. CSFs from human urine have a similar molecular weight and are also effective for mouse but not human cells (Stanley & Metcalf 1969). Molecules with a molecular weight of 35 000 have been isolated from cultures of human peripheral blood (Iscove *et al.* 1971; Austin 1971); this CSA is effective in cultures of human cells and works almost as well in cultures of mouse cells. Dr Metcalf has just told us about a material of molecular weight 16 000 which is active. Price *et al.* (1973) have described a CSA of molecular weight approximately 1300 which is active in cultures of human cells but inactive in the mouse. This degree of variability makes it difficult to agree on a single standard preparation. It is obviously inappropriate to use erythropoietin as an analogy in considering CSA.

Metcalf: Erythropoietin also probably has more than one molecular form.

McCulloch: But not like that.

Winterhalter: Which of these materials cross-reacts with the same antibody?

Metcalf: Our knowledge of immunological cross-reactivity between different sources of CSF is rather limited. Most rabbits immunized with human urine CSF produce antibodies which selectively inactivate human CSF and not mouse CSF (Stanley *et al.* 1970). However, the situation seems likely to be much more complex. Recently we have prepared antisera in rabbits to mouse lung CSF which does not inactivate mouse serum CSF or CSF produced by mouse bone-related cells (J. Sheridan & D. Metcalf, unpublished data).

Yoffey: Is Australian CSF increased at all in maternal blood during pregnancy? If so, what about the possibility that the foetal CSF has crossed the placenta?

Metcalf: We have not looked at it as exhaustively as I would like, but there does not seem to be any gross increase either in serum CSF levels or in output of CSF in the urine during pregnancy.

References

AUSTIN, P. E. (1971) Studies on conditioning factor activity for marrow cells in culture. Ph. D. Thesis, University of Toronto

AUSTIN, P. E., McCULLOCH, E. A. & TILL, J. E. (1971) Characterization of the factor in L-cell conditioned medium capable of stimulating colony formation by mouse marrow cells in culture. *J. Cell. Physiol.* **77**, 121

BRADLEY, T. R., TELFER, P. A. & FRY, P. (1971) The effect of erythrocytes on mouse bone marrow colony development. *Blood J. Hematol.* **38**, 353–359

CHAN, S. H. & METCALF, D. (1972) Local production of colony stimulating factor within the bone marrow. Role of non-hemopoietic cells. *Blood J. Hematol.* **40**, 646–653

CHAN, S. H. & METCALF, D. (1973) Local and systemic control of granulocyte and macrophage progenitor cell regeneration after irradiation. *Cell. Tissue Kinet.* **6**, 187–199

DELMONTE, L., STARBUCK, W. C. & LIEBELT, R. A. (1968) Species-dependent concentration of granulocytosis-promoting factor in mammalian tissues. *Am. J. Physiol.* **215**, 768–773

GORDON, A. S., HANDLER, E. S., SIEGEL, C. D., DORNFEST, B. S. & LoBUE, J. (1964) Plasma factors influencing leucocyte release in rats. *Ann. N.Y. Acad. Sci.* **113**, 766–789

ISCOVE, N. N., SENN, J. S., TILL, J. E. & McCULLOCH, E. A. (1971) Colony formation by normal and leukemic human marrow cells in culture: effect of conditioned medium from human leukocytes. *Blood J. Hematol.* **37**, 1

KATZ, R., GORDON, A. S. & LAPIN, D. M. (1966) Studies on the purification of leucocytosis inducing factor (L.I.F.) *J. Reticuloendothel. Soc.* **3**, 103–116

METCALF, D. (1971) Acute antigen-induced elevation of serum colony stimulating factor (CSF) levels. *Immunology* **21**, 427–436

METCALF, D. & STANLEY, E. R. (1971) Haematological effects in mice of partially purified colony stimulating factor (CSF) prepared from human urine. *Br. J. Haematol.* **21**, 481–492

MOORE, M. A. S. & WILLIAMS, N. (1972) Physical separation of colony stimulating from *in vitro* colony forming cells in hemopoietic tissue. *J. Cell. Physiol.* **80**, 195–206

MOORE, M. A. S., McNEILL, T. A. & HASKILL, J. S. (1970) Density distribution analysis of *in vitro* colony forming cells in bone marrow. *J. Cell. Physiol.* **75**, 167–179

PRICE, G. B., McCULLOCH, E. A. & TILL, J. E. (1973) A new human low molecular weight granulocyte colony stimulating activity. *Blood J. Hematol.* in press

ROHLICH, K. (1941) On the relationship between the bone substance and hemopoiesis in the bone marrow. *Z. Mikrosk-Anat. Forsch.* **49**, 425–464

SHERIDAN, J. & METCALF, D. (1972) Studies on the bone marrow colony stimulating factor (CSF). Relation of urine CSF to serum CSF. *J. Cell. Physiol.* **80**, 129–140

SHERIDAN, J. & STANLEY, E. R. (1971) Tissue sources of bone marrow colony stimulating factor. *J. Cell. Physiol.* **78**, 451–459

STANLEY, E. R. & METCALF, D. (1969) Partial purification and some properties of the factor in normal and leukemic human urine stimulating mouse bone marrow colony growth *in vitro*. *Aust. J. Exp. Biol. Med.* **47**, 467–483

STANLEY, E. R., McNEILL, T. A. & CHAN, S. H. (1970) Antibody production to the factor in human urine stimulating colony formation *in vitro* by bone marrow cells. *Br. J. Haematol.* **18**, 585–590

STEPHENSON, J. R., AXELRAD, A. A., McLEOD, D. L. & SHREEVE, M. M. (1971) Induction of colonies of hemoglobin-synthesising cells by erythropoietin *in vitro*. *Proc. Natl Acad. Sci. U.S.A.* **68**, 1542–1546

Cellular communication early in haemopoietic differentiation

E. A. MCCULLOCH, C. J. GREGORY and J. E. TILL

Institute of Medical Science and Department of Medical Biophysics, University of Toronto, and the Ontario Cancer Institute, Toronto

Abstract The production of erythrocytes, granulocytes and platelets depends on pluripotent stem cells. Alternative avenues of differentiation are regulated independently by factors acting on progeny cells committed to a specific pathway. Since morphological markers are not available for the identification of pluripotent stem cells or their committed descendants, both must be studied using functional tests.

Two classes of transition are recognized. First, reversible transitions occur between populations of rapidly proliferating and slowly proliferating or resting cells. Second, apparently irreversible transitions lead to restriction of differentiation, decrease in proliferative potential, and acquisition of sensitivity to specific regulators of a single pathway. Regulators of both reversible and irreversible transitions are required (1) to determine that a transition will be made, (2) to regulate rate of change, (3) to relate the occurrence and rates of transitions to population size at each level of differentiation.

Genetic and physiological studies have provided evidence that these multiple facets of regulation are achieved through a variety of mechanisms. Some of these act intrinsically; others affect cells from without and these external regulators provide the intercellular messages that permit the system to behave coherently. Some external regulators, like erythropoietin, act at long range; these usually affect committed rather than pluripotent cells. The latter are influenced by cell-to-cell contact or substances diffusing over short distances. It is suggested that some short-range interactions are mediated through specific cell surface components that can be characterized genetically and by their response to alloantisera.

Cell culture methods are becoming available for assaying haemopoietic progenitor cells and their regulators. Such methods have been applied to man and give promise of yielding new insights into mechanisms of haemopoietic disease.

A widely accepted model is now available for cellular events occurring early in the myelopoietic component of the haemopoietic system (Lajtha 1970; Trentin 1970; Hellman *et al.* 1970; McCulloch & Till 1971; Editorial 1972). The principal feature of the model is the postulated existence of two categories of progenitor cells. The first category consists of pluripotent stem cells, considered to be capable of differentiating into erythropoietic, granulocytic and megakaryocytic lines as well as possessing extensive capacity for self-renewal. The second category consists of a number of early committed cells, progeny of pluripotent parents but restricted in their avenues of differentiation and with insufficient capacity for self-renewal to maintain independent populations of progeny. Evidence is available that both pluripotent stem cells and early committed cells can proliferate rapidly or slowly in response to differing demands for cell production (Becker *et al.* 1965; Iscove *et al.* 1970). The transition between rapid proliferation and slow proliferation or rest (G0 state proposed by Quastler 1963, and Lajtha 1963) is considered to be reversible, but it is a basic assumption of the model that transitions associated with restrictions in pathways of differentiation or proliferative potential are irreversible under physiological conditions.

The complexity of the model has implications for regulation. First, genetic information must be available for specifying the major properties of each cell category and for control of both reversible and irreversible transitions. Genetic factors of this kind are of great biological interest since they provide the basis for the essential components of the system. However, if such primary mechanisms are rendered ineffective by mutation or disease, either the whole system or one of its essential components would become inoperative; under these conditions, survival is unlikely. Accordingly, the most fundamental mechanisms within the system have little immediate clinical importance since living patients are unlikely to present with lesions at this level.

A different group of regulatory mechanisms may be considered as permissive to, or modifiers of, the major components of the system. For example, although primary mechanisms determine whether or not a given transition can take place, secondary mechanisms must be present to modulate the frequency of the given transition relative to other potential transitions. This latter class of regulators is required to maintain appropriate population sizes at each level of the system. Permissive or rate regulators are of practical importance since lesions affecting these mechanisms are compatible with haemopoietic function at least sufficient to permit the birth of living animals and the survival of patients long enough to allow therapeutic intervention.

Chronic myelogenous leukaemia provides an example of a disease process affecting regulators of relative population size. The availability of the Philadelphia chromosome marker (Nowell & Hungerford 1961) has permitted the identification of leukaemic pluripotent stem cells capable of erythropoietic, granulopoietic and megakaryocytic differentiation (Whang *et al.* 1963). When the disease is in relapse, the flow of differentiation into the granulocytic pathway is greatly increased relative to erythropoiesis. However, when the size of the pool of leukaemic stem cells is decreased, either by treatment with cytotoxic drugs or by dilution after transplantation into a new host (Levin *et al.* 1965), erythropoiesis increases relative to granulopoiesis and the balance between them approaches normal. These relationships support the view that the leuk-aemic lesion in chronic myelogenous leukaemia affects mechanisms that relate the rate of stem cell renewal (and consequently population size) to relative frequencies of transitions to erythropoietic as compared to granulopoietic progenitors. Observations on cellular events in chronic myelogenous leukaemia, therefore, provide a basis for postulating the existence of this class of regulatory mechanism, and assessing for it a significant role in disease.

Maintenance of appropriate balances between different populations depends on information transfer within the system. A long-range messenger, erythro-poietin, is known to be the principal regulator of erythropoiesis (Krantz & Jacobson 1970). However, cellular communication may also be achieved through cell–cell contact or diffusible substances with short effective ranges. Understanding of these various mechanisms in concrete terms is only beginning. The purpose of this paper is to describe three experimental systems that show promise of yielding important new insights into short-range regulation based on cellular communication.

METHODS OF STUDY

Assays for haemopoietic cells used in our laboratory have recently been sum-marized and discussed (McCulloch & Till 1972). Essential for the study of progenitors within the system are assays based on colony formation, since more direct methods for recognizing and quantitating progenitor cells are not available. Three colony methods, the nomenclature associated with them, and the significance we attach to the interpretation of data obtained using them, are summarized in Table 1. It should be emphasized that each of these methods

TABLE 1

Colony methods for the assay of haemopoietic progenitor cells

Term	Interpretation	Detected by	References
CFU–S	Pluripotent stem cells	Spleen colony assay	Till & McCulloch 1961
CFU–C	Committed progenitors of granulopoiesis	CSA[a]-dependent colony formation in culture	Bradley & Metcalf 1966 Pluznik & Sachs 1966
CFU–E	Committed progenitors of erythropoiesis	Erythropoietin-dependent colony formation in culture	Stephenson *et al.* 1971

[a]   CSA = colony-stimulating activity for granulocytic or macrophage colonies, or both.

defines haemopoietic populations in operational terms, a fact that is emphasized by the descriptive nomenclature. Within such populations, considerable heterogeneity may exist; physical measurements based on velocity sedimentation or density centrifugation have demonstrated such heterogeneity for colony-forming units in the spleen (CFU–S) and colony-forming units in culture (CFU–C) (Worton *et al.* 1969*a*), while for the former, evidence is also available for heterogeneity in capacity for self-renewal (Worton *et al.* 1969*b*). Further, cell culture assays are highly 'ingredient-dependent'. Thus, minor variations in technique may alter the spectrum of cells detected. These considerations, combined with the absence of absolute measurements of plating efficiency for any colony assay, provide constraints on the interpretation of results.

The existence of such constraints emphasizes the need to combine colony assays with other methods. Cell separation procedures have been useful in analysing heterogeneous haemopoietic populations. For example, cell separation has been combined with pulse-height analysis to yield a visual display analogous to a contour map (Moon *et al.* 1972); such displays, or 'fingerprints', provide a quantitative approach to the identification and characterization of cells and help to liberate investigators from thraldom to the microscope.

CELLULAR COMMUNICATION: SYSTEMS OF STUDY

Requirements for cellular cooperation have been clearly demonstrated in immune responses. Usually the experimental protocol consists of a comparison between the effects of two populations tested independently or as a mixture. As a result of experiments of this design, it is now believed that in some instances a requirement exists for three cell classes, T or thymus-derived cells, B or marrow-derived cells and A or accessory cells (Osoba 1970). Similar experimental approaches have been applied to the myeloid component of the system (McCulloch & Till 1970); however, these approaches have not yielded clear-cut evidence for cellular cooperation *in vivo*. It is possible that the disruptive processes of rendering tissues into cell suspensions may destroy important spatial configurations.

Experimental systems that depend on the maintenance or establishment of spatial configurations require subtle and specific methods of manipulation. Among the most powerful of such methods is physiological genetics, which permits the identification of regulatory processes sufficiently discrete to be under the control of single genes. Two of the experimental systems to be described below are based on the principles of physiological genetics. The third is a cell culture system, where granulopoietic colony formation (see Table 1) depends on the presence of molecules with colony-stimulating activity (CSA).

S1 AND W GENES AND THE REGULATION OF MYELOPOIESIS

The most conclusive evidence for the significance of cellular communication in myelopoietic control is derived from studies of genetically anaemic mice of genotype Sl/Sl^d (Russell & Bernstein 1966; McCulloch *et al.* 1965; Bernstein 1970; Trentin *et al.* 1971). The myelopoietic defect in these animals is at the level of the pluripotent stem cell (McCulloch *et al.* 1964*a*); however, their complement of CFU–S is normal in number and properties. The lesion is demonstrated only when mice of genotype Sl/Sl^d are used as irradiated recipients for normal cells; in these hosts, colony formation is not observed (McCulloch *et al.* 1965). Further, the defect cannot be related to a long-range mediator since Bernstein (1970) and Trentin *et al.* (1971) have shown that normal splenic fragments will support colony formation after their transplantation into Sl/Sl^d mice, while similar implants of Sl/Sl^d spleen in normal hosts are not repopulated normally by CFU–S. Thus, normal haemopoietic tissue contains a class of cells or cell-derived structures, essential for colony formation, that exert their action locally. The Sl-gene product affects part of the mechanism by which such cells or structures interact with CFU–S to regulate their function. When the gene is mutant, function is impaired and the serious myelopoietic lesion of Sl/Sl^d mice is observed.

Sl gene function may belong to the category of permissive or rate-modifying regulators rather than representing a primary mechanism essential for CFU–S function. This suggestion is based on kinetic studies using not only Sl/Sl^d mice but also genetically anaemic mice of genotype W/W^v (Sutherland *et al.* 1970). In these experiments, heavily irradiated normal mice or Sl/Sl^d animals were used as recipients of marrow cells derived either from controls or W/W^v mice. At intervals after transplantation, groups of recipients were killed and their spleens and femoral marrows assayed for CFU–C and, where possible, CFU–S. The relevant findings are presented as growth curves for CFU–C (Fig. 1, redrawn from Sutherland *et al.* 1970). Both in marrow and in spleen, the growth of CFU–C was only moderately slower than normal when the graft was derived from W/W^v marrow or when the irradiated hosts were of genotype Sl/Sl^d. In Fig 1 most of the data points have been omitted; however, for emphasis, points derived from Sl/Sl^d recipients bearing grafts of $+/+$ or W/W^v origin have been retained. It is evident that the growth kinetics under these conditions are not different from those obtained when either donor or host, but not both, were defective. Thus, although both W/W^v and Sl/Sl^d animals have genetic defects

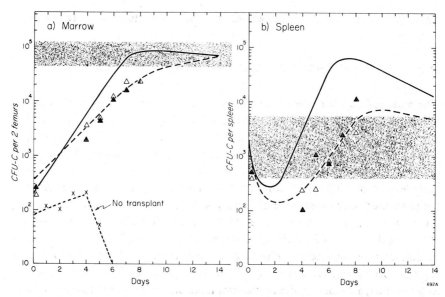

Fig. 1. Numbers of CFU–C in marrow and spleen as a function of time after transplantation of 2×10^7 marrow cells into irradiated (950 rads) recipient mice. Solid lines: both donor and host normal. Dashed lines: donors either normal or W/W^v mice and recipients either normal or Sl/Sl^d mice. ▲: W/W^v donors in irradiated Sl/Sl^d recipients. △: $+/+$ cells in irradiated Sl/Sl^d mice. Results for irradiated mice without transplanted cells are shown for marrow only as a dotted line at the bottom of *(a)*. The hatched areas indicate normal values in unirradiated control mice. (Redrawn from Sutherland *et al.* 1970.)

expressed at the level of CFU–S (McCulloch *et al.* 1964a), and although the defects have very different cellular bases (see Table 2), no additive deficit in growth was observed when the two were combined.

TABLE 2
Two genes regulating myelopoiesis

Gene symbol	Linkage group	Effect on CFU–S	Effect on growth	Interpretation
W	XVII	W/W^{v*} marrow cells do not form macroscopic colonies	Normal cells form colonies in unirradiated W/W^v mice	*W* is an intrinsic regulator of CFU–S
Sl	IV	None	Normal cells grow poorly in irradiated Sl/Sl^{d*} hosts	*Sl* is an extrinsic regulator of CFU–S

* Mice of genotypes Sl/Sl^d and W/W^v are superficially similar: both are black-eyed whites, sterile, unusually radiosensitive and have a severe macrocytic anaemia (Russell & Bernstein 1966).

It is assumed that CFU–C has a limited capacity for self-renewal; consequently, differentiation from CFU–S is considered responsible for most of the observed increase in CFU–C. If both *W* and *Sl* genes are considered to affect rate regulatory processes, the basic growth and differentiation of CFU–S might proceed at a basal level even when both gene functions are defective. Such a basal level might provide the kinetics observed in the experiments of Fig .1.

CFU REPRESSION: AN EXPERIMENTAL SYSTEM FOR THE STUDY OF CELLULAR COMMUNICATION

The lack of cellular methods for the study of Sl/Sl^d at present limits use of this genotype for the investigation of cellular communication. A second system is available whose genetic basis appears to be simple enough for experimental manipulation. This is the defective growth of C57BL/6 (B6) marrow transplanted into heavily irradiated (C57BL/6 × C3H)F1 mice (McCulloch & Till 1963). The growth defect has been shown to depend on *H-2* linked differences between donor and recipient (Cudkowicz & Stimpfling 1964); however, the usual mechanisms of immunological graft rejection do not appear to be operative. In fact, the grafts are not rejected, but rather their growth is delayed. Fig. 2 depicts data from experiments in which growth kinetics of B6 marrow transplanted into isologous and B6C3F1 hosts were compared. The lag period for both CFU–S and CFU–C in B6C3F1 hosts was long compared to that in isologous recipients; however, once growth had begun, their doubling time was similar in both hosts. The B6 origin of the regenerating cells in the F1 hosts was established using specific isoantisera capable of distinguishing between B6 and B6C3F1. The alternative conventional explanation of poor growth is graft-versus-host reaction; this is also unlikely. The B6C3F1 chimeras bearing B6 grafts appeared healthy and, as will be described later (p. 192), the degree of CFU repression is much more readily affected by manipulation of the host than of the donor. CFU repression, therefore, may be considered as an example of inappropriate regulation, and we have suggested that its basis lies in a modification of an interaction between CFU–S and 'managerial' cells with regulator functions (McCulloch & Till 1970).

Indirect evidence is available for the existence of such 'managerial' cells. Cudkowicz (1968) has shown that defective growth of parental cells is not observed in hybrid hosts when these are under three weeks of age. Further, the capacity of hybrid recipients to repress parental cells disappears approximately seven days after irradiation (Cudkowicz 1968); when such mice are reconstituted with isologous marrow cells, capacity to repress returns slowly and is not fully recovered within two months after irradiation and marrow transplantation.

These findings are compatible with the existence in haemopoietic tissue of a cell whose function is relatively radioresistant and hence does not depend upon cell proliferation. The function of this cell class is reduced slowly after injury and is even more slowly replenished in chimeras, presumably by differentiation from transplantable progenitors. These properties, very different from those of CFU–S, are those ascribed to 'managerial' cells.

As mentioned earlier, donor–host differences at the *H-2* locus are required for repression to occur (Cudkowicz & Stimpfling 1964). Cudkowicz has also obtained evidence that non-*H-2* factors are involved. Although appropriate *H-2* heterozygosity appears to be necessary for repression, such heterozygosity is not a sufficient condition. For example, repression occurs if marrow from *H-2*^{b}/*H-2*^{b} donors is transplanted into irradiated B6C3F1 but not (C3H × C3.SW)F1 recipients (Cudkowicz 1965), although both of these recipients are *H-2*^{b}/*H-2*^{k}. C3.SW are *H-2*^{b}/*H-2*^{b} congenic with C3H-*H-2*^{k}/*H-2*^{k}. Thus some non-*H-2* factor of B6 origin and absent or ineffective in C3H mice must also form part of the mechanism of repression. Other instances where the same *H-2* heterozygosity leads to repression in the presence of one genetic background and not in another have been described by Cudkowicz (1965). He has also obtained evidence that the non-*H-2* genetic factor or factors involved in repression segregate independently of *H-2*, are dominant, and involve either two independent genes with additive effects, or one gene with variable penetrance (Cudkowicz 1971). To distinguish between these latter two possibilities, progeny tests of segregants are required. Such tests are now under way in our laboratory.

The experimental approach to mechanisms in CFU repression was facilitated by the finding that isoantisera could be prepared with the capacity to modify the defective growth of B6 marrow in irradiated B6C3F1 hosts (Gregory *et al.* 1972). The derepressive activity of such antisera is demonstrated in Fig. 2. When B6C3F1 recipients of B6 marrow received active isoantisera before irradiation, the rate of regeneration of B6 CFU–S was markedly enhanced. The effect of such antisera can be studied more readily by means of a simpler assay procedure (Gregory *et al.* 1972). The standard protocol is to inject serum intraperitoneally before irradiation of B6C3F1 mice; immediately after irradiation the animals receive 5×10^5 marrow cells from B6 donors. After nine days, the spleens of groups of animals receiving either no treatment or inactive antisera have mean values of between 0.5 and seven colonies/spleen; recipients of active isoantisera contain in excess of 20 colonies/spleen.

Because of the known relationship between CFU repression and the *H-2* locus, the *H-2* specificity requirement of derepressive isoantisera was investigated (Gregory *et al.* 1972). C57BL/6 (*H-2*^{b}/*H-2*^{b}), LP (*H-2*^{b}/*H-2*^{b}), C57BL/10 (*H-2*^{b}/*H-2*^{b}) (B10) and congenic B10.BR (*H-2*^{k}/*H-2*^{k}) mice were used for this

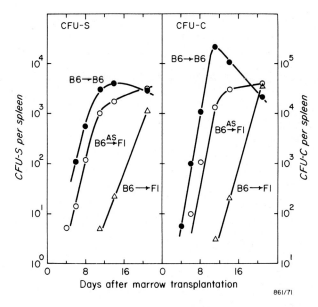

FIG. 2. Numbers of CFU–S (left) and CFU–C (right) as a function of time after transplantation of 10^6 B6 marrow cells into irradiated (950 rads) B6 or B6C3F1 recipients. Some B6C3F1 recipients received 0.5 ml of derepressive antisera (C3H anti-B10.BR) before irradiation and transplantation. The groups are indicated in the figure.

purpose. The results are presented in qualitative terms in Table 3, and in more detail elsewhere (Gregory *et al.* 1972). It is evident from the table that *H-2*

TABLE 3
The non H-2 specificity of derepressive isoantisera

Antigen[a]	Producer[b]	Result[c]
C57BL/6 or C57BL/10 (*H–2^b*)	C3H – *H–2^k*	Active
	LP – *H–2^b*	Active
	B10.BR *H–2^k*	Inactive
B10.BR (*H–2^k*)	C3H – *H–2^k*	Active
	C57BL/10 – *H–2^b*	Inactive

[a]   Spleen cells injected intraperitoneally with or without complete Freund's adjuvant. More than one injection required.
[b]   Either serum or ascites is used as a source of antibody.
[c]   Active: increase of > tenfold in colonies per spleen in irradiated B6C3F1 recipients of 5×10^5 marrow cells.
     Appropriate endogenous and normal mouse serum controls were negative.
     For details see Gregory *et al.* (1972).

differences between immunizing cells and the antibody producer were not related to the derepressive activity of the serum. Thus, B10 cells (H-2^b/H-2^b) were active in immunizing C3H but not B10.BR mice, although both the latter are H-2^k/H-2^k. Similarly, B10.BR cells elicited active antisera in C3H but not in B10 mice. Where the H-2 barrier was crossed (for example B10.BR immunized with B10 or vice versa), cytotoxic antibodies were raised, even though these sera were without derepressive capacity (Gregory *et al.* 1972). These results provide strong evidence that a cellular component, not linked to H-2, can influence CFU repression.

The results of studies of the genetic basis of repression outlined above, and the studies on derepressive isoantisera, are both consistent with non-H-2 factors being involved in repression. However, it is not yet known whether or not the non-H-2 genetic factor or factors involved in repression are genetically related to the specificity of derepressive isoantisera. Analysis of back-cross segregants should reveal the extent to which the two classes of non-H-2 factors are separable.

Genetic means have also been used to obtain evidence that derepression is mediated by an effect on non-H-2 antigens present in the irradiated recipient rather than in the donor. Like marrow cells from B6 donors, cells from C3.SW (C3H-H-2^b/H-2^b) mice are repressed in B6C3F1 recipients; this repression is also reversed if the recipients are treated with antiserum prepared in C3H mice against H-2 identical B10.BR cells. This antiserum can have no anti-H-2 activity, and, since it was raised in C3H, should contain no antibodies against C3H antigens. Accordingly, it will not react with either the H-2 or non-H-2 antigens of the marrow cells from C3.SW donors. Derepression can therefore be attributed entirely to antibodies directed against non-H-2 B10 antigens present in the B6C3F1 hosts. Such a component is essential for derepression and may be part of the mechanism of repression.

In summary, CFU repression is presented as a model system for studying cellular communication. We propose that the mechanisms of repression include modulation of the behaviour of CFU–S by short-range interaction with members of a class of 'managerial' cells. As an experimental system, CFU repression has many advantages; separate genetic control of at least two components of the mechanism has been identified. Of more importance, if the antigen or antigens responsible for the activity of derepressive antisera also form part of the mechanism of repression, such antisera may be used to identify and to alter a specific component of the mechanism. Therefore, the system can be used to develop and test concepts that involve the effects of several genes interacting to achieve haemopoietic regulation.

GRANULOPOIESIS IN CULTURE

The third system is one in which colonies of maturing granulocytes or macrophages, or both, develop in cultures containing viscid or semi-solid media (Pluznik & Sachs 1966; Bradley & Metcalf 1966; Metcalf & Bradley 1970; Worton et al. 1969a; Senn et al. 1967). These colonies are considered to arise from early committed progenitors of granulopoiesis, and the culture technique provides a useful assay procedure for cells of this class. However, the observation that colony formation depends on, or is strongly influenced by, the presence in the cultures of cell-derived molecules makes the system an interesting candidate as an experimental model of cellular interactions. The material identified by its colony-stimulating activity in such cultures will be referred to as CSA. CSA might be considered as a chemical mediator of information in granulopoietic regulation.

Various experiments have been done in an attempt to demonstrate a physiological role for molecules with colony-stimulating activity (Metcalf & Stanley 1971; Morley et al. 1971; Dale et al. 1971; Shadduck & Nagabhushanam 1971). For example, Shadduck & Nagabhushanam (1971) found that in mice rendered neutropenic by antineutrophil serum a decrease in granulocytes was associated with an increase in serum CSA. However, such a correlation is not proof of a regulatory role in vivo for CSA, since CSA might be liberated non-specifically from many tissues within the antiserum-treated mice.

A contrasting point of view would be that CSA is important only in cell cultures, providing either a nutritional requirement that is not rate-limiting in vivo, or protection for cells against damage caused by cell culture conditions. More definitive evidence in support of a physiological role of CSA could be obtained in a number of ways; for example, experiments might be done analogous to those used to demonstrate the relationship between erythropoietin and erythropoiesis (Krantz & Jacobson 1970). An alternative approach would be to find a relationship between specific perturbations of granulopoiesis and CSA-producing and responding cells. Thus, if the genetic basis of CSA production could be uncovered, the effect of mutation would establish the presence or lack of a physiological role. Or, if altered relationships between CSA production and haemopoietic response could be demonstrated as part of a disease mechanism, the validity of the interaction in vivo would be supported. In the remainder of this section an attempt will be made to discuss the role of CSA in terms of the considerations outlined above.

Man may prove a useful species for studies of the relationship between granulopoiesis in culture and in vivo. Cells from human marrow are capable of giving rise to granulopoietic colonies in culture (Senn et al. 1967; Iscove et al.

1971; Robinson & Pike 1970), and there is evidence that such human CFU–C have properties similar to those of their murine counterparts (Messner *et al.* 1972; Iscove *et al.* 1972). However, some important differences have been observed between human and mouse cultures. In cultures of human cells small colonies are observed, when no CSA is added, as long as enough cells are plated (Iscove *et al.* 1971). CSA from mouse sources, although active on mouse cells, has little or no effect when added to cultures of human cells. However, CSA active in cultures of human cells can be obtained from a limited number of human sources. These include supernatants from cultures of human peripheral leucocytes, spleen or embryo cells (Iscove *et al.* 1971; Robinson & Pike 1970; Brown & Carbone 1971; Paran *et al.* 1970). When supernatants from human leucocyte cultures are added to human marrow cultures, the size of the colonies is increased and colony formation is observed even when limiting numbers of cells are plated (Iscove *et al.* 1971). Such CSA will also stimulate colony formation in cultures of mouse cells (Chervenick & Boggs 1970).

The lack of a requirement for added CSA in human cultures of high density appears to result from the activity of cells producing CSA in the cultures. Preliminary experiments by Messner *et al.* (1973) support this view. Using the observations of the Melbourne group (Metcalf *et al.* 1972) that CSA-producing cells are separable from CFU–C, they separated human marrow into adherent and non-adherent populations. Colony formation by non-adherent cells was much more dependent on the addition of CSA than colony formation by unseparated marrow cells. Thus, human marrow appears to contain both granulopoietic progenitors and a cellular source of CSA; the two cell classes cooperate in cultures to yield granulocytic colonies, and if enough cells are present the addition of exogenous CSA has an effect only on colony size.

These findings in culture do not provide a demonstration that two cell classes are interacting meaningfully *in vivo*. However, since the observations are made in man, it is possible to examine disease states for evidence of effects of disturbed cell–cell interactions. Several features of human leukaemia make this disease particularly suitable for such purposes. First, colony formation is abnormal in untreated leukaemia. In acute myeloblastic leukaemia, colony formation is usually reduced (McCulloch & Till 1971); a reduction has also been observed in patients with pre-leukaemia many months before the overt disease develops, indicating that the change in colony-forming efficiency may be closely related to the disease process (Senn & Pinkerton 1972). In other forms of acute leukaemia (Moore *et al.* 1972) and in chronic leukaemia (Moore *et al.* 1972), colony formation may be increased or abnormal. Abnormalities in serum and urine levels of CSA and inhibitors of CSA have been reported in patients with leukaemia (Chan *et al.* 1972; Metcalf *et al.* 1972). While such changes do not appear to be clearly correlated with disease states, Metcalf *et al.* (1972) have suggested that this lack of correlation may be explained as the failure of serum or urine levels to reflect levels in haemopoietic tissue.

Some recent findings in patients with acute leukaemia will be summarized as possible examples of alterations in CSA-mediated interactions. Remission–induction in acute myeloblastic leukaemia is regularly associated with striking increases in marrow colony-forming efficiency (Cowan *et al.* 1972). However, early in remission, colony formation is markedly dependent on exogenous CSA even when marrow cells are plated at high density. These findings are similar to the observations on non-adherent cells from normal marrow and may indicate a deficient population of CSA-producing cells. As remission–induction proceeds, dependence of colony formation on exogenous CSA decreases, perhaps indicating a return towards normal in CSA-producing cells. If this hypothesis can be confirmed experimentally, it will support the view that an interaction between CFU–C and CSA-producing cells is part of the mechanism of haemopoietic regulation *in vivo*.

Unusual findings in cultures from certain patients with acute myeloblastic leukaemia (Cowan *et al.* 1973) may also be considered as manifestations of abnormal cellular interactions. In two patients confluent growth of granulocytic colonies was observed when marrow cells were plated at a concentration of 10^5 cells/ml and addition of CSA to the cultures had no effect. However, at dilutions between 10^4 and 3×10^4 cells/ml colonies were formed but their number depended heavily on the addition of CSA. These findings are consistent with a large increase in CFU–C without a concomitant increase in CSA-producing cells; in these conditions confluent growth would be observed when enough CSA-producing cells were present, while the addition of CSA would be required for cultures deficient in this class because of dilution. Finally, Aye *et al.* (1972) have recently described unusual findings in three leukaemic patients whose marrows yielded only macrophage colonies. These patients had large numbers of peripheral blood blast cells capable of multiplication in suspension culture when stimulated by supernatants from cultures of leukaemic blast cells but not by those of normal leucocytes.

It is unlikely that changes at the level of CFU–C will prove to be primary events in acute leukaemia. Malignant transformation probably occurs at the stage of pluripotent cells (Jensen & Killmann 1967) or earlier, rather than in committed progenitors. Nonetheless the lesion may be reflected in changes at the level of CFU–C and these preliminary findings in acute leukaemia provide reason to hope that detailed studies of this disease may provide the data necessary for assessing the physiological significance of molecules with colony-stimulating activity and of the cells that produce them.

CONCLUSION

Three experimental systems have been described that may yield knowledge of cellular communication. Each system has advantages and drawbacks. Genetically determined anaemias in mice provide information of unquestioned relevance to haemopoietic regulation. Unfortunately, experimental manipulations of this material are difficult and at present lack flexibility. Further, only a few mutations affecting haemopoiesis are available for study.

CFU repression is attractive since novel genetic interactions appear to be part of the mechanism. The use of specific isoantisera to manipulate the system provides a new experimental dimension with obvious potential for further useful development. The major disadvantage of CFU repression as an experimental system is that the mechanisms involved have not been proved to be physiologically operative.

Finally, studies using CSA are attractive because biologically active molecules are available and therefore analysis of the properties of these molecules may yield detailed mechanistic information. Cell culture methods are flexible and permit a large number of interesting manipulations. Perhaps of greatest importance, this system has potential for studies of diseases in man. The drawback is that CSA has not been established as a physiological regulator of haemopoiesis.

In all three systems the pros are more significant than the cons. Indeed, for both CFU repression and marrow cultures further work may dispel doubts about their relevance to physiological regulatory mechanisms.

At the beginning of this paper we stated that a generally accepted model for haemopoiesis was available. General acceptance leads to dangerous complacency. It seems improbable that our present views of the cellular structure of haemopoietic tissue will be entirely disproved; however, it is also entirely likely that the model will prove incomplete and even misleading. Data about regulator cells and their functions are beginning to provide the shadowy outlines of a better concept in which the 'generally accepted model' may be only a small part.

ACKNOWLEDGEMENTS

The work reported in this paper was supported by grants from the Medical Research Council of Canada (MT-1420), The Ontario Cancer Research and Treatment Foundation (Grant 236), and the National Cancer Institute of Canada.

References

AYE, M. T., TILL, J. E. & McCULLOCH, E. A. (1972) Growth of leukaemic cells in culture. *Blood J. Hematol.* **40**, 806–811

BECKER, A. J., McCULLOCH, E. A., SIMINOVITCH, L. & TILL, J. E. (1965) The effect of differing demands for blood cell production on DNA synthesis by hemopoietic colony-forming cells of mice. *Blood J. Hematol.* **26**, 296–308

BERNSTEIN, S. F. (1970) Tissue transplantation as an analytic and therapeutic tool in hereditary anemias. *Am. J. Surg.* **119**, 448–451

BRADLEY, T. R. & METCALF, D. (1966) The growth of mouse bone marrow cells *in vitro*. *Aust. J. Exp. Biol. Med. Sci.* **44**, 287–299

BROWN, C. H. (III) & CARBONE, P. P. (1971) In vitro growth of normal and leukemic human bone marrow. *J. Natl Cancer Inst.* **46**, 989–1000

CHAN, S. H., METCALF, D. & GUNZ, F. W. (1972) Serum inhibitors of colony factor in leukemia, in *The Nature of Leukaemia* (Vincent, P., ed.), pp. 162–171, Proc. Int. Cancer Conf., Sydney, Australia

CHERVENICK, P. A. & BOGGS, D. R. (1970) Bone marrow colonies: stimulation *in vitro* by supernatant from incubated human blood cells. *Science (Wash. D.C.)* **169**, 691–692

COWAN, D. H., CLARYSSE, A., ABU-ZAHRA, H., SENN, J. S. & McCULLOCH, E. A. (1972) The effect of remission-induction in acute myeloblastic leukemia on colony formation in culture. *Ser. Haematol.* **5**(2), 179–188

COWAN, D. H., MESSNER, H. A., SENN, J. S. & McCULLOCH, E. A. (1973) The heterogeneity of cell culture findings in patients with acute myeloblastic leukemia. *Proc. Paris Cancer Symposium.*

CUDKOWICZ, G. (1965) The immunogenetic basis of hybrid resistance to parental marrow grafts, in *Isoantigens and Cell Interactions* (Palm, J., ed.), pp. 37–56, Wistar Institute Press, Philadelphia

CUDKOWICZ, G. (1968) Hybrid resistance to parental grafts of hematopoietic and lymphoma cells, in *The Proliferation and Spread of Neoplastic Cells*, pp. 661–691, Williams & Wilkins, Baltimore

CUDKOWICZ, G. (1971) Genetic regulation of bone marrow allograft rejection in mice, in *Cellular Interactions in the Immune Response*, pp. 93–102, Karger, Basel

CUDKOWICZ, G. & STIMPFLING, J. H. (1964) Deficient growth of C57BL marrow transplanted in F1 hybrid mice. Association with histocompatibility-2 locus. *Immunology* **7**, 291–306

DALE, D. C., BROWN, C. H., CARBONE, P. P. & WOLFF, S. M. (1971) Cyclic urinary leukopoietic activity in gray collie dogs. *Science (Wash. D.C.)* **173**, 152–153

EDITORIAL (1972). Haemopoiesis. *Lancet* **1**, 1056–1057

GREGORY, C. J., McCULLOCH, E. A. & TILL, J. E. (1972) Repressed growth of C57BL marrow in hybrid hosts reversed by antisera directed against non-H-2 alloantigens. *Transplantation* **13**, 138–141

HELLMAN, S., GRATE, H. E., CHAFFEY, J. T. & CARMEL, R. (1970) Hematopoietic stem cell compartment: patterns of differentiation following radiation or cyclophosphamide, in *Hemopoietic Cellular Proliferation* (Stohlman, F., Jr., ed.), pp. 36–48, Grune & Stratton, New York

ISCOVE, N. N., TILL, J. E. & McCULLOCH, E. A. (1970) The proliferative states of mouse granulopoietic progenitor cells. *Proc. Soc. Exp. Biol. Med.* **134**, 33–36

ISCOVE, N. N., SENN, J. S., TILL, J. E. & McCULLOCH, E. A. (1971) Colony formation by normal and leukemic human marrow cells in culture: effect of conditioned medium from human leukocytes. *Blood J. Hematol.* **37**, 1–5

ISCOVE, N. N., MESSNER, H., TILL, J. E. & McCULLOCH, E. A. (1972) Human marrow cells forming colonies in culture: analysis by velocity sedimentation and suspension culture. *Ser. Haematol.* **5**(2), 37–49

JENSEN, M. K. & KILLMANN, S. (1967) Chromosome studies in acute leukaemia. Evidence for chromosomal abnormalities common to erythroblasts and leukaemic white cells. *Acta Med. Scand.* **181**, 47–53

KRANTZ, S. B. & JACOBSON, L. O. (1970) *Erythropoietin and the Regulation of Erythropoiesis*, University of Chicago Press

LAJTHA, L. G. (1963) On the concept of the cell cycle. *J. Cell. Physiol.* Suppl. 1, **62**, 143–145

LAJTHA, L. G. (1970) Stem cell kinetics, in *Regulation of Hematopoiesis* (Gordon, A. S., ed), pp. 111–131, Appleton-Century-Crofts, New York

LEVIN, R. H., WHANG, J., CARBONE, P. P. & FREIREICH, E. J. (1965) Erythroid homograft following leukocyte transfusion in a patient with acute leukemia. I. Clinical studies and implications. *Blood J. Hematol.* **26**, 587–596

MCCULLOCH, E. A. & TILL, J. E. (1963) Repression of colony-forming ability of C57BL hematopoietic cells transplanted into non-isologous hosts. *J. Cell. Comp. Physiol.* **61**, 301–308

MCCULLOCH, E. A. & TILL, J. E. (1970) Cellular interactions in the control of hemopoiesis, in *Hemopoietic Cellular Proliferation* (Stohlman, F., Jr., ed.), pp. 15–25, Grune & Stratton, New York

MCCULLOCH, E. A. & TILL, J. E. (1971) Regulatory mechanisms acting on hemopoietic stem cells: some clinical implications. *Am. J. Pathol.* **65**, 601–619

MCCULLOCH, E. A. & TILL, J. E. (1972) Leukemia considered as defective differentiation: complementary *in vivo* and culture methods applied to the clinical problem, in *The Nature of Leukaemia* (Vincent, P. C., ed.), pp. 119–134, Proc. Int. Cancer Conf., Sydney, Australia

MCCULLOCH, E. A., TILL, J. E. & SIMINOVITCH, L. (1964) Genetic factors affecting the control of hemopoiesis, in *Proc. Sixth Canadian Cancer Conference*, Honey Harbour, Ontario, pp. 336–356, Pergamon Press, London, New York

MCCULLOCH, E. A., SIMINOVITCH, L., TILL, J. E., RUSSELL, E. S. & BERNSTEIN, S. E. (1965) The cellular basis of the genetically determined hemopoietic defect in anemic mice of genotype Sl/Sl^d. *Blood J. Hematol.* **26**, 399–410

MESSNER, H., TILL, J. E. & MCCULLOCH, E. A. (1972) Density distributions of marrow cells from mouse and man. *Ser. Haematol.* **5**(2), 22–36

MESSNER, H., TILL, J. E. & MCCULLOCH E. A. (1973) Interacting cell populations affecting granulopoietic colony-formation by normal and leukemic human marrow cells. Submitted to *Blood J. Hematol.*

METCALF, D. & BRADLEY, T. R. (1970) Factors regulating *in vitro* colony formation by hematopoietic cells, in *Regulation of Hemopoiesis* (Gordon, A. S., ed.), pp. 187–215, Appleton-Century-Crofts, New York

METCALF, D. & STANLEY, E. R. (1971) Haematological effects in mice of partially purified colony stimulating factor (CSF) prepared from human urine. *Br. J. Haematol.* **21**, 481–492

METCALF, D., CHAN, S. H., STANLEY, E. R., MOORE, M. A. S., GUNZ, F. W. & VINCENT, P. C. (1972) Regulation of normal and leukaemic granulocytic cells by colony stimulating factor (CSF), in *The Nature of Leukaemia* (Vincent, P., ed.), pp. 173–186, Proc. Int. Cancer Conf., Sydney, Australia

MOON, R., PHILLIPS, R. A. & MILLER, R. G. (1972) Sedimentation and volume analysis of human bone marrow. *Ser. Haematol.* **5**(2), 163–178

MOORE, M. A. S., WILLIAMS, N. & METCALF, D. (1972) Characterization of *in vitro* colony forming cells in acute and chronic myeloid leukemia, in *The Nature of Leukaemia* (Vincent, P., ed.), pp. 135–249, Proc. Int. Cancer Conf., Sydney, Australia

MORLEY, A., RICKARD, K. A., HOWARD, D. & STOHLMAN, F. (1971) Studies on the regulation of granulopoiesis. IV. Possible humoral regulation. *Blood J. Hematol.* **37**, 14–22

NOWELL, P. C. & HUNGERFORD, D. A. (1961) Chromosome studies in human leukemia. II. Chronic granulocytic leukemia. *J. Natl Cancer Inst.* **27**, 1013–1035

OSOBA, D. (1970) Cellular cooperation in the primary immune response. The need for a uniform terminology. *Rev. Eur. Etud. Clin. Biol.* **15**, 929–933

PARAN, M., SACHS, L., BORAK, Y. & RESNITZKY, P. (1970) *In vitro* induction of granulocyte differentiation in hemopoietic cells from leukemic and non-leukemic patients. *Proc. Natl Acad. Sci. U.S.A.* **67**, 1542–1549

PLUZNIK, D. H. & SACHS, L. (1966) The induction of clones of normal mast cells by a substance from conditioned medium. *Exp. Cell Res.* **43**, 553–563

QUASTLER, H. (1963) The analysis of cell population kinetics, in *Cell Proliferation* (Lamerton, L. F. & Fry, R. J. M., eds.), vol. 18, pp. 18–34, Blackwell, Oxford

ROBINSON, W. & PIKE, B. L. (1970) Colony growth of human bone marrow cells *in vitro*, in *Hemopoietic Cellular Proliferation* (Stohlman, F., Jr., ed.), pp. 249–259, Grune & Stratton, New York

RUSSELL, E. S. & BERNSTEIN, S. E. (1966) Blood and blood formation, in *The Biology of the Laboratory Mouse* (Green, E. L., ed.), pp. 351–372, McGraw-Hill, New York

SENN, J. S. & PINKERTON, P. H. (1972) Defective *in vitro* colony formation by human bone marrow preceding overt leukaemia. *Br. J. Haematol.* **23**, 277–281

SENN, J. S., McCULLOCH, E. A. & TILL, J. E. (1967) Comparison of colony forming ability of normal and leukemic human marrow in cell culture. *Lancet* **2**, 597–598

SHADDUCK, R. K. & NAGABHUSHANAM, N. G. (1971) Granulocyte colony stimulating factor. I. Response to acute granulocytopenia. *Blood J. Hematol.* **38**, 559–568

STEPHENSON, J. R., AXELRAD, A. A., McLEOD, D. C. & SHREEVE, M. M. (1971) Induction of colonies of hemoglobin-synthesizing cells by erythropoietin *in vitro*. *Proc. Natl Acad. Sci. U.S.A.* **68**, 1542–1546

SUTHERLAND, D. J. A., TILL, J. E. & McCULLOCH, E. A. (1970) A kinetic study of the genetic control of hemopoietic progenitor cells assayed in culture and *in vivo*. *J. Cell. Physiol.* **75**, 267–274

TILL, J. E. & McCULLOCH, E. A. (1961) A direct measurement of the radiation sensitivity of normal mouse bone marrow cells. *Radiat. Res.* **14**, 213–222

TRENTIN, J. J. (1970) Influence of hematopoietic organ stroma (hematopoietic inductive microenvironments) on stem cell differentiation, in *Regulation of Hematopoiesis* (Gordon, A. S., ed.), vol. 1, pp. 161–186, Appleton-Century-Crofts, New York

TRENTIN, J. J., McGARRY, M. P., JENKINS, V. K., GALLAGHER, M. Y., SPEIRS, R. S. & WOLF, M. N. (1971) in *Morphological and Functional Aspects of Immunity* (Landahl-Kiessling, K., Alm, G. & Hanna, M. G., eds.), pp. 289–298, Plenum, New York

WHANG, J., FREI, E., TJIO, J. H., CARBONE, P. P. & BRECHER, G. (1963) The distribution of the Philadelphia chromosome in patients with chronic myelogenous leukemia. *Blood J. Hematol.* **22**, 664–673

WORTON, R. G., McCULLOCH, E. A. & TILL, J. E. (1969a) Physical separation of hemopoietic stem cells from cells forming colonies in culture. *J. Cell. Physiol.* **74**, 171–182

WORTON, R. G., McCULLOCH, E. A. & TILL, J. E. (1969b) Physical separation of hemopoietic stem cells differing in their capacity for self-renewal. *J. Exp. Med.* **130**, 91–103

Discussion

Metcalf: Does repression affect one morphological type of colony at the expense of another in your animals? If your managerial cells are involved in repression these same cells also constitute the microenvironment which determines the pathway of differentiation entered by individual stem cells. Therefore one might expect changes in the erythrocyte: granulocyte ratio in some repression situations.

McCulloch: From studies of CFU repression, managerial cells specific for either erythropoiesis or granulopoiesis are not postulated. Rather, it is suggested that differing interactions between cell surface gene-products may influence the probabilities of differentiation in one direction or another.

Metcalf: So if both of two surface patches on the managerial cell operate you get an erythroid colony and if one operates you get a granulocytic colony? Was there a difference in any of your experiments between the proportion of colonies of different types?

McCulloch: We have not been able to detect morphological differences between colonies growing in isologous recipients and those resulting from the transplantation of B6 marrow cells into B6C3F1 irradiated hybrids.

Lajtha: The phenomena which you describe as allogeneic inhibition are essentially delays in 'take rate', because you get parallel growth curves afterwards. These temporary lags have been made at the onset of CFU multiplication, which of course results in a lower colony number for a given size of graft (and time), in the F1 situation. Is that enough to say that thereby you control the pathways of differentiation? Is this not simply a question of extinction or non-extinction?

McCulloch: We interpret growth curves (Fig. 2, p. 191) as indicating a longer lag period before the beginning of exponential growth in the CFU repression situation as compared to isologous transplants. It is difficult to investigate events during this lag. Experiments using inhibitors and irradiation support the view that there is a long lag rather than a rejection of many of the grafted cells. Exponential growth is finally observed in F1 recipients and has been identified as donor rather than host.

Lajtha: This is rather crucial, is it not? If it is active, that is one thing; if it is straight extinction, or non-take, that is another thing.

McCulloch: But they do take. They finally grow.

Lajtha: Some will grow but not all; that is a very great difference.

McCulloch: It is difficult to give a definitive answer to your question, Dr Lajtha, because of problems in methodology. During the period before growth commences in the repression situation, the numbers of CFU–S or CFU–C are so small that it is difficult to make convincing measurements. One cannot solve the problem by grafting larger numbers of cells initially, since CFU repression decreases markedly for grafts greater than 10^6 nucleated marrow cells.

Winterhalter: Dr McCulloch, did you show that untreated leukaemic material did not respond to CSA, whereas after treatment the response was there?

McCulloch: I did not intend to imply that.

Metcalf: The untreated marrow responded to increasing concentrations of CSA.

Winterhalter: It responded to very high concentrations. But are the cells there unresponsive, or are they absent?

McCulloch: Colony formation by marrow cells in patients with acute leukaemia increases during remission-induction. Our chemotherapeutic regimen includes cyclophosphamide, cytosine arabinoside and vincristine, at intervals of two to three weeks (Cowan *et al.* 1972). During this increase, we postulate that cells producing CSA are also increasing. In normal human marrow, the relative concentration of CFU–C and CSA-producing cells is such that colonies are produced even without the addition of exogenous CSA; when CSA is added, the colony sizes increase but their numbers do not greatly change (Iscove *et al.* 1971). During remission–induction we see a gradually decreasing dependency of colony number on added CSA and we interpret this as indicating an increased number of CSA-producing cells.

Stohlman: We come back to the age-old problem. With human beings one is dealing with concentrations, not the total number of CFC in the bone marrow. It may be that in these circumstances, because of the amplification factor, myeloid elements are diluted; there are many more cells, it being a much more cellular marrow. You are interjecting a number of cells which were not present earlier.

McCulloch: I agree that this is a difficult problem. We have attempted to get around it by expressing the data in terms of CFU per aspirate and the general picture is similar using this method of expression. However, the absolute number of colonies is not relevant to the problem of cellular interactions since we are looking at dependence on added CSA, not at absolute colony number.

Stohlman: Let us say for the purpose of discussion that a metamyelocyte is the feeder cell or the stimulating cell which is removed. In acute leukaemia the marrow is replaced by myeloblasts, so obviously these are reduced in concentration.

McCulloch: My purpose was only to present the observations; there are not enough data to permit a mechanistic explanation. However, one does not see a correlation between the percentage of blasts in a marrow specimen and the capacity of that specimen to form colonies in culture. Accordingly, we do not believe the reduction in colony-forming capacity seen in patients with acute myeloblastic leukaemia is a consequence of dilution of their marrow by blast cells.

Winterhalter: You really showed that early in remission you have a higher concentration dependence on cells than later in remission. Could the CSA be destroyed more rapidly early in remission than later in remission? This would fit very nicely with experiments on other transformed cells with proteases on their surface (Schnebli 1972), where higher doses would have to be given to overcome the protease activity.

McCulloch: If CSA were being destroyed (a very interesting hypothesis), a greater concentration of CSA would be required to achieve maximum colony formation in patients with leukaemia than populations of normal non-adherent cells. However, in the dose-response curves, plateaus of colony formation were obtained for approximately the same concentration of added CSA for cells from patients with leukaemia going into remission and for normal non-adherent marrow cells.

Metcalf: The colony growth curves you showed, Dr McCulloch, indicated a fluctuating situation during remission development in acute granulocytic leukaemia with respect to the bone marrow content of endogenous CSF-producing cells. In remission, the frequency of these cells is often higher than in relapse and because of this cultures of cells from patients in remission are less dependent on extrinsic CSF for colony formation. However such data should not be misinterpreted as giving any information on the relative responsiveness of normal or leukaemic colony-forming cells. Such a question can only be asked after CSF-producing cells have been separated from the colony-forming cells by some separative procedure, e.g. buoyant density separation (Moore *et al.* 1973).

We have analysed the cells from more than 70 patients with acute and chronic myeloid leukaemia and in every case in which proliferation occurred in agar, that cellular proliferation was responsive to stimulation by CSF. We have never seen an example of autonomous growth in agar in which the leukaemic cells can proliferate independently of CSF. It is more difficult to determine whether there are quantitative differences between the responsiveness of normal and leukaemic cells to CSF but if differences exist they must be marginal.

McCulloch: There is no evidence to say whether the cells we are growing are normal or leukaemic.

Metcalf: From the fact that the marrow population in the untreated patient produced no colonies, I would suspect that either the cells were incapable of proliferation or produced only abortive colonies or clusters. Karyotypic analysis can be used to prove whether or not these clusters are formed by leukaemic cells if the leukaemic population has a karyotypic marker.

Stohlman: I am troubled about this concentration factor. Leukaemic cells vary under the microscope and in their responsiveness to chemotherapy. After all only 40–50% of patients with acute myeloblastic leukaemia will respond to chemotherapy and 50–60% will not. The spectrum may go from a bone marrow that is completely replaced by leukaemic elements, through an aplastic phase and then through a recovery phase. One really has to get more quantitative measurements, perhaps with bone marrow biopsies, and determine which are normal type cells, which are abnormal and so on. Otherwise one is just dealing with an abnormal concentration.

McCulloch: The changes we are seeing cannot be explained simply by dilution by blast cells. Perhaps the most compelling piece of evidence has come from a study by Senn & Pinkerton (1972), who observed three patients with pancytopenia for up to two years before overt leukaemia was recognized. The marrow was not hypercellular during this period, contained no recognizable blast cells and yielded very few colonies in culture.

Stohlman: We have three preleukaemic patients with normal concentrations of CFC.

McCulloch: When patients with leukaemia are studied using the cell culture methods, they are found to be heterogeneous (Cowan *et al.* 1972). The model of myelopoiesis (McCulloch & Till 1971) has many different sites of potential regulation and at each one a defect might occur that would lead to a leukaemic phenotype. It is now evident that leukaemic transformation is associated with alterations at cell surfaces and such alterations might lead to defective regulation when such regulation is based on cellular interaction. It is our hope to apply the culture assays to the characterization of populations in leukaemia; we believe these assays to be powerful tools for identifying specific sites and mechanisms of regulation.

Dicke: At least in our system the CFU–C has a definite capacity for proliferation. Replating of cells from 100 five-day-old colonies derived from stem cell concentrates gives rise to 800 colonies in the secondary dishes. The size of those colonies is the same as in the primary dishes. When we take 300 colonies from the same dish and the same culture, but fractionate them before putting them in secondary dishes, the number of colonies rises from 300 to 8000—27 times more colonies.

McCulloch: Your data support Dr Metcalf's point that CFU–C have limited proliferative capacity.

Dicke: But it is a high proliferative capacity.

Metcalf: *In vitro* colony-forming cells may have the capacity for three to five self-replicating divisions. If so, I would regard them as having a relatively restricted capacity for self-replication.

Dicke: After five days?

Metcalf: In assessing whether *in vitro* colonies contain colony-forming cells, one has to be very careful to consider the size of the colonies. Obviously if a colony-forming cell can generate a colony of 2000 cells, each of the original daughter cells can generate a colony of 1000 cells. However this does not mean that the first cell division was necessarily a genuine self-replicating division. In this type of work the exact size of all 'colonies' generated by cells within colonies must be determined, to exclude the possibility that reduction divisions are involved rather than self-replicatory divisions.

Dicke: I agree. I only want to emphasize that the capacity of cell proliferation is quite distinct in our culture method; such a proliferative rate, as far as I remember, has never been encountered in any other culture system being used.

References

COWAN, D. H., CLARYSSE, A., ABU–ZAHRA, H., SENN, J. S. & MCCULLOCH, E. A. (1972) The effect of remission-induction in acute myeloblastic leukaemia on colony formation in culture. *Ser. Haematol.* **5**(2), 179–188

ISCOVE, N. N., SENN, J. S., TILL, J. E. & MCCULLOCH, E. A. (1971) Colony formation by normal and leukaemic human marrow cells in culture: effect of conditioned medium from human leukocytes. *Blood J. Hematol.* **37**, 1

MCCULLOCH, E. A. & TILL, J. E. (1971) Regulatory mechanisms acting on hemopoietic stem cells: some clinical implications. *Am J. Pathol.* **65**, 601

MOORE, M. A. S., WILLIAMS, N. & METCALF, D. (1973) *In vitro* colony formation by normal and leukemic human hemopoietic cells. Characterisation of the colony-forming cells. *J. Natl Cancer Inst.* in press

SCHNEBLI, H. P. (1972) Protease-like activity associated with malignant cells. *Schweiz. Med. Wochenschr.* **102**, 1194–1197

SENN, J. S. & PINKERTON, P. H. (1972) Defective *in vitro* colony formation by human bone marrow preceding overt leukaemia. *Br. J. Haematol.* **23**, 277–281

Control of granulopoiesis

FREDERICK STOHLMAN, Jr., PETER QUESENBERRY, EERO NISKANEN, ALEC MORLEY, WILLIAM TYLER, KEVIN RICKARD, MICHEL SYMANN, FRANCIS MONETTE and DONALD HOWARD

Department of Medicine, St. Elizabeth's Hospital and Tufts Medical School, Boston, Massachusetts

Abstract We have observed that there is a log-linear relationship between the peripheral neutrophil count and the granulocytic response of the more differentiated myeloblast–promyelocyte compartment and a similar relationship with the granulocytic precursor, the committed myeloid stem cell (colony-forming cell: CFC). As neutropenia develops a serum factor capable of differentiating CFC into the myeloblast compartment is generated (colony-stimulating factor: CSF). Our data suggest that the generation of CSF is more likely related to neutrophil function than to concentration. In irradiated animals increased levels of CSF were seen at a time when neutropenia had developed and when bacteraemia and endotoxaemia were present. After injection of *Salmonella typhosa* endotoxin into normal mice, increased CSF activity was seen after 20 minutes. In the bone marrow of these animals, there was a sequential wave of differentiation from the CFC through the differentiated granulocytic compartment. Germ-free animals when irradiated failed to develop CSF, indicating that neutropenia alone is not sufficient to increase the generation of CSF, which is more likely to be a function of endotoxaemia.

Using a Millipore chamber implanted intraperitoneally into normal and neutropenic mice, we demonstrated long-range hormonal control of the production of granulocytic elements. Moreover the numbers of pluripotent stem cells in both normal and neutropenic animals increased over a five-day period; the rate of increase of CFU in the neutropenic hosts was significantly greater than that seen in normal hosts. These data are taken to indicate that here is a long-range or hormonal control of the pluripotent stem cell as well as perhaps a short-range cell–cell interaction, the evidence for which is discussed.

The use of [³H]thymidine and [³²P]diisopropylfluorophosphonate has permitted the generation of substantial information on the kinetics of the granulocytic compartment. Realistic estimates of the intravascular lifespan of the neutrophil, the definition of a marginal pool in equilibrium with the circulating granulocytic pool and estimates of transit time for the granulocytic elements in bone marrow have resulted. Thus these techniques provide a picture of the progression of neutrophil production, maturation and release as well as of the intravascular history of the granulocyte. Detailed reviews of these findings are available elsewhere (Cronkite & Vincent 1970; Athens 1970). The salient features of the system for our purposes are as follows: the differentiated myeloid compartment is not self-sustaining but is fed from a precursor compartment (colony-forming cell: CFC) committed to myelopoiesis, which in itself is derived from the pluripotent haemopoietic stem cell (colony-forming unit: CFU); the differentiated myeloblast undergoes a series of divisions while simultaneously maturing; the numbers of divisions between the myeloblast and the mature non-dividing myelocyte will vary with species and the generation time of myeloid elements may vary with perturbation; the potential for further DNA replication and division is lost in the stage of the late myelocyte but maturation in the bone marrow progresses through the metamyelocyte and polymorphonuclear cells; and release of the neutrophil from the bone marrow occurs in a 'pipeline' fashion, i.e. first in, first out. There are studies to suggest that the latter is accomplished by virtue of changes in the deformability and 'stickiness' of the neutrophil as it matures which favour release of later forms (Lichtman & Weed 1972).

While much information has been gained about the nature of these events in the differentiating myeloid compartments, until recently relatively few data were forthcoming about the forces regulating these events. Gordon and his associates (1964) reported that the leucocytosis resulting from endotoxin treatment was mediated by a plasma factor which they called leucocytosis-inducing factor (LIF). Those studies have been confirmed and extended by Boggs *et al.* (1968) who termed the factor neutrophil-inducing activity (NIA). This substance is thought to be responsible for the discharge or release of the large storage pool of bone marrow granulocytes. Beyond this, however, there was a paucity of information about the regulation of granulopoiesis. In significant measure this was due to the lack of a satisfactory label for newly released granulocytes, such as the reticulocyte or ^{59}Fe label in the case of the red cell, together with the presence of the large intermedullary storage pool and the short intravascular lifespan of granulocytes. Further, the marginal pool of granulocytes could affect peripheral granulocyte numbers without affecting production and release.

It is our purpose to present recent data on those forces regulating myelopoiesis and the pluripotent stem cell. As with any such presentation this is more of a progress report from our laboratory than a definitive final answer about the regulation of white cell production.

MATERIALS AND METHODS

The techniques which we have employed in these studies have been published in detail elsewhere. Briefly, virgin CF$_{1J}$ female mice eight to ten weeks of age were used, except in some studies on chamber implantation in which Sprague-Dawley female rats were used. Standard techniques were used for measuring peripheral blood elements and bone marrow differentials. The pluripotent stem cell (CFU) was measured by the technique of Till & McCulloch (1961); the committed myeloid stem cell (CFC) was measured by the method of Bradley & Metcalf (1966) or by the double layer technique of Bradley & Sumner (1968). Cultures of bone marrow elements were studied *in vivo* in Millipore chambers implanted intraperitoneally; this technique has been described by Boyum & Borgstrom (1970). Irradiation was delivered in some experiments from a 250 kV X-ray source and in others from a caesium source; hind-leg shielding was done with an amount of lead appropriate to the energy of the radiation source.

RESULTS AND DISCUSSION

Relationship of peripheral granulocyte level to the rate of myelopoiesis

Although it has been generally assumed that the control of myelopoiesis is in some way a function of the concentration of peripheral neutrophils, experimental documentation of the relationship has been needed. Accordingly we initiated a study in which one hind-leg of the mouse was shielded (ILS) and varying doses of irradiation were delivered to the rest of the body. In this fashion different levels of peripheral neutropenia could be achieved. At the same time the intact marrow of the shielded limb provided an index of the granulocytic response to peripheral neutropenia.

After a lethal dose of whole-body radiation the more mature granulocytic elements of the shielded limb decreased rapidly as the storage compartment was emptied in an effort to compensate for the developing neutropenia. As the latter developed, increased differentiation from the committed stem cell compartments and changes in the rate of replication within the myeloblast–promyelocyte compartment (MPC) were seen (Morley *et al.* 1971*a*). This led to an increase in the MPC which reached its peak on the fifth day after irradiation (Morley & Stohlman 1970*a*). These changes are shown in Fig. 1. Thereafter there were sequential increases in the myelocyte compartment, metamyelocytes, band cells and mature elements.

Theoretically, if the rate of myelopoiesis is regulated by some function of the

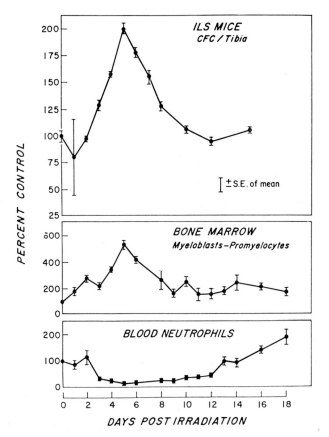

FIG. 1. CFC values in mice with one hindlimb shielded are plotted as % of control for days 1–15 after irradiation. Absolute values for the myelocyte–promyelocyte compartment and the blood neutrophil count are similarly plotted as % control. Values for CFC/tibia in ILS mice are calculated by compiling the results from at least three experiments per point. (Day 5, 13 experiments.) The average of the mean values so obtained is expressed as % of control values obtained from normal mice. Vertical bars represent the standard error. (From Rickard *et al.* 1971, reprinted from *Blood*.)

concentration of peripheral neutrophils, the MPC response in the shielded limb should reflect the degree of peripheral neutropenia. In Fig. 2 the response of the MPC compartment in the shielded limb is plotted as a function of the log of the concentrations of peripheral neutrophils. Varying degrees of neutropenia were achieved by delivering appropriate doses of radiation to the remainder of the body. Also shown is the relationship of the MPC compartment to the log of the peripheral neutrophil count in animals rendered polycythaemic by transfusion.

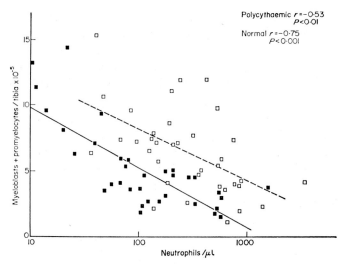

FIG. 2. Effect of polycythaemia on the size of the myeloblast–promyelocyte compartment on day 4 after various doses of irradiation. Each point shows the myeloblast–promyelocyte compartment compared with the neutrophil count from a polycythaemic (□) or normal (■) mouse. The regression lines were calculated by the method of least squares. In each case the size of the myeloblast–promyelocyte compartment is significantly ($P > 0.01$) related to the logarithm of the neutrophil count but the regression line for the polycythaemic animals lies significantly ($P > 0.01$) above that for the normal animals. (From Morley *et al.* 1970, reprinted from *Br. J. Haematol.*)

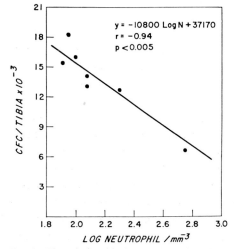

FIG. 3. The relationship between the size of the CFC compartment and the blood neutrophil count in ILS mice for days 2–8 after irradiation. CFC are the average of mean values for composite results of at least three experiments per point. Correlation coefficient *r* and the regression line are calculated from these values and are significant when $P > 0.005$. (From Rickard *et al.* 1971, reprinted from *Blood.*)

In both cases the response of the MPC compartment on the fifth day after irradiation was a linear function of the log of the peripheral white cell count. For the polycythaemic animal, however, the response was set at a higher level. We have considered the latter as evidence for stem cell competition. Thus, when the need for erythropoiesis is removed by polycythaemia more stem cells are available for differentiation into the granulocytic pathway. However, the mechanism by which priorities are adjudicated between myelopoiesis and erythropoiesis in a variety of circumstances has yet to be established.

In these studies we also examined the relationship of the committed myeloid stem cells (CFC) in the shielded limb to the degree of peripheral neutropenia. An increase in the numbers of CFC/tibia was noted and it was related temporally to the increase in the MPC compartment (Fig. 1). The increase in CFC was also a linear function of the concentration of peripheral neutrophils (Fig. 3).

These observations provided a foundation for the thesis that myelopoiesis is regulated by a feedback loop from the peripheral blood which depends on a function of the concentration of peripheral neutrophils. Feedback loops such as this have an inherent tendency to oscillate, due to the time-delay between measurement of a function and correction. In myelopoiesis the time-delay would include the time for measurement, production of a regulatory hormone, increased input from stem cells, and transit through the bone marrow. The period of the oscillation should be twice the time-delay. But we know that the concentration of granulocytes in peripheral blood does not have detectable oscillation in normal circumstances. This may in part be due to the inaccuracy of measurement of the peripheral WBC but more likely it reflects the dampening of the oscillation by a large storage pool. Removal of this pool should result in clear-cut oscillations of peripheral neutrophils and permit us to determine whether the periodicity approximates twice the transit time of myeloid elements through the bone marrow.

By administering appropriate doses of cytotoxic agents (cyclophosphamide or busulphan) to dogs, we were able to suppress myelopoiesis to such an extent that the storage pool was compromised and a cyclical neutropenia with a period twice that of the marrow transit time as measured with [3H]thymidine developed (Morley & Stohlman 1970b). Further doses of these drugs resulted in further suppression of myelopoiesis. At this point damage to the stem cell compartment was sufficiently great that a more severe and non-cyclical neutropenia resulted. These data fulfil the requirements for a feedback regulation and hence provided further evidence for such a mechanism regulating myelopoiesis.

Hormonal control of myelopoiesis

From the above we concluded that myelopoiesis is under a long-range humoral control with the characteristics of a simple feedback system. The nature of control, however, remained to be examined. One might suggest that there is a granulopoietin analogous to erythropoietin, the production of which is a function of the end-line cell and the ability of that cell to deliver oxygen to the required tissue. But in granulopoiesis a more complex situation appears to exist. Not only is there a need for increased production in the face of reduced numbers but there is also the need to provide increased numbers of white cells in the face of localized as well as generalized infection. Production of 'granulopoietin' by the neutrophil with release at the time of destruction of the cells is one possibility, but it seems unlikely to us. Such a mechanism in essence is a positive feedback which would not provide for a response to neutropenia. Further, since it is a positive feedback it should result in ever-increasing numbers of neutrophils until a 'population explosion' occurred. Thus it seemed more likely to us that the feedback mechanism involved a derivative function of the neutrophil.

There is also a need to separate out neutrophil-releasing factors from those which effect differentiation of the stem cell into the myeloid compartment. It seems possible, although unlikely, that the same substance could be responsible for both neutrophil release and differentiation of precursor cells. One might also suggest that the depletion of the storage compartment triggers a short-range intramedullary loop which is responsible for differentiation of the CFC. In view of these considerations we initiated a series of studies on the relationship of neutropenia and a derivative function—bacteraemia and endotoxaemia—to white cell production as assessed by the colony-forming technique *in vitro* and the growth of myeloid elements in Millipore chambers *in vivo*.

Production of colony-stimulating factor

In mice exposed to whole-body irradiation or with the hind-leg shielded, Morley *et al.* (1971*b*) observed that as the animals became neutropenic the ability of the serum to stimulate colony formation *in vitro* increased and peaked between the fifth and seventh days after irradiation. The increase in activity coincided with the previously described increase in myelopoiesis and CFC in the shielded limb of irradiated animals. It was of further interest that the increase in CSF coincided with the bacteraemia and associated intestinal injury in irradiated animals. Thus, the question was raised as to whether the increase in CSF might not reflect bacteraemia and endotoxaemia. We therefore studied CSF in germ-free irradiated animals. In the latter, although the degree of neutropenia was similar to that seen in conventional irradiated animals, increased CSF activity was not observed (Morley *et al.* 1972), suggesting that endotoxaemia was an important if not critical factor in CSF generation in irradiated neutropenic animals.

In view of these findings we examined the effect of endotoxin on CSF generation and myeloid response in normal animals (Quesenberry *et al.* 1972). *Salmonella typhosa* was used as a source of endotoxin. It was given in doses of from 5 μg to 250 μg intravenously or intraperitoneally. Shortly afterwards the peripheral neutrophil count dropped precipitously. This was followed by granulocytosis caused by the release of neutrophils from the marrow storage compartment (Fig. 4). There followed a decrease in CFC and a sequential wave of differentiation through the myeloid compartment. Twenty minutes after injec-

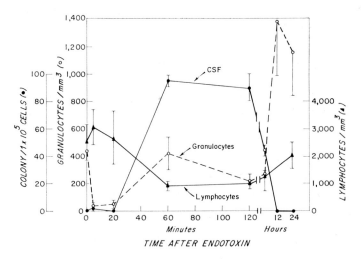

FIG. 4. Changes in serum CSF, granulocytes and lymphocytes shown as a function of time after the intravenous injection of 250 μg endotoxin (each point represents the mean ± S.E. of 10 to 12 mice). (From Quesenberry *et al.* 1972, reprinted from *New Engl. J. Med.*)

tion of endotoxin, increased CSF levels were detected in the serum. Peak levels of CSF activity were seen one to eight hours after the injection of endotoxin and the serum activity afterwards declined (Fig. 4). The levels of CSF generation were a log function of the dose of endotoxin, as shown in Fig. 5, but intravenous administration resulted in higher CSF activities than the intraperitoneal route.

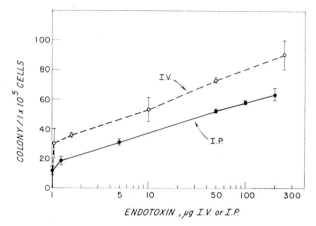

FIG. 5. Dose response curve for serum CSF two hours after endotoxin given intravenously (I.V.) or intraperitoneally (I.P.). The values expressed are the numbers of colonies developing from 1×10^5 murine marrow cells $\pm$ the standard error. (From Quesenberry *et al.* 1972, reprinted from *New Engl. J. Med.*)

After repeated injections of endotoxin, tolerance was induced and CSF activity could no longer be demonstrated. Endotoxin when given to neutropenic animals (neutrophils $< 12/\text{mm}^3$) resulted in CSF generation, indicating that granulocytes were not necessary for the production of CSF under these conditions.

A number of studies indicate that CSF may be produced in diverse sites. In our experience (Quesenberry *et al.* 1972) the addition of endotoxin to culture dishes will not affect colony production but in high concentrations (10^{-3}mM) will inhibit colony formation in the presence of a known stimulus. Interestingly enough, incubation of lung tissue, salivary gland or thymus will generate significant amounts of CSF. It would seem most reasonable, if increased granulocyte production in response to local infection were to be achieved, that the long-range hormone necessary for myeloid stimulation should be produced in diverse sites. The information available suggests that this is the case. The cells responsible for CSF generation have not been identified although monocytes and macrophages have been suggested. Vascular and connective tissue, distributed as they are throughout the body, might also be considered as possible sites of production of CSF. Definitive information on this aspect of the physiology of CSF clearly awaits the production of antibodies and the application of immunofluorescent techniques.

In vivo studies of granulopoiesis

Millipore chambers containing aliquots of normal bone marrow were implanted intraperitoneally into normal mice and rats as well as into animals pretreated with cyclophosphamide, which thus were neutropenic (Tyler *et al.* 1972). During the first 24 hours after implantation the total numbers of nucleated cells in the chambers decreased due to the death of erythroid and mature granulocytic elements. Thereafter there was a sequential increase in early proliferative cells, including myeloblasts and promyelocytes, myelocytes and more mature elements. Macrophages were also seen to grow within the chambers, suggesting either that macrophages and myeloid elements are derived from a common cell of origin or that the environmental characteristics favouring the growth of both elements are similar. In the neutropenic hosts the rate of growth of granulocytic elements was accelerated, providing further evidence that myelopoiesis is under a long-range hormonal control (Table 1).

In preliminary studies we found that [³H]thymidine labelling indexes of granulocytic elements were higher in neutropenic hosts than in controls. This may be interpreted as indicating a shorter generation time for the differentiated myeloid elements of the neutropenic animals. We also noted that serum from cyclophosphamide-treated animals increased the labelling of myeloid elements from normal bone marrow in short-term (3–6 h) liquid cultures. Presumably the same factor is operating both *in vivo* and *in vitro* to affect the generation time. The nature of this factor and the question of whether it has an identity separate from that of CSF remain to be established. The term antichalone has been suggested for serum factors capable of shortening the generation time of differentiated haemopoietic elements. On Sephadex the mobility of the factor appears to be similar to that of CSF and further studies are needed to determine the relationship of the two, if indeed they are separate regulators.

The stem cell

The CFC serves as the immediate precursor for differentiated granulopoiesis but, as previously indicated, it has limited capacity for self-renewal. Thus when depleted it is restored by influx from the pluripotent haemopoietic stem cell compartment. This compartment is frequently thought of as homogeneous and clearly delineated but in fact there is probably a significant degree of heterogeneity within the compartment and varying degress of 'stemness'. For conceptual convenience, however, we shall consider the pluripotent compartment as a

TABLE 1

Changes in cellularity in implanted Millipore chambers as a function of time after implantation

Day		Control × 10⁻³	CYᵃ 50 mg/kg	CYᵃ 100 mg/kg
	Total cellularity			
0		100	100	100
2		40.6 ± 3.4	52.9 ± 5.4	60.8 ± 8.2
5		212.9 ± 16.9	381.1 ± 35.9	701.2 ± 66.6
7		262.6 ± 27.5	455.5 ± 50.6	844.7 ± 91.8
	EPCᵇ			
2		8.8 ± 1.1	13.0 ± 1.9	12.6 ± 2.0
5		40.3 ± 6.6	59.5 ± 8.8	104.8 ± 9.6
7		16.9 ± 3.6	43.2 ± 8.1	68.4 ± 6.0
	Myelocytes			
2		5.0 ± 0.9	5.9 ± 1.0	5.8 ± 1.4
5		89.4 ± 9.2	161 ± 15.2	247.8 ± 27.8
7		85.1 ± 12.3	147 ± 21.9	259.1 ± 43.3
	Late granulocytesᶜ			
2		8.8 ± 1.0	9.3 ± 1.3	12.4 ± 2.2
5		27.8 ± 4.7	93.6 ± 18.5	208.8 ± 3.2
7		76.6 ± 12.3	151.3 ± 24.6	263.2 ± 36.7

ᵃ CY: Cyclophosphamide given 24 hours before implantation in indicated dose.
ᵇ EPC refers to early proliferating cells including myeloblasts and promyelocytes.
ᶜ Indicates metamyelocytes, bands and mature forms.
  Results are given as the mean number of cells ± standard error.

single relatively homogeneous entity. Since it occupies a central role in haemopoiesis it seemed important to examine its regulation.

It had been suggested that the pluripotent stem cell (CFU) is regulated by short-range factors and perhaps by cell–cell interaction. The observations of McCulloch & Till (1970) and those of Goodman & Grubbs (1970) have been interpreted as indicating that the regulation is of a stimulatory nature. Rencricca et al. (1970), however, reported that in mice with phenylhydrazine-induced anaemia the CFU migrated from bone marrow to spleen, where perhaps a more favourable environment for expanding erythropoiesis was present. As the CFU population decreased in the marrow the remaining CFU were seen to leave the G0 state and enter active cycle. Conversely, in the spleen, where the CFU population was increased by immigration, the CFU remained dormant or in a G0 state. Rencricca et al. (1970) suggested that if cell–cell interaction is important in the regulation of CFU it is more likely to be of an inhibitory nature, similar to contact inhibition. More recently Monette et al. (1972) examined the effect of an antigenic stimulus—Bordetella pertussis—on CFU kinetics. After a single administration of this antigen the CFU migrated from bone marrow to spleen but, unlike what happens in the anaemic animals, the CFU in the spleen were seen to enter cycle (Fig. 6). Despite an increasing number of splenic CFU, they remained in cycle for 48 hours after injection of the antigen (Fig. 6; Table 2). The number of splenic CFU continued to rise between 48 and 96 hours but this was due to migration from the bone marrow to the spleen; the splenic CFU had returned to a resting or G0 state (Fig. 6). It was proposed that this sequence of events might reflect an alteration of the cell surface membrane which interfered with the recognition process and thus permitted the CFU to enter cycle. Later re-establishment of the recognition process led to inhibition caused by population increases and the CFU entered G0.

It was therefore of interest to examine the CFU content in Millipore chambers in both normal and neutropenic animals. In this system migration can be eliminated and the effects of long-range regulation evaluated. After implantation of chambers containing normal bone marrow there was an initial decline in the CFU but after 24 hours the numbers began to increase (Table 3). At this point the cells were in active cycle as judged by the hydroxyurea technique. By the fifth day the number of CFU far exceeded those in the original marrow implant. In neutropenic (cyclophosphamide-treated) animals the total number of CFU on the fifth day after implantation was significantly greater than in control animals. Both implants were aliquots from the same marrow. Hence the increased proliferation in the neutropenic animals must have been due to host factors. A long-range regulation of CFU appears to be implicated. In this respect Gregory *et al.* (1971) suggested that an α-macroglobulin is released after treat-

TABLE 2

CFU (mean $\pm$ standard error) in tibia, spleen and peripheral blood of mice at intervals after a single injection of *B. pertussis* vaccine

Time interval (h)	Tibia		Spleen		Peripheral blood	
	Total CFU	CFU/10^6 cells	Total CFU	CFU/10^6 cells	CFU/ml	CFU/10^6 cells
Normal control	3266 ± 413	268 ± 37	4776 ± 739	34 ± 5	12.5 ± 2.1	3.5 ± 0.6
4	2744 ± 460	257 ± 47	4686 ± 1005	30 ± 6	53.1 ± 7.6	19.5 ± 2.8
14	1430 ± 278	201 ± 47	2611 ± 503	19 ± 3	21.3 ± 4.0	6.3 ± 1.2
24	1494 ± 216	268 ± 39	4251 ± 806	30 ± 5	16.7 ± 3.4	5.1 ± 1.1
36	1700 ± 272	268 ± 43	7218 ± 672	42 ± 4	——	——
48	1906 ± 206	421 ± 50	$14\ 592 \pm 1573$	80 ± 9	37.9 ± 5.9	9.7 ± 1.5
60	2453 ± 223	376 ± 35	$18\ 769 \pm 3622$	76 ± 10	136.7 ± 6.0	29.5 ± 1.3
72	2510 ± 264	381 ± 34	$36\ 215 \pm 5771$	157 ± 27	263.8 ± 26.0	35.1 ± 3.5
96	1254 ± 214	192 ± 34	$58\ 921 \pm 9486$	209 ± 35	——	——
168	1909 ± 226	236 ± 28	$49\ 074 \pm 8238$	176 ± 24	——	——

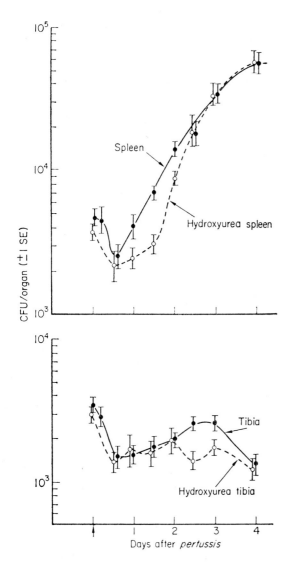

FIG. 6. Total number of tibial and splenic CFU after *B. pertussis* vaccine (solid line) and total number 2 h after administering hydroxyurea i.v. (dashed line). (From Monette *et al.* 1972, reprinted from *Cell Tissue Kinet.*)

ment of animals with cyclophosphamide and that this may account for the stimulation of stem cell growth. This possibility is currently being studied as a possible explanation for the findings in these experiments.

The regulation of the size of the CFU compartment is undoubtedly a com-

TABLE 3

Growth of CFU in Millipore chambers implanted intraperitoneally in mice

| Day | N^a | Total no. CFU (± S.E.) after indicated days of implantation | |
		Control	Neutropenic[b]
0	6	23 ± 2.9	23 ± 2.9
1	3	14 ± 6.8	13 ± 5
2	4	15 ± 3.3	17.1 ± 4
4	2	16	35
5	4	39 ± 2	60 ± 5.5

[a] N: Number of experiments.
[b] Neutropenic animals were treated with cyclophosphamide 24 hours before implantation.

plex problem involving both short-range cell–cell interaction and long-range or hormonal influences. Surely the migration of CFU in response to antigen and erythropoietin stimulation as well as the experiments described here, speak for a long-range regulation. The differences in proliferation between bone marrow and spleen in the same animals exposed to the long-range stimulus and in a number of experimental circumstances, however, suggest that local or short-range regulation is also operative. The balance between the two may determine whether pluripotent cells enter cycle or not.

ACKNOWLEDGEMENTS

Supported in part by grants NHLI-7542 and 5600 from the National Heart and Lung Institute and FR 5587 from the General Research Support Grant, National Institutes of Health.

P. Quesenberry and F. Monette were supported by Training Grant HL 5600 from the National Heart and Lung Institute, E. Niskanen is an International Post-Doctoral Fellow of the National Institutes of Health, K. Rickard is a Leukemia Society Fellow and M. Symann a Damon Runyon Fellow.

References

ATHENS, J. W. (1970) Neutrophilic granulocyte kinetics and granulocytopoiesis, in *Regulation of Hemopoiesis* (Gordon, A. S., ed.), pp. 1143–1167, Appleton-Century-Crofts, New York
BOGGS, D. R., CHERVENICK, P. A., MARSH, J. C., CARTWRIGHT, G. E. & WINTROBE, M. M.

(1968) Neutrophil releasing activity of dogs injected with endotoxin. *J. Lab. Clin. Med.* **72**, 177–185

BOYUM, A. & BORGSTROM, R. (1970) The concentration of granulocytic stem cells in mouse bone marrow determined with diffusion chamber technique. *Scand. J. Haematol.* **7**, 294

BRADLEY, T. R. & METCALF, D. (1966) The growth of mouse bone marrow cells *in vitro*. *Aust. J. Exp. Biol. Med. Sci.* **44**, 287–299

BRADLEY, T. R. & SUMNER, M. A. (1968) Stimulation of mouse bone marrow colony growth *in vitro* by conditioned medium. *Aust. J. Exp. Biol. Med. Sci.* **46**, 607

CRONKITE, E. P. & VINCENT, P. C. (1970) Granulocytopoiesis, in *Hemopoietic Cellular Proliferation* (Stohlman, F., Jr., ed.), pp. 211–288, Grune & Stratton, New York

GOODMAN, J. W. & GRUBBS, C. (1970) The relationship of the thymus to erythropoiesis, in *Hemopoietic Cellular Proliferation* (Stohlman, F., Jr., ed.), pp. 27–36, Grune & Stratton, New York

GORDON, A. S., HANDLER, E. S., SIEGEL, C. D., DORNFEST, B. S. & LOBUE, J. (1964) Plasma factors influencing leukocyte release in rats. *Ann. N.Y. Acad. Sci.* **113**, 766–779

GREGORY, S. A., FRIED, W., KNOPSE, W. H. & TROBAUGH, F. (1971) Accelerated regeneration of transplanted hematopietic stem cells in irradiated mice pretreated with cyclophosphamide. *Blood J. Hematol.* **37**, 196–203

LICHTMAN, M. A. & WEED, R. I. (1972) Alteration of the cell periphery during maturation. *Blood J. Hematol.* **39**, 301–316

McCULLOCH, E. A. & TILL, J. E. (1970) Cellular interactions in the control of hemopoiesis, in *Hemopoietic Cellular Proliferation* (Stohlman, F., Jr., ed.), Grune & Stratton, New York

MONETTE, F., MORSE, B., HOWARD, D., NISKANEN, E. & STOHLMAN, F., JR. (1972) Hemopoietic stem cell proliferation and migration following *Bordetella pertussis* vaccine. *Cell Tissue Kinet.* **5**, 121–129

MORLEY, A. A. & STOHLMAN, F., JR. (1970a) Studies on the regulation of granulopoiesis I. The response to neutropenia. *Blood J. Hematol.* **35**, 312–321

MORLEY, A. A. & STOHLMAN, F., JR. (1970b) Cyclophosphamide induced cyclical neutropenia. *New Engl. J. Med.* **282**, 643

MORLEY, A., HOWARD, D., BENNETT, B. & STOHLMAN, F., JR. (1970) Studies on the regulation of granulopoiesis. II. Relationship to other differentiation pathways. *Br. J. Haematol.* **19**, 523–532

MORLEY, A., MONETTE, F., RIZZOLI, V., HOWARD, D. & STOHLMAN, F., JR. (1971a) Studies on the regulation of granulopoiesis III. Neutrophil kinetics in irradiation-induced neutropenia. *Br. J. Haematol.* **20**, 637

MORLEY, A. A., RICKARD, K. A., HOWARD, D. & STOHLMAN, F., JR. (1971b) Studies on the regulation of granulopoiesis. *Blood J. Hematol.* **37**, 14–20

MORLEY, A., QUESENBERRY, P., BEALMEAR, P., STOHLMAN, F., JR. & WILSON, R. (1972) Serum colony stimulating factor levels in irradiated germfree and conventional CFW mice. *Proc. Soc. Exp. Biol. Med.*, **140**, 478–480

QUESENBERRY, P., MORLEY, A., STOLHMAN, F., JR., RICKARD, K., HOWARD, D. & SMITH, M. (1972) The effect of endotoxin upon granulopoiesis I. Colony stimulating factor. *New Engl. J. Med.* **286**, 227–231

RENCRICCA, N., RIZZOLI, V., HOWARD, D. & STOHLMAN, F., JR. (1970) Stem cell migration and proliferation during severe anemia. *Blood J. Hematol.* **36**, 764–775

RICKARD, K. A., MORLEY, A., HOWARD, D. & STOHLMAN, F., JR. (1971) The *in vitro* colony-forming cell and the response to neutropenia. *Blood J. Hematol.* **37**, 6–13

TILL, J. E. & McCULLOCH, E. A. (1961) A direct measurement of the radiation sensitivity of normal mouse bone marrow cells. *Radiat. Res.* **14**, 213–221

TYLER, W., NISKANEN, E., STOHLMAN, F., JR., KEANE, J. & HOWARD, D. (1972) Effect of neutropenia on myeloid growth and the stem cell in an *in vivo* culture system. *Blood J. Hematol.* **40**, 634–645

Discussion

Metcalf: Human urine CSF and two types of mouse CSF (serum from endotoxin-injected mice and partially purified lung CSF) have been tested for their capacity to cause acute release of granulocytes or colony-forming cells from the marrow but all three failed to provoke a discharge of cells (D. Metcalf, unpublished data).

If one leg of a mouse is shielded before 250 rads whole-body irradiation, production of CSF by bone-related cells rises in both the irradiated femur and the shielded femur, beginning at the same time. The rise is even higher in the shielded femur than in the unshielded femur, which suggests that there is some circulating influence capable of affecting local CSF production.

Stohlman: I am glad to hear that. In CF1 mice we saw an increase in the serum CSF in both hind-leg-shielded and whole-body-irradiated animals.

Yoffey: Pertussis has some very odd effects. Barnes & Loutit (1967) also noted this increase in circulating CFU, and Morse & Riester (1967) showed a massive discharge of lymphocytes and transitional cells from the marrow. Dr Stohlman, did you look into the morphology of the CFU in terms of the cells which were being discharged from the marrow?

Stohlman: There is a striking decline in erythroid precursors but I did not look at the lymphoid elements.

Harris: I shall be talking about the morphology of the cells which emerge into the peripheral blood later (see pp. 263–277).

Stohlman: We also examined some purified material in the Millipore chamber system, but unfortunately not enough to treat a large number of animals. We saw no effect. I don't think this is meaningful, for when we assayed this purified material, which was sent to us by Dick Stanley, in the agar system there had been a tremendous loss of activity. How well does CSF travel?

Metcalf: The ampouled human urine CSF which we supply on request as a standard is quite stable. In laboratories in which this standard induces unusually low numbers of colonies, the explanation has been that the batch of foetal calf serum used in the medium is not suitable for urine-stimulated colony formation.

Dicke: Was there a threefold increase in CFU, Dr Stohlman?

Stohlman: In the first 24 hours there is a decrease and then the CFU increase. I cannot say anything about death of the CFU. However, when we label the donor marrow, we document cell death throughout the study although there is a net increase in cells.

McCulloch: Does the concentration of CFU in the chambers stay the same or go down a little? The cell number is going up.

Stohlman: It goes down initially and then rises.

Kubanek: In your experiments did the ratio of CFC to CFU increase according to the time in the chambers?

Stohlman: We have not enough data on the CFC for me to comment.

Grigoriu: Is there any difference between the CSF level in patients with chronic leucopenia and those with acute leucopenia?

Stohlman: We have not studied this systematically. A couple of patients with drug-induced leucopenia, who were monitored very carefully, showed only a slight increase in CSF. They did not have infection. I am not sure whether this would be a function of infection or not. In the leukaemic patients and so forth, much to Dr Metcalf's horror, we have not been looking at this.

Metcalf: Like you, Dr Stohlman, we found that the capacity of mice to elevate serum CSF levels after the injection of endotoxin is quite radioresistant. Even after 1200 rads, a mouse can still respond quantitatively in exactly the same way as a normal mouse, after an injection of endotoxin or of bacterial antigen (Metcalf 1971). In our experience the only mice that have very low levels of serum CSF are germ-free animals (Metcalf *et al.* 1967). When such animals are conventionalized, serum CSF levels rise slowly. However, a germ-free mouse given an injection of endotoxin responds as quickly as a conventional animal, both in tissue production of CSF and in serum CSF levels (J. Sheridan and D. Metcalf, unpublished data). So the capacity is there; it is just not being expressed.

My extrapolation from this is that the reason why all of us in this room have measurable levels of CSF in our serum is because we all carry a significant microbiological load providing bacterial products which stimulate CSF-producing cells.

One can then legitimately raise the question: is CSF a 'normal' regulator? If a humoral factor only appears in the abnormal state, is it 'normal' in the sense that hormones or erythropoietin are 'normal'? It really depends on the degree of abnormality one accepts as part of everyday life. The 'normal' lymph node is in fact an intensely hyperplastic organ compared with the vestigial organ in germ-free animals. This hyperplasia is so common as to be regarded as 'normal' but again its origin is antigenic stimulation by microbial flora.

Hudson: Is there any CSF in foetal liver?

Metcalf: There are very high levels in foetal blood (Moore & Metcalf 1970). The yolk sac, which is the site of development of the first *in vitro* colony-forming cells, also has a very high capacity to produce CSF, yet oddly enough no granulopoiesis occurs in the yolk sac. In the yolk sac it must be presumed that local microenvironmental factors block the colony-forming cells from responding to this CSF.

Thomas: Are there any discrepancies between levels of CSF concentration, which might account for the different patterns of haemopoietic activity in the medullary cavities and in extramedullary sites (see Thomas 1971, and Fig. 10, this volume, p. 93)?

Stohlman: One can only speculate. I agree with Dr Metcalf that it is nice to think that bacterial products are what govern CSF production. There is, however, the problem of tolerance. In considering the spleen and bone marrow, we enter the problem of microenvironmental influences. If bone marrow from an adult rabbit is implanted intraperitoneally into the rat, resolution of bone, stromal formation and haemopoietic formation all follow. Then if the marrow came from a red bone marrow source, one will continue to see red bone marrow; if it came from a yellow bone marrow source it will revert to yellow bone marrow. I do not know the nature of these microenvironmental influences. Clearly the spleen of the mouse differs from that of man in this respect.

Thomas: Dr Metcalf has told us that in germ-free animals CSF levels are low, which is what we might expect. In the early embryo and in the foetus, however, where we might expect the levels to be similar to those in germ-free animals, CSF levels are high. Presumably therefore it is not that CSF production fails to be switched on in germ-free animals, but rather that CSF production which has been switched on *in utero* is switched off.

Metcalf: While a seven- or eight-day mouse yolk sac has no granulopoiesis, the foetal mouse liver generates many granulocytic cells.

Thomas: We have found very few granulocytes in human foetal liver (Thomas & Yoffey 1964) or in guinea-pig foetal liver, and in murine foetal liver we have observed very few granulocytes before the 17th day of gestation (Thomas 1966). How did you demonstrate the many granulocytic cells to which you refer?

Metcalf: We are talking about two slightly different things. The rise in *in vitro* colony-forming cells (granulocytic progenitor cells) occurs early in the foetal mouse liver and there is a peak incidence of these cells at the 12th–13th day (Metcalf & Moore 1971). However, the number of more differentiated progeny of these cells is initially very small. Again, as is the case for the yolk sac, some local inhibitory influence must prevent these granulocytic precursor cells from responding to CSF stimulation.

Because the foetus has high CSF levels it may be that, in the foetus, CSF production is not as dependent on antigenic stimulation as appears to be the case in adult life. The high level of granulopoiesis in the neonatal germ-free spleen (Metcalf & Stevens 1972) also suggests that regulation of granulopoiesis in foetal life may differ from that in adult life.

Thomas: On what evidence do you base the statement that there is granulocyte production in murine foetal liver on the ninth or tenth day of gestation?

Metcalf: I qualified that statement. I was really referring to granulocytic progenitor cells, not differentiated granulocytes.

Thomas: Transplanted foetal liver cells will certainly produce granulocytes in a suitable environment (Fig. 10, p. 93).

Metcalf: Yes.

References

BARNES, D. W. H. & LOUTIT, J. E. (1967) Haemopoietic stem cells in the peripheral blood. *Lancet* 2, 1138–1141

METCALF, D. (1971) Acute antigen-induced elevation of serum colony stimulating factor (CSF) levels. *Immunology* 21, 427–436

METCALF, D. & MOORE, M. A. S. (1971) *Haemopoietic Cells*, North-Holland, Amsterdam

METCALF, D. & STEVENS, S. (1972) Influences of age and antigenic stimulation on granulocyte and macrophage progenitor cells in the mouse spleen. *Cell Tissue Kinet.* 5, 433–446

METCALF, D., FOSTER, R. & POLLARD, M. (1967) Colony stimulating activity of serum from germfree normal and leukemic mice. *J. Cell. Physiol.* 70, 131–132

MOORE, M. A. S. & METCALF, D. (1970) Ontogeny of the haemopoietic system: yolk sac origin of *in vivo* and *in vitro* colony forming cells in the developing embryo. *Br. J. Haematol.* 18, 279–296

MORSE, S. I. & RIESTER, S. K. (1967) Studies on the leukocytosis and lymphocytosis induced by *Bordetella pertussis*. I. Radioautographic analysis of the circulating cells in mice undergoing pertussis-induced hyperleukocytosis. *J. Exp. Med.* 125, 401–408

THOMAS, D. B. (1966) Hepatic haematopoiesis in the mouse foetus. *J. Anat.* 100, 932–934

THOMAS, D. B. (1971) The differentiation of transplanted haematopoietic cells derived from bone marrow, spleen and foetal liver. *J. Anat.* 110, 297–306

THOMAS, D. B. & YOFFEY, J. M. (1964) Hepatic haematopoiesis in the human foetus. *Br. J. Haematol.* 10, 193–197

Regulation of thrombopoiesis

DAVID P. SHREINER and JACK LEVIN

Veterans Administration Hospital, University Drive, Pittsburgh, Pennsylvania and Department of Medicine, The Johns Hopkins University School of Medicine and Hospital, Baltimore, Maryland

Abstract Production of platelets by megakaryocytes appears to be controlled by the number of circulating platelets. Thrombocytopenia induced by increased destruction or removal of platelets is followed by an increase in the number, size and rate of maturation of megakaryocytes. Increased platelet production in thrombocytopenic animals can be detected by the rate and magnitude of incorporation of radioisotopic labels into megakaryocytes and platelets, and the appearance of larger and more dense platelets in the circulation.

Transfusion-induced thrombocytosis results in a decrease in the number and size of megakaryocytes, diminished platelet production, and low or undetectable levels of thrombopoietin in plasma. Suppression of thrombopoiesis appears to be related to the duration and degree of thrombocytosis. Animals with suppressed thrombopoiesis are more sensitive assay animals than normal animals for the detection of thrombopoietin in plasma.

Thrombopoietic stimulating activity (thrombopoietin) in plasma of thrombocytopenic animals can be detected by the rate and magnitude of incorporation of radioisotopes into the platelets of plasma-injected animals. Haemorrhaged animals have increased levels of thrombopoietic and erythropoietic activity in their plasma. However, it is still not clear whether or not erythropoietin has thrombopoietic activity.

Thrombopoietin can be detected even in normal plasma, when animals with suppressed thrombopoiesis are used as assay animals. However, plasma from thrombocytopenic donors contains more thrombopoietic activity than plasma from normal donors.

Thrombopoietin may act by one or more of the following mechanisms: increasing the differentiation of precursor cells into the megakaryocyte compartment, stimulating endomitosis and cytoplasmic growth of megakaryocytes, or accelerating the rate of megakaryocytic maturation. The site of action, the site of production and the chemical nature of thrombopoietin remain unknown.

Platelet production from megakaryocytes appears to be controlled by a homeostatic mechanism. Alterations of the platelet count result in changes in numbers, size and rate of maturation of megakaryocytes. These changes appear to be initiated at the level of megakaryocytic precursor cells, rather than by a direct effect on the recognizable megakaryocytes themselves.

The mechanism whereby an alteration in the platelet count affects the mega-karyocytes is thought to be mediated by a humoral regulator called 'thrombo-poietin'. An increase in the platelet count or in platelet mass appears to be followed by decreased production of platelets. Conversely, a decrease in the level of circulating platelets is followed by increased production of platelets. Evidence is presented to support the concept of a humoral control of throm-bopoiesis.

MEGAKARYOCYTOPOIESIS

Recognizable megakaryocytes have been classified according to cytoplasmic morphology by light microscopy into three types (Ebbe 1970). Stage I mega-karyocytes have basophilic cytoplasm without granulation and a high nuclear-to-cytoplasmic ratio. Stage II megakaryocytes are more mature, have more cytoplasm with less basophilia, and some granules may be present. Stage III cells have many granules, a low nuclear-to-cytoplasmic ratio, and are the most mature platelet-producing megakaryocytes. In rats, Stage I cells constitute approximately 19% of all marrow megakaryocytes, Stage II cells 25%, and Stage III cells 56% (Ebbe 1970).

Studies with tritiated thymidine have demonstrated that DNA synthesis occurs only in Stage I megakaryocytes in the rat (Ebbe & Stohlman 1965; Odell *et al.* 1970). As a result of maturation of Stage I cells, Stage II and III cells become labelled eight and 24 hours, respectively, after initial labelling of Stage I cells (Ebbe & Stohlman 1965). The intensity of the nuclear label does not change during this time, suggesting that cell division does not occur during maturation of megakaryocytes. In fact, cell division has never been observed among recognizable megakaryocytes, and mitotic figures are seen only in Stage I cells (Ebbe & Stohlman 1965; Ebbe 1970). Presumably, an unrecognizable precursor pool of cells is responsible for replenishing the megakaryocyte com-partment.

The absence of DNA synthesis in Stage II and III megakaryocytes indicates that maximum polyploidy is attained before much cytoplasmic maturation has occurred. However, Paulus (1970) has shown by electron microscopy that cytoplasmic organelles begin to form even in the earliest recognizable mega-karyocytes, when the cytoplasm appears immature by light microscopy. Endo-mitotic division occurs synchronously, so that megakaryocytes may have ploidy values of $4n$, $8n$, $16n$ or $32n$ (Odell & Jackson 1968). In rats Stage I cells may have any ploidy value from $4n$ to $32n$ (Odell & Jackson 1968). Stage II and III megakaryocytes may have any ploidy value from $8n$ to $32n$ (Odell & Jackson 1968). Megakaryocytes increase in size during maturation predominantly by cytoplasmic growth (Ebbe 1970). Although all stages of megakaryocytes may have representatives of each ploidy value, there is some evidence that cell size may be roughly correlated with DNA content or ploidy values (Ebbe 1970; Harker 1968).

The nature of the progenitor cell or cells of the megakaryocytic series has been the subject of some speculation. Most investigators agree that the transplantable stem cell normally appears to be in a relatively quiescent non-dividing state (Ebbe 1970). Since all Stage I megakaryocytes in rats are labelled one day after injection with tritiated thymidine (Ebbe & Stohlman 1965; Odell & Jackson 1968), these cells must come from a precursor pool with active DNA synthesis (Ebbe 1970). These unrecognizable active precursor cells are apparently intermediate between the quiescent pluripotent stem cells and the recognizable megakaryocytes. The intermediate precursor cells appear to be committed to the megakaryocytic series, unlike the pluripotent stem cells (Ebbe 1970). The committed precursor pool may be self-replicating, or it may be replenished from the pluripotent stem cell compartment, or both mechanisms may occur (Ebbe 1970). Further characterization of the megakaryocytic precursor cells awaits improvement in techniques designed to measure stem cell kinetics and to identify these precursor cells.

THROMBOCYTOPENIA

When thrombocytopenia is produced by increased destruction or removal of platelets from the circulation, megakaryocytopoiesis and thrombocytopoiesis are altered so as to increase the production of platelets. The number of megakaryocytes in the marrow increases approximately in proportion to the duration of the thrombocytopenia (Harker 1968). Megakaryocytes also increase in size in response to thrombocytopenia; this is first noticeable in Stage I cells, then in Stage II cells, and finally in Stage III cells (Ebbe et al. 1968a; Ebbe 1970). When the platelet count returns to normal, megakaryocyte size becomes normal in the same sequence (Ebbe 1970). This increase in size is apparently not simply a result of an increased cytoplasmic growth, because the nuclear: cytoplasmic ratio remains unaltered (Ebbe 1970). DNA content and the number of nuclei in rat megakaryocytes are increased (Harker 1968; Penington & Olsen 1970). The degree of macrocytosis attained appears to be proportional to the degree of thrombocytopenia (Ebbe 1970).

Induction of thrombocytopenia also results in acceleration of the rate of maturation of megakaryocytes. The cytoplasmic maturation time in rats with severe thrombocytopenia is only 44% of that of normal control values (Ebbe et al. 1968b). The rate of differentiation of precursor cells into the compartment of recognizable Stage I megakaryocytes is also accelerated (Ebbe et al. 1968b). During recovery from acute thrombocytopenia, rebound thrombocytosis occurs before platelet counts return to normal (Ebbe et al. 1968a; Evatt & Levin 1969). This finding has been interpreted as evidence that thrombopoiesis is stimulated by induction of thrombocytopenia.

[^{75}Se]Selenomethionine (^{75}SeM) and Na$_2$^{35}SO$_4$ are radioisotopes which initially label megakaryocytes in vivo and later appear in the circulation incorporated in platelets (Najean & Ardaillou 1969; Odell et al. 1955; Evatt & Levin 1969; Harker 1970). Induction of acute thrombocytopenia increases the level and the rate of incorporation of these radioisotopes into platelets during the recovery phase (Harker 1970; Penington 1969). The incorporation of radioisotopic labels into platelets is a more sensitive indicator of the rate of thrombocytopoiesis than is the concentration of circulating platelets (Evatt & Levin 1969; Harker 1970; Shreiner & Levin 1970). Thrombocytopenia due to increased platelet destruction or removal is associated with the appearance of larger and more dense platelets in the circulation (McDonald et al. 1964; Minter & Ingram 1967). Young platelets have been shown to be larger and heavier than old platelets by studies of differential centrifugation and labelling with radioisotopes (Amorosi et al. 1971; McDonald et al. 1964; Minter & Ingram 1967).

THROMBOCYTOSIS

Transfusion-induced thrombocytosis is followed by rebound thrombocytopenia on the fifth to eighth day after cessation of transfusions (Cronkite 1957; Odell et al. 1967; Evatt & Levin 1969). This finding has been interpreted as evidence for suppression of platelet production. However, rebound thrombocytopenia is less reproducible than the rebound thrombocytosis that follows acute thrombocytopenia (Ebbe 1970). Incorporation of ^{75}SeM and Na$_2$^{35}SO$_4$ into platelets is decreased in animals with transfusion-induced thrombocytosis (Shreiner & Levin 1970; Harker 1970). Suppression of thrombopoiesis is related to the duration and degree of thrombocytosis (Levin 1970; Harker 1968, 1970; Ebbe 1970).

Animals with transfusion-induced thrombocytosis have a decrease in the number and size of megakaryocytes, and fewer nuclear lobes are seen (Odell *et al.* 1967; Harker 1968). Maximum microcytosis occurs in Stage III cells only after the fourth day of hypertransfusion, whereas in thrombocytopenic animals maximum macrocytosis occurs after two days (Ebbe 1970). In contrast to the accelerated rates of megakaryocytic maturation in thrombocytopenic animals, no change in the rate of maturation in animals with thrombocytosis has been detected, and the rate of differentiation from the precursor pool appears unchanged (Ebbe *et al.* 1966).

These studies suggest that thrombopoiesis is less sensitive to the suppressive effect of thrombocytosis than to the stimulatory effect of thrombocytopenia.

RELATIONSHIP BETWEEN THROMBOPOIESIS AND ERYTHROPOIESIS

Certain clinical observations suggest that there is an inverse relationship between the erythrocyte count and the platelet count. Patients with hae-morrhagic anaemia and iron deficiency frequently have thrombocytosis (Harker & Finch 1969). Megakaryocytes are usually increased in number, but not in size, in these patients. Furthermore, postsplenectomy thrombocytosis, which usually subsides within two to three months, persists in patients with continuing haemolytic anaemia (Hirsh & Dacie 1966). In contrast, patients with cyanotic congenital heart disease often have low platelet counts, which are inversely related to the mean haemoglobin level (Gross *et al.* 1968).

Rats with polycythaemia induced by hypoxia or hypertransfusion have slightly decreased platelet counts (De Gabriele & Penington 1967*a*). However, polycythaemic rats respond like normal rats by increasing their platelet counts at similar rates after induction of thrombocytopenia by platelet antiserum. Furthermore, injections of erythropoietin which increased erythropoiesis did not alter platelet counts. The same authors also showed that nephrectomized rats have a normal recovery of the platelet count after acute thrombocytopenia. These studies suggest that thrombopoietin and erythropoietin are different substances.

In haemorrhaged rabbits incorporation of [75]SeM into platelets is increased, and plasma from haemorrhaged rabbits increases the incorporation of isotope into platelets when injected into normal rabbits (Shreiner & Levin, unpublished). Shreiner and Levin (unpublished) found that the injection of a partially purified preparation of human erythropoietin into rabbits increases the incorporation of [75]SeM into platelets, but a dose-response effect could not be demonstrated. However, the preparation of human erythropoietin was derived from patients with haemorrhagic anaemia due to hookworm infestation, and these patients may have had thrombocytosis and increased levels of thrombopoietin. Therefore, the studies with human erythropoietin may be similar to the experiments with haemorrhaged rabbits. The lack of a dose-response effect with the preparation of erythropoietin suggests that the apparent thrombopoietic effect of this preparation of erythropoietin may be non-specific or due to contamination of the erythropoietin with some other substance. Although haemorrhage is associated with thrombocytosis and increased levels of thrombopoietic stimulating activity, it is not clear whether this is due to increased levels of erythropoietin, or of thrombopoietin, or both. It is conceivable that platelet loss during haemorrhage and consumption of platelets in the haemostatic process may lead to increased production of thrombopoietin. It is also conceivable that erythropoietin may have a thrombopoietic effect, possibly by stimulation of undifferentiated stem cells.

In an attempt to clarify these observations, the incorporation of ^{75}SeM into the platelets of hypoxic mice was studied. After six days of hypoxia, the mean haematocrit had increased 23% above controls and the mean platelet count had decreased 24% below controls. However, incorporation of ^{75}SeM into platelets was unchanged when calculated as % ^{75}SeM in the total estimated platelet mass, and was actually increased 52% when calculated as % ^{75}SeM per million platelets (Shreiner, unpublished).

These results could be explained by assuming that the platelet concentration in plasma remained unchanged, since the percentage increase in haematocrit is similar to the percentage decrease in platelet count of whole blood. In this instance the total number of circulating platelets and the plasma volume would be unaltered. It is also possible that splenic enlargement and sequestration of platelets may account for the decrease in platelet count (De Gabriele & Penington 1967c; Rolovic & Baldini 1970), because the mouse spleen rapidly becomes erythropoietically active and hypertrophic in response to erythropoietin (Filmanowicz & Gurney 1961; Papayannopoulou & Finch 1972).

If the total numbers of circulating platelets were decreased in hypoxic mice by an increased rate of removal of older platelets from the circulation, while platelet production remained unchanged, the incorporation of ^{75}SeM per million circulating platelets would appear increased. If platelet production were decreased, incorporation of ^{75}SeM should also be decreased. Thus, it is not possible from these experiments to determine whether platelet production is normal or increased in hypoxic mice, but the decrease in platelet count cannot be accounted for by decreased thrombopoiesis.

If splenic pooling of platelets were responsible for the thrombocytopenia in hypoxic mice, the increased ^{75}SeM incorporation per platelet is compatible with increased thrombopoiesis. The increased incorporation of ^{75}SeM into platelets may underestimate platelet production, because there appears to be a tendency for young platelets to pool in the spleen (Shulman *et al.* 1968). In the normal human being, hypoxia may be associated with an increased platelet count (Siri *et al.* 1966). However, people chronically exposed to high altitudes do not have thrombocytosis (Aster 1972).

In another group of experiments, plasma from hypoxic mice was injected into normal mice. The mean reticulocyte count increased 129% above controls, but the mean platelet count and incorporation of ^{75}SeM into platelets was not significantly different from controls (Shreiner, unpublished). Thus, although acute hypoxia may possibly be associated with increased thrombopoiesis, there is no definite evidence that erythropoietin has thrombopoietic activity. Further studies are in progress using different assay techniques. Preliminary experiments using hypoxic splenectomized mice suggest that erythropoietin does not have thrombopoietic activity.

HUMORAL CONTROL OF THROMBOPOIESIS

Evidence for the humoral control of thrombopoiesis has been summarized in several recent reviews (Levin 1970; Abildgaard & Simone 1967; Cooper 1970). After the induction of acute thrombocytopenia, rebound thrombocytosis occurs before platelet levels return to normal (Ebbe *et al.* 1968a; Evatt & Levin 1969). Conversely, transfusion-induced thrombocytosis is followed by a rebound thrombocytopenia on the fifth to eighth days after cessation of transfusions (Cronkite 1957; Odell *et al.* 1967). These findings suggest that there are positive and negative feedback mechanisms which increase platelet production in response to thrombocytopenia and decrease production in response to thrombocytosis.

Evidence for humoral control of platelet levels by the spleen has been inconclusive (Abildgaard & Simone 1967). The rise in platelet count that occurs after splenectomy has usually been attributed to removal of the splenic platelet pool. However, the increase in platelet count that occurs after splenectomy for traumatic injury to the spleen is much greater than can be accounted for by absence of splenic pooling, and is also greater than the 30 to 50% rise that follows other surgical procedures (Aster 1972). This may be due to absence of a humoral inhibitor of thrombopoiesis, since animal studies have shown that reimplantation of a small portion of the spleen prevents postsplenectomy thrombocytosis, even when the spleen is enclosed in a cell-impermeable chamber (Tarnuzi & Smiley 1967).

Many early studies purported to show thrombopoietic activity in plasma, urine or tissue extracts by the increase in platelet count after their injection into animals. However, Odell *et al.* (1964) have shown that the platelet count can be altered by a variety of non-specific stimuli. Also, the platelet count in peripheral blood depends on the rate of platelet destruction or removal, as well as platelet production. Nevertheless, various investigations have suggested the presence of thrombopoietic stimulating activity in normal human plasma (Spector 1961; Linman & Pierre 1962), plasma from thrombocytopenic donors (Abildgaard & Simone 1967; Spector 1961; Odell *et al.* 1961; De Gabriele & Penington 1967*b*; Schulman *et al.* 1965), and plasma from patients with myeloproliferative disorders (Kelemen *et al.* 1958; Linman & Pierre 1963). Two families have been reported in which a plasma factor necessary for normal thrombopoiesis was apparently lacking (Schulman *et al.* 1965; Vildosola & Emparanza 1962). Thrombocytopenia in these patients was corrected by infusions of normal plasma.

Isotopic techniques have been used recently to detect thrombopoietic stimu-

TABLE 1

Isotopic methods for the detection of thrombopoietic activity in plasma, *in vivo*

Isotope	Recipient	Test plasma	% Increase in incorporation of isotope in platelets	Reference
^{75}SeM[a]	Normal rabbit	Normal rabbit	None	Evatt &
		Thrombocytopenic rabbit	36 %	Levin (1969)
^{75}SeM[a]	Hypertransfused rabbit	Normal rabbit	0– 93%[b]	Shreiner &
		Thrombocytopenic rabbit	52–107%[b]	Levin (1970)
		Thrombocythaemic rabbit	None	
^{75}SeM[a]	Normal mouse	Normal human	None	Penington
		Thrombocytopenic human	89–201 %[b]	(1970)
$Na_2^{35}SO_4$	Normal rat	Normal rat	0– 56 %	Cooper (1970)
		Thrombocytopenic rat	35–118 %	
	Normal mouse	Normal mouse	None	
		Thrombocytopenic mouse	58–106 %[b]	
$Na_2^{35}SO_4$	Hypertransfused rat	Normal rat	116 %	Harker (1970)
		Thrombocytopenic rat	304 %	
		Thrombocythaemic rat	None	

[a]   [^{75}Se]Selenomethionine
[b]   Incorporation of isotope was proportional to the dose of plasma given.

lating activity (Table 1). It has been reported that $Na_2{}^{35}SO_4$ and ^{75}SeM label all stages of megakaryocytes and are not directly incorporated into circulating platelets to any significant degree (Odell et al. 1955; Najean & Ardaillou 1969; Evatt & Levin 1969; Odell & McDonald 1964). After incorporation into mega-karyocytes, radioactivity appears in circulating platelets. The rate and degree of incorporation of the isotope into platelets can be used as a measure of thrombopoiesis.

Using ^{75}SeM, Evatt & Levin (1969) were not able to demonstrate thrombo-poietic activity in normal rabbit plasma when such plasma was given to normal rabbits (Table 1). This confirmed previous observations that normal plasma did not raise platelet counts of normal recipients when the donor and recipient were of the same species (Spector 1961; Odell et al. 1961). However, plasma from thrombocytopenic donors produced a significant increase in incorporation of ^{75}SeM in the platelets of normal recipients, suggesting that such plasma contains a substance that increases platelet production (Evatt & Levin 1969). Cooper (1970) reported similar findings in rats and mice using $Na_2{}^{35}SO_4$ (Table 1). Penington (1970) also found no detectable thrombopoietic activity in normal human plasma, using normal mice injected with ^{75}SeM as assay animals (Table 1). He did find variable increases in the incorporation of ^{75}SeM in platelets of mice injected with plasma from thrombocytopenic patients.

Animals with suppressed thrombopoiesis due to hypertransfusion of platelets are more sensitive assay animals for the detection of thrombopoietic activity. Shreiner & Levin (1970) and Harker (1970) have demonstrated thrombopoietic activity in the plasma of both normal and thrombocytopenic animals when such plasma was given to rabbits or rats with transfusion-induced thrombocytosis (Table 1). Plasma from thrombocytopenic donors produces a greater incorpora-tion of isotope into platelets than plasma from normal donors. A dose-response relationship is demonstrable for both normal plasma and plasma from throm-bocytopenic animals (Shreiner & Levin 1970). Plasma from animals with transfusion-induced thrombocytosis has no detectable thrombopoietic activity (Shreiner & Levin 1970; Harker 1970).

Recently, a haemagglutination-inhibition assay for thrombopoietin has been reported (McDonald 1971). A thrombopoietically active fraction from sheep sera, determined by its ability to increase the $Na_2{}^{35}SO_4$ incorporation into the platelets of thrombocythaemic mice, was used to immunize rabbits in order to produce an antithrombopoietin. Immune sera from the rabbits produced agglutination of red cells sensitized with the thrombopoietically active serum fraction. Inhibition of haemagglutination was achieved by preincubation of test sera containing thrombopoietin with the rabbit immune sera. In this manner thrombopoietic activity was measured in the sera of sheep with thrombocytopenia. Further studies will be nessecary to confirm the usefulness of this assay.

The physicochemical nature of thrombopoietin is still unknown. Reports concerning the heat stability of thrombopoietin are conflicting (Abildgaard & Simone 1967; Schulman *et al.* 1965). Most workers consider thrombopoietin to be a protein, possibly a glycoprotein (Linman & Pierre 1963). It has variously been claimed to be an α-globulin, a β-globulin, and an albumin (Abildgaard & Simone 1967). In preliminary investigations from our laboratories, a non-dialysable, thrombopoietically active plasma fraction has been tested in the bioassay system using ^{75}SeM (Evatt *et al.*, 1972). Electrophoretic analysis of this fraction demonstrated a large albumin component, a lesser amount of β-globulin, and a trace of α-globulin, but no gammaglobulin (Shreiner, unpublished). Further fractionation and purification of this plasma fraction is in progress.

CONCLUSIONS

Thrombopoiesis is responsive to the level of circulating platelets, apparently by means of a humoral, thrombopoietic stimulating factor (thrombopoietin). Thrombopoietin is increased in plasma in response to thrombocytopenia and is decreased or absent in response to transfusion-induced thrombocytosis. Although animals subjected to haemorrhage appear to have increased platelet production, it has not been demonstrated that erythropoietin has thrombopoietic activity.

Thrombopoietin may act by increasing the maturation rate of megakaryocytes, by increasing the differentiation of precursor cells into the megakaryocyte compartment, or by stimulating nuclear division at the precursor cell or stem cell level. An increase in the number and size of megakaryocytes in response to a thrombopoietic stimulus is followed by an increase in the number and size of the platelets in the circulation. Young platelets are usually larger and more dense than old platelets.

The exact mechanism and site of action, the site of production and the chemical nature of thrombopoietin remain unknown. There is some evidence that thrombopoietin may be bound or adsorbed onto the platelet membrane (De Gabriele & Penington 1967b). In this case, levels of thrombopoietin would be dependent on the total number of circulating platelets, including those sequestered in the spleen. Thrombopoietin appears to be a non-dialysable protein with biological effects that are different from erythropoietin. The development of more sensitive and simple assay methods will, it is hoped, lead to further characterization of thrombopoietin, and the discovery of the mechanism that senses platelet levels or platelet mass.

ACKNOWLEDGEMENTS

These investigations were supported in part under Contract No. COO-3014-3 between the United States Atomic Energy Commission and The Johns Hopkins University, and, in part, by a Graduate Training Grant, TI-AM-5260 from the National Institute of Arthritis and Metabolic Diseases, United States Public Health Service.

References

ABILDGAARD, C. F. & SIMONE, J. V. (1967) Thrombopoiesis. *Semin. Hematol.* **4**, 424–452

AMOROSI, E., GARG, S. K. & KARPATKIN, S. (1971) Heterogeneity of human platelets. IV. Identification of a young platelet population with [^{75}Se]selenomethionine. *Br. J. Haematol.* **21**, 227–232

ASTER, R. H. (1972) in *Hematology* (Williams, W. J., Beutler, E., Erslev, A. J. & Rundles, R. W., eds.), pp. 1050–1054, McGraw-Hill, New York

COOPER, G. W. (1970) in *Regulation of Hematopoiesis* (Gordon, A. S., ed.), vol. 2, pp. 1611–1629, Appleton-Century-Crofts, New York

CRONKITE, E. P. (1957) in *Homeostatic Mechanisms (Brookhaven Symp. Biol.*, No. 10), pp. 96–110, Brookhaven National Laboratories, Upton, N.Y.

DE GABRIELE, G. & PENINGTON, D. G. (1967a) Physiology of the regulation of platelet production. *Br. J. Haematol.* **13**, 202–209

DE GABRIELE, G. & PENINGTON, D. G. (1967b) Regulation of platelet production: 'Thrombopoietin.' *Br. J. Haematol.* **13**, 210–215

DE GABRIELE, G. & PENINGTON, D. G. (1967c) Regulation of platelet production: 'Hypersplenism' in the experimental animal. *Br. J. Haematol.* **13**, 384–393

EBBE, S. (1970) in *Regulation of Hematopoiesis* (Gordon, A. S., ed.), vol. 2, pp. 1587–1610, Appleton-Century-Crofts, New York

EBBE, S. & STOHLMAN, E., JR., (1965) Megakaryocytopoiesis in the rat. *Blood J. Hematol* **26**, 20–35

EBBE, S., STOHLMAN, F., JR., DONOVAN, J. & HOWARD, D. (1966) Megakaryocytopoiesis in the rat with transfusion-induced thrombocytosis. *Proc. Soc. Exp. Biol. Med.* **122**, 1053–1057

EBBE, S., STOHLMAN, F., JR., OVERCASH, J., DONOVAN, J. & HOWARD, D. (1968a) Megakaryocyte size in thrombocytopenic and normal rats. *Blood J. Hematol.* **32**, 383–392

EBBE, S., STOHLMAN, F., JR., DONOVAN, J. & OVERCASH, J. (1968b) Megakaryocyte maturation rate in thrombocytopenic rats. *Blood J. Hematol.* **32**, 787–795

EVATT, B. L. & LEVIN, J. (1969) Measurement of thrombopoiesis in rabbits using ^{75}selenomethionine. *J. Clin. Invest.* **48**, 1615–1626

EVATT, B. L., LEVIN, J. & SCHREINER, D. P. (1972) Effects of fractions of plasma proteins from thrombocytopenic rabbits on thrombopoiesis in rabbits and mice. *Blood J. Hematol.* **40**, 926 (Abstr.)

FILMANOWICZ, E. & GURNEY, C. W. (1961) Studies on erythropoiesis. XVI. Response to a single dose of erythropoietin in polycythemic mouse. *J. Lab. Clin. Med.* **57**, 65–72

GROSS, S., KEEFER, V. & LIEBMAN, J. (1968) The platelets in cyanotic congenital heart disease. *Pediatrics* **42**, 651–658

HARKER, L. A. (1968) Kinetics of thrombopoiesis. *J. Clin. Invest.* **47**, 458–465

HARKER, L. A. (1970) Regulation of thrombopoicsis. *Am. J. Physiol.* **218**, 1376–1380

HARKER, L. A. & FINCH, C. A. (1969) Thrombokinetics in man. *J. Clin. Invest.* **48**, 963–974

HIRSH, J. & DACIE, J. V. (1966) Persistent post-splenectomy thrombocytosis and thrombo-embolism: a consequence of continuing anaemia. *Br. J. Haematol.* **12**, 44–52

KELEMEN, E., CSERHATI, I. & TANOS, B. (1958) Demonstration and some properties of human thrombopoietin in thrombocythaemic sera. *Acta Haematol. (Basel)* **20**, 350–355

LEVIN, J. (1970) in *Formation and Destruction of Blood Cells* (Greenwalt, T. J. & Jamieson, G. A., eds.), pp. 143–150, Lippincott, Philadelphia

LINMAN, J. W. & PIERRE, R. V. (1962) Thrombocytosis-promoting activity of normal plasma. *Proc. Soc. Exp. Biol. Med.* **110**, 463–466

LINMAN, J. W. & PIERRE, R. V. (1963) Studies on thrombopoiesis: III. Thrombocytosis-promoting effects of 'thrombocythemic' and 'polycythemic' plasmas. *J. Lab. Clin. Med.* **62**, 374–384

McDONALD, T. P. (1971) The hemagglutination-inhibition assay for thrombopoietin. *Blood J. Hematol.* **38**, 818 (abstr.)

McDONALD, T. P., ODELL, T. T., JR. & GOSSLEE, D. G. (1964) Platelet size in relation to platelet age. *Proc. Soc. Exp. Biol. Med.* **115**, 684–689

MINTER, N. & INGRAM, M. (1967) Density distribution of platelets. *Blood J. Hematol.* **30**, 551 (abstr.)

NAJEAN, Y. & ARDAILLOU, N. (1969) The use of ^{75}Se-methionine for the *in vivo* study of platelet kinetics. *Scand. J. Haematol.* **6**, 395–401

ODELL, T. T., JR. & JACKSON, C. W. (1968) Polyploidy and maturation of rat megakaryocytes. *Blood J. Hematol.* **32**, 102–110

ODELL, T. T., JR. & McDONALD, T. P. (1964) Two mechanisms of sulfate-S^{35} uptake by blood platelets of rats. *Am. J. Physiol.* **206**, 580–584

ODELL, T. T., JR., TAUSCHE, F. G. & GUDE, W. D. (1955) Uptake of radioactive sulfate by elements of the blood and the bone marrow of rats. *Am. J. Physiol.* **180**, 491–494

ODELL, T. T., JR., McDONALD, T. P. & DETWILER, T. C. (1961) Stimulation of platelet production by serum of platelet-depleted rats. *Proc. Soc. Exp. Biol. Med.* **108**, 428–431

ODELL, T. T., JR., McDONALD, T. P. & HOWSDEN, F. L. (1964) Native and foreign stimulators of platelet production. *J. Lab. Clin. Med.* **64**, 418–424

ODELL, T. T., JR., JACKSON, C. W. & REITER, R. S. (1967) Depression of the megakaryocyte-platelet system in rats by transfusion of platelets. *Acta Haematol. (Basel)* **38**, 34–42

ODELL, T. T., JR., JACKSON, C. W. & FRIDAY, T. J. (1970) Megakaryocytopoiesis in rats with special reference to polyploidy. *Blood J. Hematol.* **35**, 775–782

PAPAYANNOPOULOU, T. & FINCH, C. A. (1972) On the *in vivo* action of erythropoietin: a quantitative analysis. *J. Clin. Invest.* **51**, 1179–1185

PAULUS, J. M. (1970) DNA metabolism and development of organelles in guinea pig mega-karyocytes: a combined ultrastructural, autoradiographic and cytophotometric study. *Blood J. Hematol.* **35**, 298–311

PENINGTON, D. G. (1969) Assessment of platelet production with ^{75}Se-selenomethionine. *Br. Med. J.* **4**, 782–784

PENINGTON, D. G. (1970) Isotope bioassay for 'thrombopoietin'. *Br. Med. J.* **1**, 606–608

PENINGTON, D. G. & OLSEN, T. E. (1970) Megakaryocytes in states of altered platelet pro-duction: cell numbers, size and DNA content. *Br. J. Haematol.* **18**, 447–463

ROLOVIC, Z. & BALDINI, M. (1970) Megakaryocytopoiesis in splenectomized and hypersplenic rats. *Br. J. Haematol.* **18**, 257–268

SCHULMAN, I., ABILDGAARD, C. F., CORNET, J. SIMONE, J. V. & CURRIMBHOY, Z. (1965) Studies on thrombopoiesis. II. Assay of human plasma thrombopoietic activity. *J. Pediatr.* **66**, 604–612

SHREINER, D. P. & LEVIN, J. (1970) Detection of thrombopoietic activity in plasma by stimul-ation of suppressed thrombopoiesis. *J. Clin. Invest.* **49**, 1709–1713

SHULMAN, N. R., WATKINS, S. P., JR., ITSCOITZ, S. B. & STUDENTS, A. B. (1968) Evidence that the spleen retains the youngest and hemostatically most effective platelets. *Trans. Assoc. Am. Physicians Phila.* **81**, 302–313

SIRI, W. E., VAN DYKE, D. C., WINCHELL, H. C., POLLYCOVE, M., PARKER, H. G. & CLEVELAND, A. S. (1966) Early erythropoietin, blood and physiological responses to severe hypoxia in man. *J. Appl. Physiol.* **21**, 73–80

SPECTOR, B. (1961) *In vivo* transfer of a thrombopoietic factor. *Proc. Soc. Exp. Biol. Med.* **108**, 146–149

TARNUZI, A. & SMILEY, R. K. (1967) Hematologic effects of splenic implants. *Blood J. Hematol.* **29**, 373–384

VILDOSOLA, J. & EMPARANZA. E. (1962) Hereditary familial thrombocytopenia. *Proc. X Int. Congr. Paediatr.*, Lisbon, p. 36 (abstr.)

Discussion

Metcalf: What are the properties of the active serum factor?

Shreiner: Thrombopoietic activity is not dialysable from plasma. A crude fraction of plasma that precipitates between 60 and 80% saturation with $(NH_4)_2SO_4$ contains all the detectable thrombopoietic activity. Thrombopoietic activity can be concentrated by this technique. Such a plasma fraction significantly increases radioisotope incorporation into platelets when injected into normal animals. Other properties of the thrombopoietically active fraction are under investigation.

Stohlman: The platelet is notoriously very sensitive to haemorrhage and develops what is called reactive thrombocytosis. In the iron-deficient subject with gastrointestinal bleeding it is almost uniformly true clinically that the platelet count increases. In the haemorrhaged animal, you probably have the same problem, together with a loss of platelets.

Several years ago, using erythropoietin from the urine of patients with red cell aplasia and normal platelets and white cells, Shirley Ebbe could not find an effect on platelet production, by a variety of measurements. One must be careful about the source material, for it may be contaminated with thrombopoietin or produce a non-specific reactive thrombocytosis.

Winterhalter: What is the advantage of using methionine over using an amino acid mixture with any isotope that you choose?

Shreiner: There is probably no particular advantage. We chose this labelled amino acid because selenium-75 is a gamma emitter and is easier to detect than a β-emitter. ^{75}Se-labelled methionine is also readily available and has a relatively long physical half-life.

Winterhalter: What is known about the incorporation of selenomethionine in protein biosynthesis? There might be some snag there.

Shreiner: ^{75}Se-labelled methionine is metabolized in the same manner as ^{35}S-labelled methionine.

Lajtha: Didn't Van Dyke produce thrombocytosis consistently with erythropoietin in monkeys?

Shreiner: Van Dyke (1964) showed no consistent change in the leucocyte or platelet counts of monkeys injected with erythropoietin. Van Dyke *et al.* (1963) also used a urine preparation from a patient with aplastic anaemia and thrombocytopenia. Therefore, there is some question as to whether the thrombocytosis produced by this material was due to erythropoietin or whether increased levels of thrombopoietin were also present.

Lajtha: Urine from which erythropoietin could be separated would be a very useful material for trying to separate thrombopoietin.

You have already shown a discrepancy between the selenomethionine curve and platelet count changes. With a label which is immunized to a relatively small extent, despite this variation in its general metabolism by the liver and so on, this might make tremendous differences in the apparent incorporation rate. How can one control this? It is a vulnerable system.

Shreiner: We have always been looking for a better way to do this. Unfortunately, we have no isotope that is specific for platelets.

Lajtha: Wouldn't sulphate to some extent be safer? It is quite non-specific in that respect, but it is highly concentrated in platelet precursors. You can flood the body; apart from the myeloid cells, very little would be utilized. You can check and monitor plasma levels and there might be less pitfalls than with selenomethionine.

Shreiner: Penington (1969) tried $^{35}SO_4$ and simply stated that this agent was unreliable in his laboratory. Other people seem to have been successful with this isotope (Cooper 1970; Harker 1970).

McCulloch: You showed the incorporation of selenomethionine into platelets. What would happen if you used the same stimulus and looked at reticulocytes or granulocytes? The changes you have observed are small and might be the result of non-specific stimulation.

Shreiner: I have not studied granulopoiesis or erythropoiesis.

Astaldi: Does removal of the spleen influence the effect of the stimulating factor on platelet counts?

Shreiner: The effect of splenectomy on changes in platelet count in response to stimulating factor is not known. In the hypoxia experiments, platelet counts did not decrease in splenectomized animals during hypoxia. We suspect that the fall in platelet counts that occurred in mice with intact spleens may have been due to sequestration of platelets in a large spleen. Splenic erythropoiesis in response to hypoxia becomes very prominent in the mouse and may result in splenic hypertrophy.

Stohlman: Normally the response to thrombocytopenia is an increase in numbers but you have documented an increase in mass. Do you feel that producing cells that are perhaps 10 or 20% larger than normal, rather than increasing the numbers of platelets by 20%, would be more haemostatically effective?

Shreiner: It is especially hard to document significant increases in platelet numbers in rodents. The platelet count of a rabbit can vary by as much as 200 000/mm³ from one day to the next. The platelet count is unreliable as a measurement of platelet production. The platelet count depends also on the rate of removal of platelets from the circulation. The isotope incorporation into platelets seems to be more constant than the platelet count.

Stohlman: Which is the critical feature haemostatically—size, numbers or both?

Shreiner: Young platelets are more effective haemostatically than old platelets (Shulman *et al.* 1968; Karpatkin 1969; Johnson *et al.* 1971). Amorosi *et al.* (1971) and Minter & Ingram (1971) have shown that young platelets are larger and more dense than old platelets. Therefore, an increase in platelet size or an increase in total platelet mass would suggest a greater proportion of young, haemostatically more effective platelets. The absolute numbers of platelets would seem to be less critical.

Metcalf: I suppose it is a truism to say that what the megakaryocyte field needs is a good *in vitro* megakaryocyte cloning technique to solve some of these problems. Two separate processes may be going on independently—cellular proliferation and cytoplasmic maturation with the production of platelets. Nakeff & Dicke (1972) reported that megakaryocytes could proliferate in thin layer agar cultures and that this proliferation was stimulated by thrombocytopenic serum. What progress has been made with this work, Dr Dicke?

Dicke: No more progress has been made since then.

Stohlman: All the megakaryocytes you showed were stage III, Dr Dicke. It was rather early in culture and this could be a maturing phenomenon rather than a proliferating phenomenon.

Dicke: Stage I megakaryocytes have also been observed. However, Dr Nakeff never detected dividing megakaryocytes.

Lajtha: Didn't Shirley Ebbe and also Ted Odell find essentially a shift in the maturation pattern rather than in number?

Stohlman: Stimulated animals show an increase in the rate of transit and an increase in the size of megakaryocytes in the bone marrow. In spite of what Dr Shreiner has said, I am not sure that Harker's method (1970) is a good way to quantify the megakaryocytes of a bone marrow.

Shreiner: Harker (1968) has reported an increase in the number of megakaryocytes as well as an increase in size in response to thrombocytopenia.

Winterhalter: I agree that one should check for *de novo* protein synthesis in other cellular components, but I do not think you can say it is just injection of gunk, because surely the normal plasma did the same thing as the saline, namely nothing. So plasma is actually a huge heap of gunk, if you want to look at it that way, and just one additional and specialized bit of gunk present in the stimulating plasma then does the trick.

There is a special beauty in the fact that you can do something like platelet kinetics, since presumably you only label the youngest elements in the bone marrow. If you really want to find out whether younger platelets are stickier than older ones you could do it this way. This is a very promising system.

Yoffey: What do you think is the life of a megakaryocyte in bone marrow?

Shreiner: In rats, rabbits and mice it is approximately three days. In human beings it is not precisely known, but it is estimated to be five to six days.

Hudson: Do your experiments provide any evidence for a platelet releasing factor distinct from this stimulating factor?

Shreiner: We measure the rate of appearance and maximum levels of labelled platelets in the circulation. The isotope has been shown to label all stages of megakaryocytes. The maximum level of labelled platelets occurs three days after injection of the isotope and corresponds to the maturation time of three days for megakaryocytes. For that reason I think we are not merely measuring a releasing factor.

Winterhalter: Is the labelling pattern of the earliest labelled platelets that are released the same as the pattern at the peak? If you hit them just the day before they come out in the blood you may label a different protein than if you hit the youngest megakaryocytes.

Shreiner: It has not been studied in quite that manner. An initial labelling occurs in the first eight hours that is different from labelling that occurs at 24 hours and later. This transient binding to circulating platelets is of low degree and does not last very long. The ratio of labelled heavy platelets to labelled light platelets is greatest in the early stages of labelling and decreases with time (Amorosi *et al.* 1971). Differential labelling of platelet proteins with ^{75}Se-labelled methionine as a function of time has not been studied.

References

AMOROSI, E., GARG, S. K. & KARPATKIN, S. (1971) Heterogeneity of human platelets. IV. Identification of a young platelet population with (^{75}Se)selenomethionine. *Br. J. Haematol.* **21**, 227–232.
COOPER, G. W. (1970) The regulation of thrombopoiesis, in *Regulation of Hematopoiesis* (Gordon, A. S., ed.), vol. 2, pp. 1611–1629, Appleton-Century-Crofts, New York

HARKER, L. A. (1968) Kinetics of thrombopoiesis. *J. Clin. Invest.* **47**, 458–465

HARKER, L. A. (1970) Regulation of thrombopoiesis. *Am. J. Physiol.* **218**, 1376–1380

JOHNSON, C. A., ABILDGAARD, C. F. & SCHULMAN, I. (1971) Functional studies of young versus old platelets in a patient with chronic thrombocytopenia. *Blood J. Hematol.* **37**, 163–171

KARPATKIN, S. (1969) Heterogeneity of human platelets. II. Functional evidence suggestive of young and old platelets. *J. Clin. Invest.* **48**, 1083–1087

MINTER, F. M. & INGRAM, M. (1971) Platelet volume: density relationships in normal and acutely bled dogs. *Br. J. Haematol.* **20**, 55–68.

NAKEFF, A. & DICKE, K. A. (1972) Stem cell differentiation into megakaryocytes from mouse bone marrow cultured with the thin layer agar technique. *Exp. Hematol.* **22**, 58–60

PENINGTON, D. G. (1969) Assessment of platelet production with ^{75}Se-selenomethionine. *Br. Med. J.* **4**, 782–784

SHULMAN, N. R., WATKINS, S. P., JR., ITSCOITZ, S. B. & STUDENTS, A. B. (1968) Evidence that the spleen retains the youngest and hemostatically most effective platelets. *Trans. Assoc. Am. Physicians Phila.* **81**, 302–313

VAN DYKE, D. (1964) Response of monkeys to erythropoietin of rabbit, sheep, and human origin. *Proc. Soc. Exp. Biol. Med.* **116**, 171–174

VAN DYKE, D., LAWRENCE, J. H., POLLYCOVE, M. & LOWY, P. (1963) Preliminary results from the use of erythropoietin in human volunteers, in *Hormones and the Kidney* (*Mem. Soc. Endocrinol.*, No. 13; Williams, P. C., ed.), pp. 222–230, Academic Press, New York

Size and proliferation of stem cell compartments in mice after depression of erythropoiesis

B. KUBANEK, O. BOCK, W. HEIT, E. BOCK and E. B. HARRISS

Schwerpunktgruppe Hämatologie, Universität Ulm

Abstract Evidence is presented that a decreased demand for erythropoiesis is associated with a rise of the myeloid stem cell compartment of the total body. This would certainly agree with the concept that competition occurs between erythropoiesis and myelopoiesis. Neither the level at which this competition occurs nor the regulation mechanism involved can be defined from the results reported here. The changes seen in the different stem cell compartments after a single dose of hydroxyurea or [³H]thymidine suggest that the recovery of the more differentiated stem cell compartments has priority over the pluripotent compartment. However, it remains to be decided whether this is accomplished by a high capacity for self-replication on the part of the committed stem cells or by an increased influx from the pluripotent stem cell compartment or, as is more likely, by both mechanisms simultaneously. Results are presented which emphasize that serious limitations in the measurement of the erythropoietin-responsive cell and its proliferation rate arise from the long biological half-life of erythropoietin and the different kinds of damage inflicted on the stem cell compartments by different agents specific for the S phase and subsequent regeneration mechanisms.

Differentiated erythroid, myeloid and megakaryocytic cell compartments are not self-sustaining but are constantly fed from a precursor compartment. Although the morphological identity of the progenitor cells has not yet been established with certainty, there are functional differences which allow a distinction to be made between the colony-forming unit (CFU), which is assumed to be the pluripotent stem cell, and subsequent 'stem cells' which seem to be already committed to a specific pathway of differentiation. In normal steady state conditions the pluripotent stem cells are to a large extent resting (G0) (Becker *et al.* 1965), whereas experimental evidence (Stohlman *et al.* 1968; Lajtha *et al.* 1969) shows that one of their progeny, the erythropoietin-responsive cell (ERC), is in cycle even when erythropoiesis is suppressed. However, estimates of the proliferative state of ERCs differ considerably (Morse *et al.*

1970; Lajtha et al. 1969). Similar evidence has been presented for proliferation of the myeloid-committed stem cell, as detected by a culture assay on soft agar (Lajtha et al. 1969; Iscove et al. 1970).

It is the committed stem cell and not the pluripotent stem cell which is thought to be the target for specific humoral regulators of differentiated haemopoiesis. Of these humoral regulators only erythropoietin has been demonstrated with certainty. Its principal function is apparently to differentiate the committed stem cell into morphologically recognizable erythroid elements by initiating haemoglobin synthesis. Its influence on the pluripotent stem cell is less well defined. We (Kubanek et al. 1968) and others (Marsh et al. 1968) observed that mice receiving repeated doses of erythropoietin showed a significant increase in splenic pluripotent stem cells. Bone marrow CFU were either unaffected or showed a slight decrease. Migration from the bone marrow to the spleen was put forward as a tentative explanation in addition to a direct effect of erythropoietin on the stem cell. Shortly afterwards Rencricca et al. (1970) concluded, from experiments in which they studied the pattern of response after severe anaemia, that the increase in splenic CFU occurred predominantly, if not solely, from migration of CFU from the bone marrow. Thus, changes of splenic CFU are probably not due to a direct action of erythropoietin on the pluripotent stem cell but rather to migration of stem cells to an organ which possesses a more favourable micro-environment for red cell production and the capacity to expand more readily than the bone marrow.

Further experimental evidence that erythropoietin does not act directly on the CFU comes from the observation of Schooley (1966) that the doubling time of CFU in polycythaemic hosts is unaffected by the presence or absence of erythropoietin. However, it is evident from the observation of Rencricca et al. (1970) that a high demand for erythroid differentiation will eventually feed back to the stem cell level, since the turnover of femoral CFU was markedly increased several days after severe erythroid hyperplasia. The nature of the control mechanism regulating differentiation of pluripotent stem cells (CFU) after depletion of the committed compartment is unknown, but it seems to operate as a negative feedback mechanism.

On the other hand we (Shadduck et al. 1969) and others (Hurst et al. 1969) observed that after erythropoietin production had ceased in previously hypoxic mice, differentiation of erythropoietin-sensitive cells decreased and there was a moderate rebound of the CFU. Several observations indicate that the decreased demand for erythropoiesis noted after a plethoric state has been established is followed after prolonged plethora by an increase of agar colony-forming units (ACU) (Bradley et al. 1967) and CFU (Schooley 1969). However, the kinetics of these changes and the interrelationship between these functionally distinguishable compartments are poorly understood. Accordingly we measured at frequent intervals the size as well as the proliferation of CFU, ACU and the erythropoietin response in ex-hypoxic mice kept plethoric for five weeks by transfusions of homologous red cells. Several questions relevant to this issue and to problems of estimating the proliferative state of these various populations of stem cells will be discussed in the light of available experimental evidence and new observations reported here.

STEM CELL COMPARTMENTS DURING PROLONGED PLETHORA

The femoral and splenic contents of CFU were measured as described previously (Kubanek et al. 1968). The ACU were estimated by a modified method of Bradley & Metcalf (1966). We will use the term ERC in this paper for the erythroid response to a standard dose of erythropoietin measured by a 48-hour incorporation of ^{59}Fe in the peripheral blood, although we are aware that this method gives only indirect information about the erythropoietin-responsive stem cell compartment. The fraction of cells in DNA synthesis should indicate whether changes in the various cell compartments are caused to some extent by alterations in the turnover state of these populations. We therefore estimated the proportion of cells in S phase, using the method of Morse et al. (1970), injecting a high dose of hydroxyurea two hours before assaying CFU and ACU or injecting the erythropoietin. The details are given in the second part of this paper.

Fig. 1 shows that the ERC decreases over the first ten days after hypoxia and remains at this level throughout the experiment. Estimates of the proliferative state of the ERC compartment—interpreted with all the caution necessary, as will be demonstrated later—reveal that about the same proportion of cells are in DNA synthesis from day 5 onwards, throughout the experiment. The numbers of femoral ACU are below normal on day 0 after hypoxia, then they increase above the normal control level and remain high throughout the experiment. The femoral content of CFU is always slightly higher than immediately after the mice are returned to ambient pressure but is not different from that of normal controls, although there is some fluctuation, and there is a fairly high proliferation rate (27% in S phase). The splenic ACU are high above the normal controls on return to atmospheric pressure and with some variations they remain at this level until they exhibit a further rise after the 20th day of plethora. There are about three times as many as in the normal controls, with a high rate of turnover (48% in S phase) immediately after hypoxia; the numbers and proliferation rate decline about proportionately to the fall of nucleated cell counts up to the tenth day. A late rise of the splenic CFU with a concomitant increase

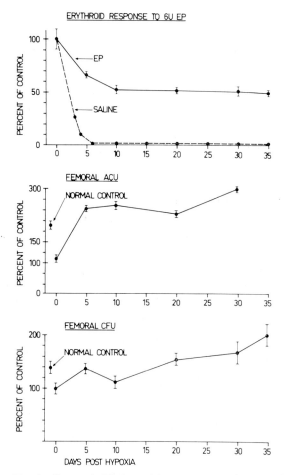

Fig. 1. Changes in ERC, total femoral CFU and ACU expressed as % of the values on day 0 after hypoxia. The animals were kept plethoric by hypertransfusions (vertical bars represent s.e.m.). EP: erythropoietin

in proliferation was observed at the 30th day. We can therefore summarize the experimental findings as follows: (1) A decreased demand for erythroid differentiation is followed by a reduction of the ERC compartment with no measurable change in the proliferation rate; (2) This decline in erythropoietin responsiveness is associated with an increase in the total content of ACU in the body and a slight increase in CFU; (3) There is an unexpected late rise of ACU and CFU in the spleen, with a concomitant increase in proliferation rate of the splenic CFU.

The question arising from these observations on the fate of the erythropoietin-sensitive cell during prolonged plethora is whether a true commitment to erythroid differentiation alone is acquired with the first step of differentiation from the pluripotent stem cell—especially when the ERC continue to proliferate, albeit more slowly, owing to a prolonged G1, as postulated by Kretschmar (1966) and shown experimentally by Morse et al. (1970). In polycythaemic animals transplanted with bone marrow the ERC compartment develops in the absence of erythropoietin (Bleiberg et al. 1965) but only to a certain size (O'Grady & Lewis 1970). Optimum restoration of this compartment under such conditions requires continual stimulation by erythropoietin (Kubanek 1972). This is in accord with the hypothesis that proliferation is slower in the absence of erythropoietin. However, even with a maximally prolonged generation time of about 30 hours for the ERC, as estimated by Morse et al. (1970), and a constant rate of differentiation from the pluripotent compartment, one would expect the ERC to accumulate after prolonged plethora.

Our experimental evidence suggests that the erythropoietin-sensitive cells are not in a resting state after prolonged plethora. In spite of this, even long after differentiation into the recognizable erythropoietic cells has stopped, erythropoietin-responsive cells tend to decrease rather than accumulate. At the moment therefore, one can only speculate about the control mechanisms regulating the size of the ERC compartment. A death function in this compartment, proposed by Stohlman et al. (1968), is a possible mechanism but is difficult to envisage teleologically. Dedifferentiation of the committed stem cells seems unlikely. An alternative possibility was put forward by Schooley (1969), who suggested from similar observations that when differentiation of the ERC ceased, decreased differentiation of CFU into the ERC compartment might result, with a consequent increase in size of the CFU compartment. This increase would be only moderate when there is simultaneously an enhanced differentiation into the committed myeloid stem cell compartment. Such a mechanism seems possible in view of the sustained increase in the total body content of ACU during the plethoric state reported here and previously observed by Bradley et al. (1967) at a single point in time after hypertransfusion. On the other hand a reduction in femoral ACU was observed when a higher demand for erythroid differentiation was induced by bleeding (Bradley et al. 1967; Metcalf 1969) or after stimulation with erythropoietin (Rickard et al. 1971).

Also relevant to this question is the observation of Morley et al. (1970) that the severity of neutropenia in irradiated mice with one leg shielded was less in polycythaemic than in normal mice, and that myelopoiesis appeared to recover earlier. These findings suggest a competition for stem cells (Hellman et al. 1970) which presumably occurs at the level of differentiation from the pluripotent stem cell compartment. However, one could also speculate that there is a flux from the 'committed' myeloid to the 'committed' erythroid stem cell compartment, and vice versa, following different demands for one or the other. This concept would certainly be against a strict commitment and the question arises of whether there is an age structure in the committed compartment in which cells step by step acquire a higher sensitivity to a specific humoral regulator, while losing their capacity for self-replication and movement into another line of differentiation. An age structure of this nature would certainly imply that there are a number of subpopulations of proliferating stem cells which cannot be distinguished with the current rather crude functional tests.

An unexpected finding was the late increase in splenic ACU and CFU, with a high proliferation rate of the latter. One possibility which has to be considered is that a change in splenic architecture and environment, caused by the prolonged hypertransfusion and increased destruction of red cells, might lead to more migrating stem cells being captured, rather than to physiological homeostasis. In this connection it is noteworthy that a short-term hypertransfusion does not change plating efficiency (Schooley 1966). However, a change in 'plating efficiency' alone would not explain the higher turnover state of CFU. One could speculate that a change in the local environment or repeated transfusions of homologous red cells stimulated the proliferation rate of CFU, as has been shown for a number of factors (McCulloch & Till 1970; Monette *et al.*, 1972). But it then remains to be determined why this occurs 20 days after the first injection of washed homologous red cells and not earlier.

KINETICS OF THE DIFFERENT STEM CELL COMPARTMENTS AFTER ADMINISTRATION OF HYDROXYUREA OR [³H]THYMIDINE

The different estimates of the proliferative state of the ERC obtained with hydroxyurea and with tritiated thymidine *in vivo* led us to study the kinetics of the different stem cell compartments after treatment with these two agents, which seem to be the only ones useful for selectively killing cells in S phase. Tritiated thymidine will kill cells in DNA synthesis when given in lethal doses either *in vitro* (Becker *et al.* 1965) or *in vivo* (Smith *et al.* 1962; Lajtha *et al.* 1969). Hydroxyurea has a selective lethal effect on haemopoietic cells in DNA synthesis when administered *in vivo* (Morse *et al.* 1970). Moreover hydroxyurea has a very short $T^1/_2$ of 13 minutes in the mouse; it slows down progression of cells from G1 into the S phase and is therefore killing only those cells that are in S phase at the time of administration (Rajewsky *et al.* 1971).

Much information is available on the proliferative state of the various functionally different stem cells. Table 1 summarizes some of the data obtained

TABLE 1

Percentages of the different stem cell compartments in DNA synthesis 2 hours after the injection into mice of a single dose of hydroxyurea (HU) or [^{3}H]thymidine (^{3}H-TdR)

	CFU (%)		ACU (%)		ERC (%)	
	^{3}H-TdR	HU	^{3}H-TdR	HU	^{3}H-TdR	HU
Lajtha et al. (1969)	∼ 10	—	45	—	76*	—
Morse et al. (1970); Stohlman (1972)	—	10–20	—	30–50	—	∼ 20*
Bock, Heit and Kubanek (unpublished)	10–20*	10–20*	∼ 35*	∼ 35*	70–75*	∼ 20*

*   Polycythaemic mice

when hydroxyurea or [^{3}H]thymidine were used *in vivo*. One can conclude that the immediate precursor of the pronormoblast is in cycle, but the estimates of its proliferative state vary considerably. When plethoric rodents with erythroid hypoplasia are labelled with a flash dose of tritiated thymidine and subsequently stimulated with erythropoietin, 40–60% of the emerging pronormoblasts are labelled (Stohlman *et al.* 1968). However, the erythroid response measured by incorporation of ^{59}Fe in the peripheral blood is reduced by as much as 75% when a suicidal dose of [^{3}H]thymidine (0.8 mCi) is injected under similar experimental conditions. In contrast, Morse *et al.* (1970) reported only a 20% reduction in the erythroid response in the polycythaemic mouse after hydroxyurea, both when hydroxyurea and erythropoietin were given simultaneously and when erythropoietin was given four hours after hydroxyurea. It was implied that this reduction was due to the death, presumably in DNA synthesis, of a population of cells responding to erythropoietin. Morse *et al.* (1970) concluded that the generation time of the erythropoietin-sensitive stem cell compartment is about 30 hours when there is no demand for erythropoiesis. On the other hand Lajtha *et al.* (1969) infer from the killing effect of [^{3}H]thymidine *in vivo* that the erythropoietin-sensitive cell is in a rapid state of turnover even when there is no demand for erythropoiesis. It should perhaps be noted that, *in vivo*, the killing agents hydroxyurea and tritiated thymidine gave similar results when used on a similar time schedule for measuring the proliferative state of CFU or ACU.

These findings raise the question of whether experimental results obtained with these S-phase-specific agents are comparable, particularly when more than a few hours have elapsed between administration of the agent and measurement of the size of the stem cell compartment, since later effects may be indirect rather than direct. This is particularly valid for the erythropoietin-sensitive cell for which we have no appropriate *in vitro* assay. Repair mechanisms, recruit-

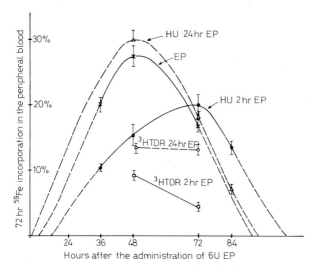

FIG. 2. Erythropoietic response expressed as % of ^{59}Fe injected intravenously 72 hours before the animal was killed. Erythropoietin was given either alone (EP), or 2 h after [^{3}H]thymidine (^{3}H-TdR 2 hr EP) or hydroxyurea (HU 2 hr EP), or 24 hours after thymidine (^{3}H-TdR 24 hr EP) or hydroxyurea (HU 24 hr EP) (vertical bars represent S.E.M.).

ment due to the relatively long half-life of erythropoietin, and further damage due to reutilization of [^{3}H]thymidine may influence the erythropoietic response measured some days later. Attempts were therefore made to compare the erythroid response, in the polycythaemic mouse, to a standard dose of erythropoietin given after hydroxyurea or [^{3}H]thymidine. Six units of erythropoietin injected into a plethoric mouse produced the well-known bell-shaped response curve (Fig. 2) with a maximum at 48 hours and a decline thereafter, as measured by incorporation of ^{59}Fe in the peripheral blood (^{59}Fe was injected intravenously 72 hours before the animal was killed). When hydroxyurea was given two hours before erythropoietin, the maximum response was shifted to 72 hours and was only 70% of that in the group treated with erythropoietin only (80% when a number of experiments were pooled). Hydroxyurea given 24 hours before erythropoietin produced no significant change in the erythroid response from that seen in the group treated with erythropoietin alone, but there was a suggestion of an overshoot in most experiments. These data would suggest that recovery from injury inflicted on the ERC by hydroxyurea is fast, as previously observed (Morse *et al.* 1970). The reduction of the erythroid response after an *in vivo* dose of [^{3}H]thymidine to about 30% of the response in controls was more severe than with hydroxyurea and showed only a slight recovery after 24 hours.

The discrepancy between the estimates of the proliferative state of the ERC

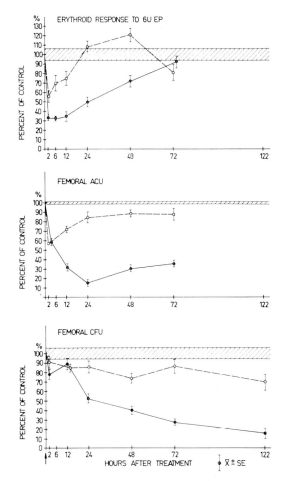

Fig. 3. The effect of hydroxyurea (1 g/kg) (○—○) compared to that of [³H]thymidine (0.8 mCi/kg) (●—●) on the erythroid response and on the total femoral ACU and CFU of plethoric CBA mice, expressed as % of the non-treated plethoric control (vertical bars represent s.e.m.).

obtained with [³H]thymidine and with hydroxyurea raises the question of whether the extensive decrease in the erythroid response seen 50 hours after the administration of [³H]thymidine is really a measure of the true proliferative state of the ERC compartment. It might be an artifact due to continuous damage inflicted on the precursor compartment and recognizable cell compartments by reutilization of tritiated thymidine. Femoral and splenic CFU and ACU and the response to a standard dose of erythropoietin in the polycythaemic mouse were therefore estimated as a function of time after a single dose of either 0.8 mCi

[³H]thymidine per mouse or 1 g hydroxyurea/kg.

Fig. 3 shows that after a single dose of thymidine the CFU content of the femur was reduced to about 80% of the control level up to the 12th hour. During the next 120 hours it decreased to less than 20% of the initial value. Splenic CFU tended to follow a similar pattern. After hydroxyurea the initial reduction in the femoral CFU was similar to that seen with tritiated thymidine, but afterwards no appreciable decrease was seen. The splenic CFU content after hydroxyurea revealed more variation but no definite pattern of fluctuation could be demonstrated, due to the limited times and short period of observation after injury. The small effect of hydroxyurea on the femoral CFU is at variance with the observations of Morse *et al.* (1970) on the polycythaemic mouse and with those of Vassort *et al.* (1971) on the normal mouse: both these groups see a significant decrease in femoral CFU after similar doses of hydroxyurea.

Preliminary data (Fig. 3) on the ACU in the femur show comparable initial reductions after [³H]thymidine and hydroxyurea (43% and 41%) but a different pattern thereafter. After the second hour a continuous rise of ACU occurs in the animals treated with hydroxyurea, whereas in the [³H]thymidine-treated group the lowest point of about 15% of the control is reached at 24 hours and a slow recovery seems to occur thereafter.

The erythroid response 48 hours after erythropoietin, given at various times after hydroxyurea or tritiated thymidine, was measured by the 72-hour ⁵⁹Fe incorporation in the peripheral blood. After hydroxyurea recovery was fast for the first 12 hours, with a slight overshoot lasting up to the 72nd hour. In contrast, after [³H]thymidine erythropoietin responsiveness recovered slowly and did not reach control values before 72 hours.

The unexpected severe decrease in CFU after a single dose of thymidine must be in part due to reutilization of DNA breakdown products from cells which were initially heavily labelled, particularly since only 10–20% of the CFU are sterilized by intranuclear [³H]thymidine after two hours; this dose of [³H]-thymidine is cleared from the plasma to trace levels within less than an hour and is either incorporated into DNA or appears as tritiated water equilibrating with the total body water of the animal (Steel 1962). It is well known that DNA break-down products are normally reutilized for DNA synthesis locally and system-ically (Feinendegen 1967). Ebbe & Stohlman (1964) inferred that the red cell nucleus is a probable source of reusable DNA components. Another source of catabolized nuclear material may originate in the ineffective cell production seen in the myeloid series (Maloney *et al.* 1963). Heininger *et al.* (1971) report a 40% reutilization but this work was done with tracer doses of [³H]thymidine and can only give limited information about reutilization after doses of thy-midine high enough to cause considerable cell death, phagocytosis and, subsequently, local reutilization in the haemopoietic organs. In addition Heininger *et al.* (1971) view the bone marrow merely as a closed system with respect to thymidine reutilization. In our experimental conditions, i.e. in the plethoric mouse, the bulk of reutilized labelled DNA is probably yielded from myeloid cells and megakaryocytes.

A further reason for the fall in CFU probably lies in a considerable loss through differentiation being caused by a high demand, since the committed erythroid and myeloid stem cell compartments are initially depleted and also suffer damage from reutilization of labelled DNA (see Fig. 3). Removal of CFU by differentiation will thus add to the loss that occurs through cells being sterilized by intranuclear irradiation with ^{3}H; it also explains the late decrease seen in the CFU compartment even though it is turning over rapidly. At this time recovery of the committed precursor compartments is already occurring.

One could therefore suggest that repopulation of the committed compartment has priority over the restoration of the pluripotent stem cell compartment which has a high rate of differentiation into the committed compartments. Relevant to this question may be the observation of Reissmann & Samorapoompichit (1970), who found that after the CFU had been eradicated with busulphan, erythropoiesis and myelopoiesis recovered without any measurable CFU being present.

Alternatively one might suggest that the committed compartments have a high ability for self-replication, particularly as Blackett (1967) observed that chronically irradiated rats exhibit a near-normal erythropoietic response even though the pluripotent stem cell compartment is severely reduced. However, this view seems to be highly hypothetical since the rate of influx from the pluripotent to the committed stem cell compartment under such conditions is not known.

The question therefore is, what is the real state of turnover of the ERC compartment? Because of the relatively long availability of erythropoietin one certainly underestimates the damage to the ERC caused by hydroxyurea with a short $T^1/_2$. This can be inferred from the data of Schooley (1965), who showed that the response to erythropoietin can be reduced by 85% if anti-erythropoietin is given six hours later. For this reason erythropoietin will be present at effective levels for some hours, whereas hydroxyurea falls rapidly to non-lethal levels; the shortening of G1 and the recruitment of pluripotent stem cells mean that the size of the erythropoietin-sensitive compartment will be overestimated when measured hours or days later, irrespective of whether numbers of absolute red cell precursors or reticulocytes or incorporation of ^{59}Fe are used as criteria. On the other hand, a high dose of [^{3}H]thymidine *in vivo* will overestimate the proliferative rate of the ERC compartment, since reutilization of tritiated compounds causes prolonged damage to the proliferating cell compartments. Probably a better estimate of the proliferation of the ERC is obtained from the labelling index after a flash label of [³H]thymidine in a plethoric mouse stimulated with a subsequent dose of erythropoietin, since less reutilization of the label will occur under such conditions. Available data on the labelling of the pronormoblasts in stimulated plethoric mice suggest that in the precursor compartment (ERC), 40–60% of the cells are in the S phase (Hanna 1967; Stohlman et al. 1968). On the other hand the persistence of a labelling index of approximately 60% in a myeloblast–promyelocyte compartment 24 hours after injection was taken as an indication of the proliferative state of the myeloid precursor compartment by Morley et al. (1971). Hence we would speculate that the ERC and ACU compartment may be in a similar state of proliferation. A distinction of the ACU and ERC compartment into two compartments, as postulated by Lajtha et al. (1969) on the basis of [³H]thymidine suicide data, seems to be unjustified in the light of our findings. A better appraisal of the proliferative activity of ERC under different conditions remains to be made by a direct method, probably an in vitro assay such as that of Stephenson & Axelrad (1971).

ACKNOWLEDGEMENTS

This work was supported in part by grants from the Bundesministerium für Bildung und Wissenschaft, Deutsche Forschungsgemeinschaft and Euratom (Contract No. 079-69-1 BIAC).

References

BECKER, A. J., McCULLOCH, E. A., SIMINOVITCH, L. & TILL, J. E. (1965) Blood J. Hematol. 26, 296

BLACKETT, N. M. (1967) Br. J. Haematol. 13, 915

BLEIBERG, J., LIRON, M. & FELDMAN, M. (1965) Transplantation 3, 706

BRADLEY, T. R. & METCALF, D. (1966) Aust. J. Exp. Biol. Med. Sci. 14, 287

BRADLEY, T. R., ROBINSON, W. & METCALF, D. (1967) Nature (Lond.) 214, 511

EBBE, S. & STOHLMAN, F., Jr. (1964) Proc. Soc. Exp. Biol. Med. 116, 971

FEINENDEGEN, L. E. (1967) in Tritium Labelled Molecules in Biology and Medicine, p. 267, Academic Press, London

HANNA, I. R. A. (1967) Nature (Lond.) 214, 355

HEININGER, H. J., FEINENDEGEN, L. E. & BÜRKI, K. (1971) Blood J. Hematol. 37, 340

HELLMAN, S., GRATE, H. E., CHAFFEY, J. T. & CARMEL, R. (1970) in Hemopoietic Cellular Proliferation (Stohlman, F., Jr., ed.), pp. 36–48, Grune & Stratton, New York

HURST, J. M., TURNER, M. S., YOFFEY, J. M. & LAJTHA, L. G. (1969) Blood J. Hematol. 33, 859

ISCOVE, N. N., TILL, J. E. & McCULLOCH, E. A. (1970) Proc. Soc. Exp. Biol. Med. 134, 33

KRETSCHMAR, A. L. (1966) Science (Wash. D.C.) 152, 367

KUBANEK, B. (1972) in Synthesis, Structure and Function of Hemoglobin (Martin, H. & Nowicki, L., ed.), p. 13, Lehmanns, München

KUBANEK, B., TYLER, W. S., FERRARI, L., PORCELLINI, A., HOWARD, D. E. & STOHLMAN, F., JR. (1968) *Proc. Soc. Exp. Biol. Med.* **127**, 770

LAJTHA, L. G., POZZI, L. V., SCHOFIELD, R. & FOX, M. (1969) *Cell Tissue Kinet.* **2**, 39

MALONEY, M. A., WEBER, C. L. & PATT, H. M. (1963) *Nature (Lond.)* **197**, 150

MARSH, J. C., BOGGS, R., CHERVENICK, P. A., CARTWRIGHT, G. E. & WINTROBE, M. M. (1968) *J. Cell. Physiol.* **71**, 65

McCULLOCH, E. A. & TILL, J. E. (1970) in *Hemopoietic Cellular Proliferation* (Stohlman, F. Jr., ed.), p. 15, Grune & Stratton, New York

METCALF, D. (1969) *Br. J. Haematol.* **16**, 397

MONETTE, F. C., MORSE, B. S., HOWARD, D. E., NISKANEN, E. & STOHLMAN, F., JR. (1972) *Cell Tissue Kinet.* **5**, 121

MORLEY, A., HOWARD, D. E., BENNET, B. & STOHLMAN, F., JR. (1970) *Br. J. Haematol.* **19**, 523

MORLEY, A., MONETTE, F. C., RIZZOLI, V., HOWARD, D. E. & STOHLMAN, F., JR. (1971) *Br. J. Haematol.* **20**, 637

MORSE, B., RENCRICCA, N. J. & STOHLMAN, F., JR. (1970) in *Hemopoietic Cellular Proliferation* (Stohlman, F., Jr. ed.), p. 160, Grune & Stratton, New York

O'GRADY, L. F. & LEWIS, J. P. (1970) *J. Lab. Clin. Med.* **76**, 445

RAJEWSKY, M. D., HULSER, D. F. & FEBRICIUS, E. (1971) *Z. Krebsforsch.* **76**, 266

REISSMANN, K. R. & SAMORAPOOMPICHIT, S. (1970) *Blood J. Hematol.* **36**, 287

RENCRICCA, N. J., RIZZOLI, V., HOWARD, D. E., DUFFY, P. & STOHLMAN, F., JR. (1970) *Blood J. Hematol.* **36**, 764

RICKARD, K. A., RENCRICCA, N. J., SHADDUCK, R. K., MONETTE, F. C., HOWARD, D. E., GARRITY, M. & STOHLMAN, F., JR. (1971) *Br. J. Haematol.* **21**, 537

SCHOOLEY, J. C. (1965) *Blood J. Hematol.* **25**, 795

SCHOOLEY, J. C. (1966) *J. Cell. Physiol.* **68**, 249

SCHOOLEY, J. C. (1969) in *Comparative Cellular and Species Radiosensitivity* (Bond, V. & Sugahara, T., ed.) p. 125, Igaku Shoin, Tokyo

SHADDUCK, R. K., KUBANEK, B., PORCELLINI, A., FERRARI, L., TYLER, W. S., HOWARD, D. E. & STOHLMAN, F., JR. (1969) *Blood J. Hematol.* **34**, 477

SMITH, W. W., BRECHER, G., STOHLMAN, F., JR. & CORNFIELD, J. (1962) *Radiat. Res.* **16**, 201

STEEL, G. G. (1962) in *Tritium in Physical and Biological Sciences*, vol. 2, International Atomic Energy Authority, Vienna

STEPHENSON, J. R. & AXELRAD, A. A. (1971) *Blood J. Hematol.* **37**, 417

STOHLMAN, F., JR. (1972) in *In Vitro Culture of Hemopoietic Cells* (Proceedings of a workshop/symposium held in Rijswijk, 1971) (van Bekkum, D. W. & Dicke, K. A., eds.), p. 109, Radiobiological Institute TNO, Rijswijk

STOHLMAN, F., JR., EBBE, S., MORSE, B. S., HOWARD, D. E. & DONOVAN, J. (1968) *Ann. N.Y. Acad. Sci.* **149**, 156

VASSORT, F., FRINDEL, E. & TUBIANA, M. (1971) *Cell Tissue Kinet.* **4**, 423

Discussion

Yoffey: In our studies on the effects of hypoxia, with quantitative marrow changes, the rise in the erythroid cells was nearly always associated with a fall in the myeloid cells (Harris *et al.* 1966; Yoffey *et al.* 1967, 1968). One possible explanation was stem cell competition. Another was the crowding out of myeloid cells into the bloodstream, but we never saw any evidence of neutrophilic leucocytosis. We did get a lymphocytosis, but not a neutrophilia.

The other side of the story seems to be that when one stimulates granulo-poiesis powerfully, for the first 24 hours there is a marked fall in proerythroblasts (Yoffey *et al.* 1964).

What interested me most were the variations in sensitivity to erythropoietin. When we studied the reactions of bone marrow at 3050 and 6100 m we also studied the spleen. At 3050 m hypoxia there was a significant increase in erythropoiesis. At 6100 m there was an even more marked increase in the erythroid population of the marrow, as one might expect. At the same time we got the expected result for reticulocyte grading. At 6100 m the myeloid fall is much greater than at 3050 m hypoxia. Again, there was no evidence of crowding out, so presumably the fall in myeloid cells would be due to a greater demand on stem cells for erythroid differentiation, leaving fewer available for myelopoiesis.

Another point of interest in these experiments was the differential response of the spleen at 3050 and 6100 m. At 3050 m no splenic erythropoiesis was evident, as shown by the failure of the spleen to gain weight, and confirmed by histologic-al examination. But at 6100 m there was massive splenic erythropoiesis, as shown both by the development of erythropoietic foci and by a tremendous in-crease in weight. If erythropoiesis is due in both cases to endogenous erythro-poietin, which must presumably be secreted even at 3050 m—to account for the increased marrow erythropoiesis—why doesn't it produce splenic erythropoiesis at 3050 m? Are there erythroid precursor cells with different degrees of sen-sitivity to erythropoietin in the spleen and bone marrow? Or is there migration of ERC (erythropoietin-reacting cells) to the spleen at 6100 but not 3050 m? Whatever the explanation, the distinction between the two groups is very striking.

In rebound erythropoiesis is undoubtedly depressed. If it is true that the ERC proliferate even in these depressed erythropoietic marrows then when one restimulates one would expect a more massive increase in erythropoiesis in this marrow than in normal marrow. Again, as I showed earlier, there was no in-crease, but in a rebound marrow stimulated by secondary hypoxia there was if anything a slightly diminished response: not only was it slower but also, when it finally reached its peak, it was a little less.

If the ERC turn over so rapidly, the only thing we can suggest is that somehow they must be discharged from the marrow. We have looked again and again for the alleged 'death' function, particularly since doing our ultrastructural studies, but have seen no indication of it whatever. If the ERC die, they do so without leaving anything which can be detected morphologically.

· In your graph of hypoxia (Fig. 1, p. 246) you show the agar colony-forming units (ACU) at one day, and the first increase at five days, Dr Kubanek. Is there a change between one and five days?

Kubanek: I would agree that it would be very important to study the interrelationship of the different compartments during the first few days but we just have not done it.

Hudson: There is one other difference, in the guinea pig, between the response at 3050 m and that at 6100 m of simulated altitude. At 6100 m, in severe hypoxia to which the animal cannot adapt, eosinophil granulocytes are present in increased numbers in the circulation while numbers in the marrow are decreased (Hudson *et al.* 1967). Strangely enough this seems to affect the eosinophils particularly (Grant & Hudson 1969: Sibley & Hudson 1970), although it also affects the other types of granulocyte.

Metcalf: The difference between the effects of hydroxyurea and tritiated thymidine is puzzling. How good is the evidence that hydroxyurea *in vivo* kills cells in the S phase, or permanently prevents their multiplication? Is it possible that these cells recover? I cannot think of an *in vivo* system where one can be 100% sure that all the cells have been killed. Other changes may happen. If you had damaged the gut in such a situation and so had an increased entry of microbial organisms, then you might get a secondary stimulation of the granulo-cytic compartment. Perhaps these experiments should be repeated in germ-free animals to see whether the difference persists.

Kubanek: One good piece of evidence for killing or permanent damage of cells is the substantial decrease of nucleated cells in the femur and spleen 12–24 hours after the injection of hydroxyurea even in the polycythaemic mice. Cell death can also be observed in bone marrow smears by a marked increase of degenerating cells and cell debris after the administration of hydroxyurea. Similar observations have been reported by Morse *et al.* (1969). Other evidence for cell death comes from unpublished experiments of our group in which the specific activity of [³H]thymidine-labelled bone marrow falls rapidly six hours after a flash label of [³H]thymidine followed by a high dose of hydroxyurea. It seems to be very unlikely that the recovery of the ACU is mainly caused by stimulation of granulopoiesis after the entry of bacteria through the gut damaged by hydroxyurea, since the ERC also recover earlier than after a suicidal dose of [³H]thymidine.

Stohlman: Morse showed that in normal bone marrow hydroxyurea kills DNA-synthesizing cells. There is a drop in the tritiated thymidine uptake to absolute zero, within minutes. Within an hour or two the DNA synthesis and thymidine uptake resume. I think one can demonstrate clear-cut death and clear-cut recovery within the time cycle that one would anticipate. It has also been extensively documented that tritiated thymidine is reutilized. We saw this with megakaryocytes. Heininger *et al.* (1971) in extensive studies compared iododeoxyuridine with tritiated thymidine. Iododeoxyuridine is not reutilized to anywhere near the extent that thymidine is. In most of our studies we used a two-hour period to determine whether the pluripotent cells were in cycle or not. The problems of gut injury, endotoxaemia and so on presumably would not affect the short-term kill.

Kubanek: One cannot compare studies of reutilization done with tracer doses of [^{3}H]thymidine, like those of Heininger *et al.* (1971), with ours, in which suicidal doses were used, since a far greater amount of [^{3}H]thymidine is available for reutilization due to a greater breakdown of cells. From Heininger's observations it appears that there is a substantial local reutilization in the bone marrow; the reutilized material is not tritiated thymidine but probably larger breakdown products of DNA.

Lajtha: Hydroxyurea is a general enzyme poison for various steps during DNA synthesis. It is also extremely sensitive to intracellular deoxyribonucleotide pools. The CFU cell type can be triggered into DNA synthesis within an hour with cyclic AMP or isoprenaline and we can measure how soon they are in S phase according to the criterion of [^{3}H]thymidine or hydroxyurea killing. [^{3}H]-Thymidine kills them off in about 30 minutes; with hydroxyurea they are not killed until two hours, that is not until the cells have used up some of their intracellular deoxyribonucleotide pools. If you provide extra deoxyribonucleotides in small amounts you can protect the cells against hydroxyurea. We do not know what the pools are in the erythropoietin-responsive cells, and we will not know until we have some *in vitro* tests. Also I do not think it is fair to talk nowadays of an ERC compartment. It is a heterogeneous population of cells with a stage (or stages) at which they are already committed, but they are not yet sensitive to erythropoietin. What the distribution of the cell cycle time is in the steady state in this pERC (potential ERC) population and in the final stage, which is already responsive to erythropoietin (the ERC 'proper'), we do not know. The 50% drop which you see, Dr Kubanek, and which we can confirm because we see the same thing, may well be the result of this last division, which is the erythropoietin-sensitive stage of this maturation process.

Kubanek: I used the term ERC for the erythroid response to a standard dose of erythropoietin and I hope I made it clear at the beginning of my paper that with this method we only obtain limited information about an erythropoietin-responsive stem cell compartment. But you are referring to an ERC and a pERC population, which means that one black box is divided into two. The erythroid committed compartment may well be a heterogeneous population which can be separated into several black boxes for the sake of building a better model than our current one, but we have very little experimental evidence for that.

Lajtha: That is why we cannot settle the argument but just point out the conceptual difficulties. It is not a homogeneous population. Therefore, any change in the inhomogeneity can produce this phenomenon. As far as reutilization is concerned, as you pointed out, it is not a low molecular weight reutiliza-tion; one can try to block it with cold thymidine and this will not make any difference. The reutilization—if any—has to be at the macromolecular level and would have to be very efficient indeed. There is no evidence for this in culture when prelabelled and unlabelled cells are kept together. The degree of reutiliza-tion in macromolecular terms, which would be required for killing, is almost a quarter of the total DNA equivalent per cell. Any 'reutilization' less than that will not kill the cells.

McCulloch: Do those who believe in stem cell competition consider it is occurring in a population of stem cells, or as a phenomenon that occurs during the expansion of a population derived from a single stem cell?

Yoffey: We do not know. Our evidence from quantitative studies on marrow is that when erythropoiesis is strongly stimulated, granulopoiesis seems to be depressed; and when granulopoiesis is strongly stimulated the more primitive erythropoietic stem cells are depressed, at any rate for a time. How one would interpret that over a 24- or 48-hour period, I do not know.

McCulloch: Studies of cells removed by so much differentiation from stem cells are not likely to bear on the problem.

Kubanek: I think competition occurs in a compartment not already com-mitted, at the stem cell level, but this is just speculation at the moment.

Lajtha: What Dr McCulloch is saying, I think, is that with a complex inter-locked population system, using stimuli and states which are anything but physiological, we cannot justifiably say that we are measuring the composition of any particular population if we perform the measurement after 24 hours. That would be called 'soft' science.

Metcalf: Spleen colonies can be regarded as micropopulations in which one pathway of differentiation has been selectively permitted or encouraged. How-ever, the stem cells in such colonies remain multipotent, so intracolony differ-entiation does not appear to operate as far back as the stem cell—or, if so, some stem cells must escape commitment by this differentiating influence.

However at the level of the whole animal it seems to be possible to stimulate one pathway of differentiation at the expense of another. For example, Freund's complete adjuvant is a powerful stimulus for granulopoiesis and mice injected with Freund's adjuvant simultaneously become anaemic (McNeill 1970).

Astaldi: Antagonism between erythroid and granulocytic cell series certainly occurs after phenylhydrazine, but there are other conditions which may change the orientation of stem cells. I wonder if there are immune reactions which would implicate the lymphoid system in stem cell differentiation.

Yoffey: The spleen colony technique which has been devised by Till & McCulloch (1961) is very intriguing, but does it really represent what is going on in normal bone marrow? To take but one example, you have repeatedly emphasized the 'decline' phenomenon in CFU, Dr McCulloch. In the bone marrow, however, CFU are present throughout life. To explain this you surmised that colony-forming units in the marrow were in a 'protected' situation. We have tried, without success, to identify these 'protected' situations, although this of course does not prove that they do not exist.

McCulloch: CFU-S in the marrow are mostly in a state of rest; the same cells could persist from the first year of life to the 50th and never function in any way. They supply a huge reserve; presumably this reserve has survival value and functions during recovery after injury. Indeed, the irradiation experiments provide excellent evidence that CFU-S is the cell that is primarily responsible for repopulation of tissues after any kind of injury and particularly after irradiation.

Even though most of the CFU-S population is quiescent, they play an important role in normal haemopoietic function. Evidence in support of this view is obtained from studying mice with mutations that affect the function of CFU-S either intrinsically or extrinsically. In mice of genotype W/W^v (genetically determined defect intrinsic to CFU-S) and mice of genotype Sl/Sl^d (genetically determined defect extrinsic to CFU–S), there is severe macrocytic anaemia and increased sensitivity to radiation damage. It is doubtful that these sick animals would survive under any conditions except the protected environment of the laboratory. Thus, mutations that affect the function of CFU–S have a profound effect on haemopoiesis and these observations provide evidence that the population of CFU–S is essential for normal function.

Stohlman: Sometimes we use terms as a convenient handle. We refer to the CFU as 'a homogeneous compartment' and another term for a homogeneous compartment is 'committed compartment'. Stem cell competition is a convenient term that I use to indicate that the cells may differentiate along the granulocytic, the erythropoietic or the megakaryocytic pathways. If CFU from the bone marrow are transplanted into a lethally irradiated animal, there is less chance that they will go along the megakaryocytic pathway than if one uses CFU from the spleen. Why this should be I do not know. There must be something that adjudicates the priorities. Reissmann's data (Reissmann & Samorapoompichit 1970) indicate that after busulphan, which reduces the CFU to zero, one continues to have myelopoiesis and erythropoiesis, and neither erythropoietic nor myelopoietic stimuli affect the other cell line. Thus, there does not appear to be any competition at this level. On the other hand, if one irradiates a polycythaemic mouse with a hind leg shielded, more myeloid cells are produced than in a normal or non-polycythaemic animal. If the hosts are pretreated with cyclophosphamide, for example, as Hellman *et al.* (1970) have done, there is a better chance of getting a normal granulocytic colony than an erythropoietic colony. The term 'stem cell competition' as I use it embraces the priorities that must be sorted out, in a number of circumstances, before the stem cell goes one way or the other.

Rosse: There is much evidence now that lymphocytes are produced in extremely large numbers in the marrow, yet we find no colonies, either by the spleen colony assay or the *in vitro* assay, which produce lymphocytes. Can some *in vitro* erythroid colonies be regarded as lymphocyte producers rather than erythroblast producers? Why is there a lack of lymphocytic colonies when lymphocyte production is so marked in all animals—at least rodents—whose marrow produces erythroid, granulocytic and megakaryocytic colonies?

Thomas: While it is quite true that in sections many of the colonies established in the spleen, and in the medullary cavities (Fig. 7, p. 86), of a mouse radiation chimera appear to consist exclusively of erythroblasts or granulocytes or mega-karyocytes, cell suspensions prepared from spleen colonies always contain lymphocytes and transitional cells, which can be detected in smears. The absence of colonies which are composed predominantly of lymphocytes may reflect the relatively late restoration of most lymphocyte populations (Fig. 1*a*, *b*, p. 76). The time scale for restoration of erythroblast and granulocyte populations is quite different from that for restoration of most lymphocyte populations. By the time the lymphocyte population of the murine spleen is restored it is too late for discrete, isolated colonies of any variety to persist in the spleen.

Rosse: What about the *in vitro* system?

Thomas: I don't know.

Kubanek: Dr McCulloch, do you think there is a fixed rate of differentiation of stem cells into the granulopoietic or erythropoietic progenitor pools, as you proposed in your stochastic model (Till *et al.* 1964) which does not change in any circumstances?

McCulloch: That model (Till *et al.* 1964) did not suggest that rates of differentiation did not change but rather that a choice between renewal and differentiation occurred at random with fixed probabilities. These probabilities could change and such a change could lead to a different pattern of differentiation at the level of the whole haemopoietic population. I have yet to see any evidence that disproves this view.

Harris: Is it true to say that a man is as old as his marrow CFU!?

McCulloch: No.

Harris: I thought you said that the CFU could live for 50 years.

McCulloch: CFU may remain latent for 50 years and there is good evidence for this in man. In irradiation accidents, radiation-induced abnormalities have been seen many years after the irradiation. However, there is no evidence that function of haemopoietic stem cells is depleted over the normal lifespan of a man and hence their properties are not obviously related to the normal processes of ageing.

Yoffey: Would you equate those cells with normal healthy cells? The radiation damage, while not completely destroying the cell's capacity to enter into mitosis, given a powerful stimulus, may nevertheless interfere with its normal developmental capacities.

McCulloch: I know of no evidence that bears on human stem cells. However, in the mouse colonies derived from irradiated cell populations they appear to be physiologically normal.

References

GRANT, J. B. F. & HUDSON, G. (1969) A quantitative study of blood and bone marrow eosinophils in severe hypoxia. *Br. J. Haematol.* **17**, 121–127

HARRIS, P. F., HARRIS, R. S. & KUGLER, J. H. (1966) Studies of the leucocyte compartment of guinea pig bone marrow after acute haemorrhage and severe hypoxia. Evidence for a common stem cell. *Br. J. Haematol.* **12**, 419–432

HEININGER, H. J., FEINENDEGEN, L. E. & BÜRKI, K. (1971) *Blood J. Hematol.* **37**, 340

HELLMAN, S., GRATE, H. E., CHAFFEY, J. T. & CARMEL, R. (1970) Hematopoietic stem cell compartment: patterns of differentiation following radiation or cyclophosphamide, in *Hemopoietic Cellular Proliferation* (Stohlman, F., Jr., ed.), p. 36, Grune & Stratton, New York

HUDSON, G., SMITH, N. C. W., WILSON, R. S. & YOFFEY, J. M. (1967). Eosinophil granulocytes and hypoxia. *Nature (Lond.)* **213**, 818–819

MCNEILL, T. A. (1970). Antigenic stimulation of bone marrow colony-forming cells. III: Effect *in vivo. Immunology* **18**, 61–72

MORSE, B., RENCRICCA, N. J. & STOHLMAN, F., JR. (1969) *Proc. Soc. Exp. Biol. Med.* **130**, 986

REISSMANN, K. R. & SAMORAPOOMPICHIT, S. (1970) Effect of erythropoietin on proliferation of erythroid stem cells in the absence of transplantable colony-forming units. *Blood J. Hematol.* **36**, 287

SIBLEY, Y. D. L., & HUDSON, G. (1970). Eosinophil leucocytes and recovery from severe hypoxia. *Acta Haematol. (Basel)* **43**, 31–39

TILL, J. E. & MCCULLOCH, E. A. (1961) A direct measurement of the radiation sensitivity of mouse bone marrow cells. *Radiat. Res.* **14**, 213–222

TILL, J. E., MCCULLOCH, E. A. & SIMINOVITCH, L. (1964) A stochastic model of stem cell proliferation, based on the growth of spleen colony forming cells. *Proc. Natl Acad. Sci. U.S.A.* **51**, 29

YOFFEY, J. M., MAKIN, G. S., YATES, A. K., DAVIS, C. J. F., GRIFFITHS, D. A. & WARING, I. S. (1964) The discharge of granulocytes from guinea-pig bone marrow in response to intravenous T. A. B. vaccine: a quantitative study. *Ann. N. Y. Acad. Sci.* **113**, 790–799

YOFFEY, J. M., SMITH, N. C. W. & WILSON, R. S. (1967) Studies on hypoxia. V. Changes in the bone marrow during hypoxia at 10 000 and 20 000 feet. *Scand. J. Haematol.* **4**, 145–157

YOFFEY, J. M., JEFFREYS, R. V., OSMOND, D. G., TURNER, M. S., TAHSIN, S. C. & NIVEN, P. A. R. (1968) Studies on hypoxia. VI. Changes in lymphocytes and transitional cells in the marrow during the intensification of primary hypoxia and rebound. *Ann. N. Y. Acad. Sci.* **149**, 179–192

Effects of anaemia on DNA-synthesizing cells in peripheral blood and observations on their origin

P. F. HARRIS

Department of Human Morphology, The Medical School, University of Nottingham

Abstract Prolonged and severe anaemia results in increased levels of unusual forms of DNA-synthesizing mononuclear cells in the peripheral blood. Their increase is phasic, with an initial peak on the fifth day, when the anaemia is maximal, and a later peak at 15 days.

The mononuclear cells are a heterogeneous population. There are three basic types: type 1 have the morphology of blast cells, type 2 resemble transitional cells of the bone marrow and type 3 resemble early forms of monocyte. The ratio of the three types is 1.5: 1.5: 1, transitional cells and blasts forming 75% of the total. Flash-labelling with [³H]thymidine shows that all three types are capable of DNA synthesis but that they have different turnover rates. The highest incidence of labelling is in the transitional cell group (35%), the next highest in the blasts (25%), and the lowest in the monocytic group (10%).

There is strong evidence that the mononuclear cells originate in the bone marrow. The pattern of their increase closely parallels that of other cells which also increase in the blood during the anaemia but are normally confined to the marrow or present only in very low numbers in the blood. There is evidence that some of the atypical mononuclears may actually divide as they circulate in the blood.

Anaemia can be added to an already established list of circumstances in which DNA-synthesizing cells increase in the peripheral blood. A common factor in all these circumstances is an increased stress on stem cells. The DNA-synthesizing cells in the blood may represent a postnatal migration stream of stem cells which is boosted during haemopoietic stress to counteract cellular depletion in lympho-reticular tissues or to extend haemopoiesis into sites which are normally inactive. Thus, during the anaemia there was evidence of extensive lymphocyte depletion in the thymus and a lymphocytosis during the anaemia was prevented by previous thymectomy. Moreover, a tenfold increase in splenic weight was associated with extensive extramedullary erythropoiesis.

Although the presence of cellular elements in the blood has been known for about 300 years (Swammerdam 1665; Leeuwenhoek 1669), white cells in the peripheral blood were regarded until very recently as the final phase in a process of birth and maturation which starts in the bone marrow and culminates in the discharge of mature or nearly mature cells into the bloodstream. Stem cells were thought to be confined to haemopoietic organs except in certain pathological conditions.

Recent advances in experimental haematology have shown that any consideration of haemopoietic stem cells must now recognize that there is a haemic phase for some of these cells. This phase, which is present before birth and continues afterwards, is an example of a cell migration stream which has great functional and clinical implications.

The development and use of thermonuclear weapons during the Second World War provoked research on a massive scale to study the effects of X-irradiation and ways of ameliorating its damage in tissues. It was this research, and the research which it later generated, that has led to our present knowledge and complete reappraisal of the more dynamic aspects of nucleated cells in the peripheral blood. In retrospect, our current understanding of the potentialities of cells in peripheral blood evolved from four groups of experiments. Firstly, early attempts to correct the leucopenia associated with irradiation included the transfusion of whole blood or leucocyte-rich fractions into severely irradiated animals (Brecher et al. 1953; Cronkite & Brecher 1955; Congdon et al. 1952, 1956). Slight improvements in mortality rates were noted but these were usually attributed to the protective phagocytic functions of the transfused leucocytes in combating infections which complicate post-irradiation leucopenia. At that time it was not thought that transfused blood cells might include cells capable of repopulating depleted marrow. It is hardly surprising that marrow transfusions soon replaced transfusions of blood leucocytes in attempts to protect against irradiation injury and many such experiments were performed.

In the second group of experiments haemopoietic tissue, either spleen or bone marrow, was shielded while the remainder of the body was lethally irradiated. This effectively increased the chances of survival and hastened recovery even when the shielded tissue was itself subsequently destroyed by irradiation. Of the possible ways by which shielding might protect, one interpretation was that haemopoietic cells derived from shielded spleen or marrow might be repopulating the depleted tissues by migrating into them from the bloodstream (Jacobson et al. 1949, 1950, 1951; Gershon-Cohen et al. 1951; Storer et al. 1952; Kaplan & Brown 1952).

A third and vital finding was that even in normal circumstances a small group of cells within the leucocytic fraction are actually synthesizing DNA as they circulate in the blood. This was shown by labelling with [³H]thymidine and morphologically they were found to be a heterogeneous group (Bond et al. 1959). These cells have a distinctive morphology and must have been seen by the earlier haematologists but, like the 'drumstick' neutrophil, their significance was not realized until much later. They may have been termed 'atypical cells'. The development of autoradiography had to come before their significance could be appreciated.

The final group of experiments contributing to our current knowledge of certain blood leucocytes followed logically from the discovery of DNA-synthesizing cells in the blood, with its implications of proliferative potential. The functional potentialities of these cells were tested in various laboratories. Blood leucocyte transfusions were found to protect successfully against lethal whole body X-irradiation (Merwin 1959; Popp 1960; Goodman & Hodgson 1962; Malinin et al. 1965) and produce repopulation of myeloid and lymphoid tissues, indicating that at least some of these cells are multipotent stem cells. Further refinements have included the quantitative assay of stem cells in the peripheral blood with the splenic colonization techniques pioneered by Mc-Culloch and Till (Cole 1963; Barnes & Loutit 1967a).

What is the origin of these stem cells which circulate in the peripheral blood, and how are they released into it? Do their levels ever vary? What are their identities and what is their functional significance? We already have answers to some of these questions and in the experiments to be described I hope to add a little more information to this subject.

EXPERIMENTS

An experiment was designed to investigate the effects of a massive and prolonged demand for erythropoiesis on populations of bone marrow cells and blood leucocytes, with special reference to the appearance of early forms of nucleated cells in the peripheral blood.

Severe anaemia was produced by repeated injections of phenylhydrazine and was maintained for two weeks in young male albino guinea pigs. Full cytological surveillance of blood cells was made before, and at regular intervals during, the anaemia. The experimental details have been published elsewhere (Harris & Kugler 1971). By adjusting the doses of phenylhydrazine the red cell count was kept in the range $1.5–2.0 \times 10^6$ (Fig. 1). To detect DNA-synthesizing cells circulating in the blood the technique of 'flash'-labelling with [³H]thymidine was employed. Blood smears were processed using a stripping-film technique of autoradiography. All counts of white cells in blood smears and of cells in the autoradiographs were made using an oil-immersion objective at a magnification of $\times$ 1200. In addition the maximum diameters of any unusual forms of nucleated cells observed during the counts were measured with a micrometer eyepiece.

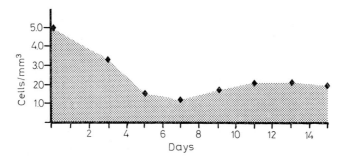

FIG. 1. RBC levels in peripheral blood during phenylhydrazine-induced anaemia (data of Harris & Kugler 1971).

FINDINGS

Quantitative studies

Increased levels of unusual forms of mononuclear cells were noted in the peripheral blood soon after the onset of the anaemia, and persisted throughout the experiment. The pattern of the increase is very distinctive (Fig. 2) and may provide the key to the origin of these cells (see below). Two peak levels were noted, the first on the fifth day (56 ± 16 cells/mm³ blood) and the second at the end of the experiment (72 ± 19 cells/mm³ blood). These peaks closely resemble the pattern of increase of DNA-synthesizing cells in the peripheral blood of X-irradiated dogs found by Bond *et al.* (1961).

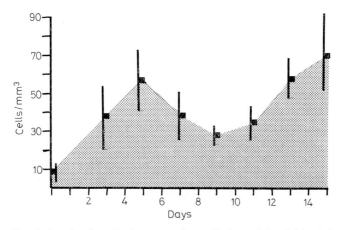

FIG. 2. Levels of atypical mononuclear cells in peripheral blood during phenylhydrazine-induced anaemia (data of Harris & Kugler 1971).

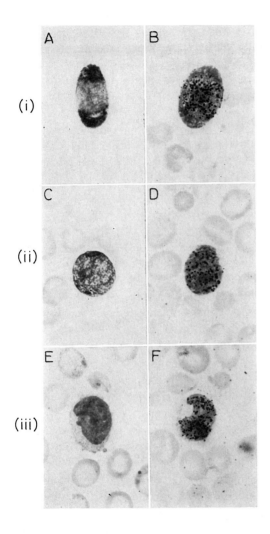

FIG. 3. (i) *Blast cells*, peripheral blood
   Cell A: MacNeal's tetrachrome × 900
   Cell B: labelled with [³H]thymidine; MacNeal's tetrachrome × 900
   (ii) *Transitional cells*, peripheral blood
   Cell C.   MacNeal's tetrachrome × 900
   Cell D: labelled with [³H]thymidine; MacNeal's tetrachrome × 900
   (iii) *Monocytoid cells*, peripheral blood
   Cell E: MacNeal's tetrachrome × 900
   Cell F: labelled with [³H]thymidine; MacNeal's tetrachrome × 900
   (From Harris & Kugler 1971, *J. Anat.*)

Qualitative studies

Morphologically, the mononuclear cells are a heterogeneous group. In general they accord with the description of DNA-synthesizing cells in the peripheral blood of other species (Bond *et al*. 1959, 1961). There are three basic types, each of which is able to incorporate [³H]thymidine actively into its DNA.

Type 1: Blast cells. These are large cells with an average diameter of 16 μm (range 12–20 μm). Their shape is round or oval and they have deeply basophilic cytoplasm. This may be restricted to the poles of the cell or form a complete rim around the nucleus (Fig. 3). The nuclear chromatin varies in appearance: in some it is clumped but in others it is more leptochromatic. About 25% of these cells are labelled after a single intravenous pulse of [³H]thymidine.

Type 2: Transitional cells. These cells are smaller than the blasts, the average diameter being approximately 13 μm (range 11–19 μm). They are round or oval and, like transitional cells in bone marrow, have an extremely high nuclear : cytoplasmic ratio (Fig. 3). Cytoplasm is usually minimal, forming a very thin rim around the nucleus or lying in a nuclear 'Hof'. The nuclear chromatin is typically leptochromatic. In blood smears prepared from one of the anaemic guinea pigs the actual pattern of the nuclear chromatin was recorded graphically using a Beckman recording spectrodensitometer. The nucleus of the transitional cell contrasts clearly with that of the lymphocyte (Fig. 4).

The incidence of labelling in these cells after a single [³H]thymidine injection is 35%.

Type 3: Monocytoid cells. These are large, oval cells (average diameter 15 μm, range 11–19 μm). The cytoplasm is pale and relatively abundant. Characteristically the nucleus has an irregular or folded contour (Fig. 3). After a single pulse of [³H]thymidine, 10% of these cells became labelled.

The relative proportions of the three types of cell, blast, transitional and monocytoid, is approximately 1.5 : 1.5 : 1. Thus, 75% of these unusual mononuclears are either blast or transitional cells.

DISCUSSION

The origin of atypical mononuclear cells in peripheral blood

Of the various organs which constitute the lymphoreticular system, several might release immature cells into the circulation—either through sinusoidal

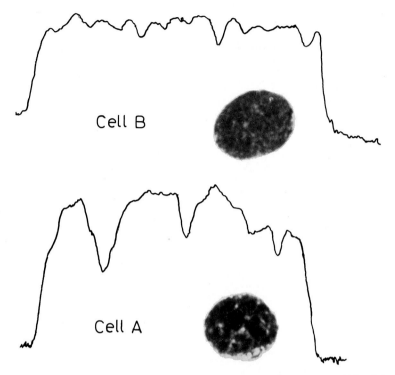

F‍IG. 4. Spectrodensitometer tracings of mononuclear cells in peripheral blood during phenyl-hydrazine-induced anaemia.   Cell A: lymphocyte.   Cell B: transitional cell.

walls, as in bone marrow and spleen, or through lymphatico-venous communications, particularly after antigenic stimulation.

The present experiments strongly support a myelogenous origin for the unusual mononuclears appearing in the blood during anaemia. Thus, increased levels of cells which are normally confined to the marrow or are present in the blood only in small numbers were noted during the anaemia, the pattern of their increase in the blood closely resembling that of the mononuclears (Fig. 5). These cells include polychromatic and basophilic erythroblasts, metamyelocytes, myelocytes and stab neutrophils. Moreover, eosinophilia and monocytosis developed during the anaemia and the peaks of these cells also coincide with the initial rise in mononuclears (Fig. 6).

A further indication of a myelogenous origin is that a substantial proportion of the unusual mononuclears are transitional cells. These are normally resident in the marrow and it is here that they have been particularly studied (Harris *et al.* 1966; Rosse & Yoffey 1967; Yoffey 1970).

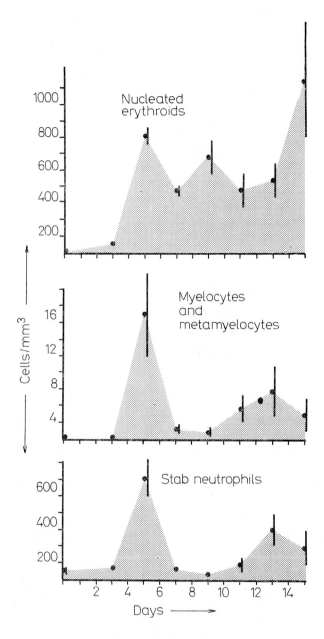

Fɪɢ. 5. Levels of nucleated erythroid cells, myelocytes, metamyelocytes and stab neutrophils in peripheral blood during phenylhydrazine-induced anaemia (from data of Harris & Kugler 1971).

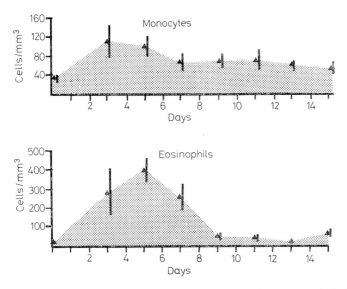

FIG. 6. Levels of eosinophils and monocytes in peripheral blood during phenylhydrazine-induced anaemia.

Mechanism of the increase

One interpretation of the pattern of increase of the DNA-synthesizing mononuclear cells in the blood is that it provides evidence of cyclical discharge from the marrow, the levels going down when cells are lost from the bloodstream by seeding or death. It may coincide with waves of maturation in erythroid clones which are eventually shed into the sinusoids. Although feedback mechanisms influence cell production in the bone marrow, the actual mechanism of cell release is obscure and presents a challenging and fundamental problem. From electron microscope studies of bone marrow in anaemic rats Weiss (1965) suggested that cells entered the blood either through existing apertures in the sinusoidal wall, or through new ones created by pressure from adjacent cells or even by the caving-in of whole segments of the walls. The latter would certainly explain the presence *en masse* of the wide variety of immature cells found in the blood during anaemia. In the present studies, injections of a fine carbon suspension failed to detect any obvious generalized leakage from the sinusoids.

Little is known of the haemodynamics of marrow circulation during anaemia. There is evidence that in some conditions associated with erythropoietic stimulation the intramedullary pressure falls (Kalser *et al.* 1951; Herzig & Root

1959). Cumming (1962) detected reflex vasodilatation in the bone marrow of hypoxic rabbits and it could be expected that increased permeability might accompany this. The persistence in the blood of supranormal levels of monocytes, eosinophils and nucleated erythroid cells throughout the anaemia suggests a general increase in permeability of the sinusoidal walls.

Leakage of immature myeloid cells into the blood also poses questions about the role of the cell membrane and whether cell adhesiveness alters during haemopoietic stress.

Although marrow discharge appears to account for much of the increase in atypical mononuclear cells in the blood during anaemia, findings in the present studies suggest that there may be a second mechanism. In the peripheral blood mitotic figures were identified in cells similar in size and shape (Fig. 7) to the mononuclears. Thus, their numbers could increase whilst they are actually circulating in the blood but the extent to which this occurs is unknown in the absence of data on their intravascular lifespan.

The potentialities of the mononuclear cells

All the mononuclear cells are capable of DNA synthesis. The transitional cells are of special interest. In the past considerable attention has been paid to these cells in the bone marrow and to their possible role as precursors of red cells, granulocytes and lymphocytes (Yoffey 1970). The present studies emphasize that in addition to the marrow considerable attention must now be given to transitional cells in the peripheral blood. Their presence in the blood has already been emphasized under certain conditions of haemopoietic stress, especially during recovery from sublethal irradiation and after transfusion of regenerating bone marrow cells (Harris et al. 1963; Harris & Kugler 1964). Not only is the transitional cell a dominant cell in human foetal marrow (Yoffey et al. 1961) but also we have recently observed these cells in foetal blood and in foetal and postnatal thymus.

The three types of atypical mononuclears found in the present studies may well include multipotent cells. Hodgson et al. (1972) have recently described an increase in splenic and agar colony-forming units (CFU) in the peripheral blood of mice made anaemic by phenylhydrazine. The peak level of the CFU occurred on the fifth day and this coincides with the first peak of DNA-synthesizing mononuclear cells in the blood of the anaemic guinea pigs. Barnes & Loutit (1967a) detected colony-forming units in the peripheral blood of antigenically stimulated mice and the timing of the peak level in their experiments is comparable with the initial peak found in the present studies.

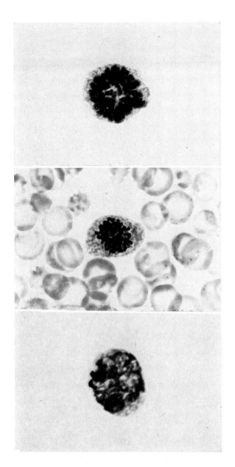

FIG. 7. Mitotic figures in peripheral blood during phenylhydrazine-induced anaemia. (From Harris & Kugler 1971, *J. Anat.*)

In the experiments of Lajtha *et al.* (1969) stem cells in bone marrow of mice were assayed by three different techniques and found to have three different turnover rates, with [³H]thymidine being used as an S phase killing agent. The cells with the highest turnover were erythropoietin-sensitive. A second group with a moderate turnover responded to agar culture by forming granulocytes and a third group, with the slowest turnover, formed mixed colonies after splenic colonization. It is of interest that the present studies also showed three groups of mononuclear cells, each with a different incidence of labelling with [³H]thymidine, and probably therefore of turnover rates.

The groups with the highest labelling were the transitional cells, these being followed by the blast cells, whilst the lowest incidence of labelling was in cells having the appearance of early monocytes.

Those who oppose the transitional cell as a form of multipotent haemopoietic stem cell have proposed 'monocytoid' cells in this role (Tyler & Everett 1966; Barnes & Loutit 1967b). Recent studies using Millipore diffusion chambers indicate that other types of stem cells which have non-haemopoietic potential are present in the blood. The experiments of Stirling & Kakkar (1969) indicate that there is a cell capable of producing connective tissue, whilst those of Lalykina & Fridenshtein (1969) indicate a cell having osteogenic properties, this cell also being present in the thymus but not in lymph nodes. Whether this indicates the existence in the peripheral blood of a cell with the potentialities of primitive mesenchyme or that different stem cells are present, each with a relatively limited potential, has yet to be proved.

Significance of the increase in DNA-synthesizing mononuclear cells

Is the increase in mononuclear cells inevitable and purely incidental to the reticulocyte release after massive erythropoietic stimulation of the marrow, or is it more purposeful? Together with earlier reports, the present findings indicate a common circumstance, namely haemopoietic stress, when the mononuclear cells increase in number in the blood. These stresses include irradiation, antigenic stimulation, the perinatal period and anaemia.

Current concepts of foetal haemopoiesis favour a dynamic situation in which stem cells from the earliest centres of haemopoiesis are carried in the bloodstream and eventually seed other haemopoietic sites. Thus, as development proceeds, multipotent cells originating in the blood islands of the yolk sac migrate to the thymus and liver, and later to the spleen and bone marrow (Moore & Owen 1967; Metcalf & Moore 1971). Does this migration stream which is so active in foetal haemopoiesis continue in a modified form postnatally, the focus for cell export changing from the yolk sac to the bone marrow? There is evidence that it does (Metcalf & Moore 1971). Is this migration stream cyclical and does haemopoietic stress boost migration so that sites becoming depleted of cells are restocked? Was there any evidence of cell depletion in the lymphomyeloid tissues of the anaemic guinea pigs or any other situation in which stem cells from the bloodstream might be required for seeding or restocking? There are three situations in which this type of mechanism might be required.

Firstly, lymphocyte depopulation on an extensive scale was found in the cortex of the thymus, with evidence of cell emigration to the interlobular septa where lymphatics lie. It was not detected in other lymphoid organs. More-over, a brisk lymphocytosis in the peripheral blood in the early stages of the anaemia was abolished by thymectomy (Harris & Kugler 1970). It is known that even in normal circumstances the thymus has a definite requirement for stem cell inflow and that this continues into adult life (Metcalf & Moore 1971).

A second situation which might involve stem cells in the peripheral blood is suggested by the enormous splenomegaly found in the anaemic guinea pigs, the splenic weight increasing tenfold, from 0.417 ± 0.02 to 4.35 ± 0.30 g. Histolo-gically, there was extensive extramedullary erythropoiesis and this might require considerable importation of stem cells.

A third possibility during prolonged anaemia is that stem cells circulating in the blood could seed into bone marrow which is normally inactive or becoming depleted of stem cells as the result of increasing demands. A seeding mechanism of this kind could account for the conversion of yellow marrow into active red marrow which frequently accompanies increased haemopoiesis. Direct evidence for cell migration into bone marrow from the bloodstream was found in studies of anaemic guinea pigs by Osmond (1965) who noted [^{3}H]thymidine labelled cells in the marrow. Also, after severe irradiation of haemopoietic tissues accompanied by partial shielding of marrow, Lord (1967) found that the number of erythropoietic stem cells in the blood markedly increased. Presum-ably the erythropoietic cells originated from the shielded marrow. In studies of autologous bone marrow implants, Tavassoli & Crosby (1968) found that haemopoietic repopulation occurred only when the sinusoidal circulation was restored. This would, of course, coincide precisely with the opportunity for stem cells to migrate from the bloodstream into the implant, or favour the access of haemopoietic factors.

References

BARNES, D. W. H. & LOUTIT, J. F. (1967a) Effects of irradiation and antigenic stimulation on circulating haemopoietic stem cells of the mouse. *Nature (Lond.)* **213**, 1142–1143

BARNES, D. W. H. & LOUTIT, J. F. (1967b) Haemopoietic stem cells in the peripheral blood. *Lancet* **2**, 1138–1141

BOND, V. P., FLIEDNER, T. M., CRONKITE, E. P., RUBINI, J. R., BRECHER, G. & SCHORK, P. K. (1959) Proliferative potentials of bone marrow and blood cells studied by *in vitro* uptake of H^3-thymidine. *Acta Haematol. (Basel)* **21**, 1–15

BOND, V. P., FLIEDNER, T. M., CRONKITE, E. P. & ANDREWS, G. (1961) Deoxyribonucleic acid synthesizing cells in the blood of man and dog exposed to total body radiation. *J. Lab. Clin. Med.* **57**, 711–717

BRECHER, G., WILBUR, K. M. & CRONKITE, E. P. (1953) Transfusion of separated leukocytes into irradiated dogs with aplastic marrows. *Proc. Soc. Exp. Biol. Med.* **84**, 54–56

COLE, L. J. (1963) Haemopoietic restoration in lethally X-irradiated mice injected with peritoneal cells. *Am. J. Physiol.* **204**, 265–267

CONGDON, C. C., UPHOFF, D. & LORENZ, E. (1952) Modification of acute irradiation injury in mice and guinea pigs by injection of bone marrow: a histopathologic study. *J. Natl Cancer Inst.* **13**, 73–107

CONGDON, C. C., MCKINLEY, T. N., JR., SUTTON, H. & URSO, P. J., JR. (1956) The effect of transfusions of blood showing extreme leucocytosis on survival of X-irradiated mice. *Radiat. Res.* **4**, 424–434

CRONKITE, E. P. & BRECHER, G. (1955) The protective effect of granulocytes in radiation injury. *Ann. N.Y. Acad. Sci.* **59**, 815–833

CUMMING, J. D. (1962) A study of blood flow through bone marrow by a method of venous effluent collection. *J. Physiol. (Lond.)* **162**, 13–21

GERSHON–COHEN, J., HERMEL, M. B. & GRIFFITH, J. Q., JR. (1951) The value of small lead shields against the injurious effect of total body irradiation. *Science (Wash. D.C.)* **114**, 157–158

GOODMAN, J. W. & HODGSON, G. S. (1962) Evidence for stem-cells in the peripheral blood of mice. *Blood J. Hematol.* **19**, 702–714

HARRIS, P. F. & KUGLER, J. H. (1964) The use of regenerating bone marrow to protect guinea pigs against lethal irradiation. *Acta Haematol. (Basel)* **32**, 146–167

HARRIS, P. F. & KUGLER, J. H. (1970) Some observations on the lympho-reticular system in anaemic guinea pigs; evidence suggesting thymic lymphocyte emigration. *J. Anat.* **107**, 389–390

HARRIS, P. F. & KUGLER, J. H. (1971) Unusual mononuclear cells in guinea pig peripheral blood during anaemia. *J. Anat.* **108**, 1–12

HARRIS, P. F., HAIGH, G. & KUGLER, J. H. (1963) Quantitative studies of mitoses and DNA-synthesizing cells in bone marrow and blood of guinea pigs recovering from sublethal whole body gamma irradiation. *Br. J. Haematol.* **9**, 385–405

HARRIS, P. F., HARRIS, R. S. & KUGLER, J. H. (1966) Studies of the leucocyte compartment in guinea pig bone marrow after acute haemorrhage and severe hypoxia; evidence for a common stem cell. *Br. J. Haematol.* **12**, 419–432

HERZIG, E. & ROOT, W. S. (1959) Relation of sympathetic nervous system to blood pressure of bone marrow. *Am. J. Physiol.* **196**, 1053–1056

HODGSON, G. S., BRADLEY, T. R. & TELFER, P. A. (1972) Haemopoietic stem cells in experimental haemolytic anaemia. *Cell Tissue Kinet.* **5**, 283–288

JACOBSON, L. O., MARKS, E. K., GASTON, E. O., ROBSON, M. J. & ZIRKLE, R. E. (1949) The role of the spleen in radiation injury. *Proc. Soc. Exp. Biol. Med.* **70**, 740–742

JACOBSON, L. O., SIMMONS, E. L., MARKS, E. K., ROBSON, M. J., BETHARD, W. F. & GASTON, E. O. (1950) The role of the spleen in radiation injury and recovery. *J. Lab. Clin. Med.* **35**, 746–770

JACOBSON, L. O., SIMMONS, E. L., MARKS, E. K., GASTON, E. O., ROBSON, M. J. & ELDRIDGE, J. H. (1951) Further studies on recovery from radiation injury. *J. Lab. Clin. Med.* **37**, 683–697

KALSER, M. H., IVY, H. K., PEVSNER, L., MARBARGER, J. P. & IVY, A. C. (1951) Changes in bone marrow pressure during exposure to simulated altitude. *J. Aviat. Med.* **22**, 286–294

KAPLAN, H. S. & BROWN, M. B. (1952) Effect of peripheral shielding on lymphoid tissue response to irradiation in C57 black mice. *Science (Wash. D.C.)* **116**, 195–196

LAJTHA, L. G., POZZI, L. V., SCHOFIELD, R. & FOX, M. (1969) Kinetic properties of haemopoietic stem cells. *Cell Tissue Kinet.* **2**, 39–49

LALYKINA, K. S. & FRIDENSHTEIN, A. YA. (1969) Induction of osteogenesis in lymphoid cell populations in guinea pigs. *Bull. Exp. Biol. Med.* **67**, 676–679

LEEUWENHOEK, A. VAN (1669) in *Antoni van Leeuwenhoek*, Latin text of his 65th letter to the Royal Society (Sept. 7th, 1688) [1962. Facsimile, De Graaf, Nieuwkoop]

LORD, B. I. (1967) Improved erythropoietic recovery in lethally irradiated rats after transfusion of buffy coat cells from the blood of partially shielded, heavily irradiated donors. *Nature (Lond.)* **214**, 924–925

MALININ, T. I., PERRY, V. P., KERBY, C. C. & DOLAN, M. F. (1965) Peripheral leukocyte infusion into lethally irradiated guinea pigs. *Blood J. Hematol.* **25**, 693–702

MERWIN, R. W. (1959) Repopulation of haematopoietic tissues of X-irradiated mice by cells from leukemoid blood. *Proc. Soc. Exp. Biol. Med.* **101**, 9–12

METCALF, D. & MOORE, M. A. S. (1971) *Haemopoietic Cells*, North-Holland, Amsterdam

MOORE, M. A. S. & OWEN, J. T. T. (1967) Stem cell migration in developing myeloid and lymphoid systems. *Lancet* **2**, 658–659

OSMOND, D. G. (1965) Radioautographic studies of blood-borne cells and lymphocyte turnover in the bone marrow of anaemic guinea pigs. *J. Anat.* **99**, 208

POPP, R. A. (1960) Erythrocyte repopulation of X-irradiated recipients of nucleated peripheral blood cells of normal mice. *Proc. Soc. Exp. Biol. Med.* **104**, 722–724

ROSSE, C. & YOFFEY, J. M. (1967) The morphology of the transitional lymphocyte in guinea pig bone marrow. *J. Anat.* **102**, 113–124

STIRLING, G. A. & KAKKAR, V. V. (1969) Cells in the circulating blood capable of producing connective tissue. *Br. J. Exp. Pathol.* **50**, 51–56

STORER, J. B., LUSHBAUGH, C. C. & FURSCHNER, J. E. (1952) The protective effect of shielded ectopic bone marrow against total body X-irradiation. *J. Lab. Clin. Med.* **40**, 355–366

SWAMMERDAM, J. (1665) in *Antoni van Leeuwenhoek*, Latin text of his 65th letter to the Royal Society (Sept. 7th, 1688) [1962. Facsimile, De Graaf, Nieuwkoop]

TAVASSOLI, M. & CROSBY, W. H. (1968) Transplantation of marrow to extramedullary sites. *Science (Wash. D.C.)* **161**, 54–56

TYLER, R. W. & EVERETT, N. B. (1966) A radioautographic study of haemopoietic repopulation using irradiated parabiotic rats. *Blood J. Hematol.* **28**, 873–890

WEISS, L. (1965) Functional interrelationships of vascular and hematopoietic compartments in experimental hemolytic anaemia: an electron microscopic study. *J. Morphol.* 467–538

YOFFEY, J. M. (1970) in *Regulation of Hematopoiesis* (Gordon, A. S., ed.), vol. 2, pp. 1421–1454, Appleton-Century-Crofts, New York

YOFFEY, J. M., THOMAS, D. B., MOFFAT, D. J., SUTHERLAND, I. H. & ROSSE, C. (1961) Non-immunological functions of the lymphocyte, in *Biological Activity of The Leucocyte (Ciba Found. Study Group* No. 10), pp. 45–54, Churchill, London

Discussion

Metcalf: The lymphoid follicles you showed in the thymus are seen in certain situations in the mouse. In AKR mice, all thymus glands develop such follicles before thymic lymphomata develop (Metcalf 1966). However, thymic weight loss is the best general index of stress.

The blood films you showed reminded me of *Eperythrozoon coccoides* infection in mice where the red cells and particularly the reticulocytes are infected by punctate parasites. Such infections flare up after stress to the animals. Might a similar organism become activated in the guinea pig after stress and produce red cells with this morphology?

Harris: I interpret these red cell appearances as punctate basophilia.

Yoffey: Tyler & Everett (1966) effected parabiosis between rats, lethally irradiated one animal, labelled the other, and obtained what they thought were stem cells passing from the non-irradiated parabiont to the irradiated one. When they analysed the morphology of these stem cells, they described them as 'monocytoid'. The monocytoid group, as described in this and later papers (Everett & Tyler 1968; Tyler & Everett 1972), seem to be rather pleomorphic. Everett & Tyler (1968) depict cells which are 'considered to be monocytoid in type'. Some of these cells have a horseshoe nucleus and one can understand why they are termed monocytoid, but they also illustrate cells which have a round nucleus, which I think one could with equal significance call lymphocytoid. As you know, terms such as lymphocytoid and lymphoidocyte have cropped up in haematological literature since the start of the century. What puzzles us is that we cannot identify monocytoid cells in our ultrastructural studies of marrow, in regions where one would expect to find stem cells. Incidentally, the description of monocytoid cells given by Tyler & Everett (1966) would apply equally to transitional cells. I do not know whether monocytoid cells are slightly modified forms of transitional cells. More work is needed on their distribution and histogenesis in normal marrow.

Rosse: I briefly referred (p. 129) to some studies on the haemopoietic re-populating capacity of cells recovered from subcutaneous exudates (Tyler *et al.* 1972). These cells were collected 18 hours after implanting sterile coverslips under the skin of mice and I examined their morphology in relation to lympho-cytes. Such cells are extremely fragile; on standard smears it is impossible to determine their identity, so we looked at them in wet preparations with supra-vital staining. From differential counts on these very early exudate cells only about 5 % can be identified as small lymphocytes. Most of the cells contain a vacuolar apparatus, which of course takes up neutral red, but they are quite distinct from the very occasional neutral red vacuoles which one finds in small lymphocytes. So I am quite satisfied that at this very early stage—and in fact one cannot collect cells earlier because so few are present—they are not lym-phocytes. Their efficiency in inducing erythroid repopulation in the spleen is less than that of whole bone marrow cells: 10^5 bone marrow cells are as efficient as 10^6 subcutaneous exudate cells.

Osmond: We have observed an influx of cells from the bloodstream into the bone marrow of anaemic guinea pigs (Osmond 1965). Erythropoiesis was stimulated by repeated cardiac puncture for two weeks. Tritiated thymidine was then given by intracardiac injection, while the circulation to one hindlimb was temporarily occluded, so that the [³H]thymidine was incorporated through-out the body, excluding the occluded limb. Subsequently, some highly labelled cells appeared in the initially occluded marrow. They increased in numbers during the first 20–30 hours after [³H]thymidine administration. Their morphology corresponded quite closely to the cells described by Dr Harris as appearing in the blood. The most frequent group of cells consisted of a range of mononuclear cells, among which monocytoid cells were quite prominent. Thus, some circulating labelled cells apparently homed into the marrow but their functional potential remains uncertain. We have seen them in mitosis in the marrow, with a halving of their mean grain count between 20 and 30 hours, but have not detected any labelled erythroid progeny arising from them.

Harris: In severe anaemia, when there is a massive demand for increased production of red cells, yellow marrow is transformed into active red marrow. This could be a purely local phenomenon but it might also result from seeding of the yellow marrow by haemic stem cells which enter it from the circulating blood.

Astaldi: Do these cells circulate from one side to the other?

Harris: We have not studied cross-circulation.

Yoffey: This question of stem cells migrating into and out of the marrow is one which we have all worried about for many years. The Harwell group (Harris *et al.* 1964; Ford *et al.* 1966; Barnes & Loutit 1967) showed that in normal marrow, as compared to the irradiated marrow which so many people have used to test for stem cell migration, there is some, but relatively little, entry of new stem cells into the marrow. Dr Harris, you seemed to get a marked fall of lymphocytes in the marrow in the first days.

Harris: The fall was found after two weeks, which was when we examined the marrow.

Yoffey: What happened to the transitionals in the marrow during that time?

Harris: There was no significant change in their levels.

Yoffey: Petrakis *et al.* (1961) made a similar observation on connective tissue arising from blood cells. Again, one has the old problem of whether the fibroblast comes from the lymphocyte, or from the monocyte forming a macrophage and then a fibroblast. Shelton & Rice (1959) derived the fibroblast directly from the lymphocyte.

Harris: Stirling & Kakkar (1969) showed that there is a cell circulating in the peripheral blood which is capable of producing connective tissue. It would be interesting to look at this with the electron microscope.

Hudson: I was intrigued by your suggestion that in some way these cells might be involved in the conversion of yellow marrow into red marrow. We know very little about this phenomenon. In prolonged severe hypoxia in guinea pigs, in spite of a tremendous increase in the red marrow, even at the expense of bone, there was no conversion of yellow marrow into red (Hudson 1958). With very severe stimulation did you find extension of the red marrow?

Harris: We did not look for this, but it occurred to us that this was another possible situation in which stem cells might be recruited from the peripheral blood.

Hudson: Did you weigh the adrenals in these animals? With 6100 m hypoxia —taking up Dr Metcalf's suggestion—adrenal weight increased enormously (Sibley & Hudson 1970), which would tie in with the suggestion that this is a stress situation.

Micklem: In studies of circulating stem cells we have given part-body irradiation with shielding of the hindlimbs, followed by injection of T6 chromosome-marked bone marrow cells (Ford *et al.* 1966). During the first week a fairly stable situation is set up in which the irradiated marrow contains about 80 % donor cells and the non-irradiated marrow about 10 %, so there is a certain amount of shifting round during that time. After that there is little or no further change, even after two years. Thus the humeri, which were not irradiated, always have a minority of donor cells, and the femurs, which were irradiated, always have a majority. Recently we have tried to equalize the populations in these tissues by various means, including whole-body irradiation. Surprisingly, a dose of 600 R was needed to achieve equalization; 350 R had no effect at all. So one has to do an enormous amount of damage to the haemopoietic system to get an influx of marrow stem cells contributing to regeneration.

Yoffey: Harris *et al.* (1964) parabiosed T6T6 to ordinary mice, and I think they established a marrow equilibrium at about 3–4 % of migrating cells.

Micklem: Although the lymph nodes and spleen approached a 50:50 equilibrium during the first eight weeks after parabiosis, there was still less than 10 % exchange in the bone marrow after six months (Ford 1966). Most of that exchange seems to have occurred during the first four weeks, so maybe an equilibrium was established at this low level.

Thomas: This is analogous to the situation in natural chimeras, which may result in equilibration at a much higher level. Maybe the level at which equilibration occurs depends partly on the number of circulating stem cells? Foetal blood, which contains stem cells, contains quite numerous transitional cells (Thomas & Yoffey, unpublished data) but very few monocytes or monocytoid cells. There may be some interesting correlations here but it would be imprudent to guess the outcome of investigations which are currently being conducted in our laboratory.

Micklem: I doubt whether the level of equilibrium is determined simply by the number of circulating stem cells. In our system, where there is one population of marked cells in the forelimbs and another in the hindlimbs, the number of circulating CFU can be increased considerably by injecting *Bordetella pertussis* organisms without causing any equalization. Probably it is environmental factors within the bone marrow which determine whether or not stem cells will enter and proliferate, rather than the number of stem cells available in the circulation.

Grigoriu: In experiments with peripheral leucocytes from normal unbled rabbits, we have cultured in Millipore chambers cells previously incubated *in vitro* with erythropoietin-rich serum (unpublished data). Smears made four to ten days later showed, as already reported (Grigoriu *et al.* 1971), that as well as erythroblasts there were some cells of a different size, but larger than a small lymphocyte, with a loose chromatin structure and intense basophilic cytoplasm, reminiscent of the transitional lymphocytes of J. M. Yoffey or P. F. Harris.

In another experiment (unpublished results), I started from the same idea as you, Dr Harris, namely that the cells committed to erythropoiesis and supposedly circulating in the peripheral blood of anaemic patients should have a high proliferative capacity. I checked my assumption by autoradiography after incubating peripheral leucocytes with tritiated thymidine. Considering all the cases of anaemia together, the results were rather confusing; however, when we looked at particular types of anaemias the situation was different. Thus, peripheral leucocytes from patients with iron-deficient anaemias showed a normal labelling index, as they did in thalassaemia or enzymopenic anaemias. In autoimmune anaemias the labelling index ranged from normal to very high, but most of these patients were on corticosteroid treatment which made the results uncertain. Some of the aplastic anaemias showed a very high labelling index. Since we excluded the patients with infections, we may say that in such cases an immune mechanism might be involved.

From these preliminary results we could infer that chronic anaemia *per se* does not generate higher than normal proliferative activity in peripheral blood. I wonder whether a high labelling index of the peripheral leucocytes could indicate an immune mechanism in anaemic patients. Since I am not sure whether the autoradiography was sufficiently sensitive for this kind of experiment, we are now investigating the proliferative capacity of peripheral leucocytes in anaemic patients by the liquid scintillation method.

Stohlman: In human beings, as opposed to the guinea pig, in chronic hypoxic conditions such as congenital haemolytic anaemias haemopoiesis expands into the areas of yellow marrow, and in thalassaemic patients the marrow may be so active as to thin out the bone to such an extent that the patients break their bones easily. Surely there are many species differences which must be taken into account.

Winterhalter: But you surely would not expect to see this over something like two or three weeks?

Stohlman: No. Further, phenylhydrazine affects more than just the red cells. For example, if one continues to give phenylhydrazine, liver damage is seen.

Yoffey: Could it be just a time phenomenon? There probably are species differences in addition, but these human anaemias have usually been going on for a long time. Huggins & Blocksom (1936) implanted rat tails into subcutaneous tissues of the abdominal wall, and said that because of the increase in temperature the fatty marrow of the caudal vertebrae became red. Recently this has been disputed (Maniatis *et al.* 1971), but I cannot remember how long the experiments were followed.

Stohlman: The only thing I wanted to clear up was that in chronic haemolytic anaemias the stem cell may move into places where it does not ordinarily replicate and differentiate.

Rosse: The distribution of fatty and red marrow seems to be constant yet the number of fat cells found in red marrow is affected extremely rapidly by haemopoietic stimulation; even within a very short time after an animal has been placed in a decompression chamber one can notice the disappearance of fat cells from haemopoietic red marrow preceding erythroid hyperplasia. The mechanisms that regulate the number and distribution of what appear to be similar cells might be different in different tissues.

Stohlman: Do you mean the disappearance of fat cells, or of fat from the fat cells?

Rosse: A fat cell is seen as a fat globule surrounded by cytoplasm and nucleus, and these structures disappear during the early phase of erythropoietic stimulation. What becomes of the cell that contained the fat, or what it looks like when the fat has disappeared, I do not know.

Stohlman: The number of fat cells is said to be determined at birth. A person is fat or thin not because of the number of adipose cells but because of their fat content.

Rosse: I do not know what happens in other tissues, but in the marrow we certainly see these changes in fat, and I do not see fat in the marrow which would appear to be outside cells.

Yoffey: Fat is fat, but is it all the same kind of fat? I think marrow fat differs from fat elsewhere, but whether or not this is so, one can indeed, as Dr Rosse has commented, see the fat cells rapidly shrinking and apparently disappearing when an animal is given a severe erythropoietic stimulus. Whether they completely disappear or whether the nucleus and shrunken cell body remain and become a fat cell again later on, I do not know. My own feeling is that they disappear, because if erythropoiesis is then depressed for any length of time, one finds far more fat cells than are ever seen in normal marrow. One could argue that this simply means that in normal marrow when a number of fat cells are present there are also a number of fat cell precursors. That may not be very convincing, but it is true that in prolonged rebound or in transfusion polycythaemia greatly increased numbers of fat cells are seen. Probably the moment you gave your animals erythropoietin in repeated doses (three times a day for 23 days), Dr Stohlman, you would find all the fat cells disappearing.

Stohlman: I am not disputing the theory that there is loss of fat from the marrow; I just raised the question as to whether it is a loss of adipose cells or a loss of their *fat* content.

Harris: In my irradiation experiments I saw a whole spectrum of cells, from what we would call a reticulum cell with just a few vacuoles right up to coalescence into what looks like a fully-formed fat cell. My guess is that these cells are part of the reticular stromal cell system and they revert to that if they lose their fat.

Winterhalter: I am surprised that phenylhydrazine is used so widely to make animals anaemic although I realize there is no other good way of doing this without other side effects. But phenylhydrazine must have a very general effect on proteins and an animal being treated with it should not be considered as a 'physiologically' anaemic animal. One could plasmaphorese the animal instead —take the blood out, spin it down, put the plasma back in and maybe supplement it with the iron that the animal has lost. I predict that this would make a much more 'physiological' kind of anaemia than giving phenylhydrazine.

Harris: I fully agree that this is very important. We used phenylhydrazine because it was a simple method, from our point of view, of producing anaemia.

Rosse: Commercially available erythropoietin is obtained from animals made anaemic with phenylhydrazine. Commercial erythropoietin in the guinea pig produces marked and measurable effects in the marrow, other than erythropoietic effects—a measurable stimulation of granulocytopoiesis, for instance. This may be related to the point you made, Dr Winterhalter.

References

BARNES, D. W. H. & LOUTIT, J. F. (1967) Migration streams of haematopoietic stem cells. *Haematol. Lat.* 10, 1–11

EVERETT, N. B. & TYLER, R. W. (1968) Studies on lymphocytes: relationship to mononuclear cells of inflammatory exudates. *Biochem. Pharmacol.* Suppl., 185–196

FORD, C. E. (1966) Traffic of lymphoid cells in the body, in *The Thymus (Ciba Found. Symp.)*, p. 131–151, Churchill, London

FORD, C. E., MICKLEM, H. S., EVANS, E. P., GRAY, J. G. & OGDEN, D. A. (1966) The inflow of bone marrow cells to the thymus: studies with part-body irradiated mice injected with chromosome-marked bone marrow and subjected to antigenic stimulation. *Ann. N.Y. Acad. Sci.* 129, 283–296

GRIGORIU, G., ANTONESCU, M. & IERCAN, E. (1971) Evidence for a circulating stem cell. Newly formed erythroblasts found in autologous leukocyte-filled diffusion chambers inserted into bled rabbits. *Blood J. Hematol.* 37, 187–195

HARRIS, J. E., FORD, C. E., BARNES, D. W. H. & EVANS, E. P. (1964) Evidence from parabiosis for an afferent stream of cells. *Nature (Lond.)* **201**, 886–887

HUDSON, G. (1958) Effect of hypoxia on bone-marrow volume. *Br. J. Haematol.* **4**, 239–248

HUGGINS, C. & BLOCKSOM, B. H. (1936) Changes in the outlying bone marrow accompanying a local increase of temperature within physiological limits. *J. Exp. Med.* **64**, 253–274

MANIATIS, Z., TAVASSOLI, M. & CROSBY, W. H. (1971) Factors affecting the conversion of yellow to red marrow. *Blood J. Hematol.* **37**, 581–586

METCALF, D. (1966) Histologic and transplantation studies on the preleukemic thymus of the AKR mouse. *J. Natl Cancer Inst.* **37**, 425–442

OSMOND, D. G. (1965) Radioautographic studies of blood-borne cells and lymphocyte turnover in the bone marrow of anaemic guinea pigs. *J. Anat.* **99**, 208

PETRAKIS, N. L., DAVIS, M. & LUCIA, S. P. (1961) The *in vivo* differentiation of human leuco-cytes into histiocytes, fibroblasts, and fat cells in subcutaneous diffusion chambers. *Blood J. Hematol.* **17**, 109–118

SHELTON, E. & RICE, M. E. (1959) Growth of normal peritoneal cells in diffusion chambers: a study in cell modulation. *Am. J. Anat.* **105**, 281–341

SIBLEY, Y. D. L. & HUDSON, G. (1970) Eosinophil leucocytes and recovery from severe hypoxia. *Acta Haematol. (Basel)* **43**, 31–39

STIRLING, G. A. & KAKKAR, V. V. (1969) Cells in the circulating blood capable of producing connective tissue. *Br. J. Exp. Pathol.* **50**, 51–56

TYLER, R. W. & EVERETT, N. B. (1966) A radioautographic study of hemopoietic repopulation using irradiated parabiotic rats. *Blood J. Hematol.* **28**, 873–890

TYLER, R. W. & EVERETT, N. B. (1972) Radioautographic study of cellular migration using parabiotic rats. *Blood J. Hematol.* **39**, 249–266

TYLER, R. W., ROSSE, C. & EVERETT, N. B. (1972) The hemopoietic repopulating potential of inflammatory exudate cells. *J. Reticuloendothel. Soc.* **11**, 617

Ageing, haemopoietic stem cells and immunity

H. S. MICKLEM, D. A. OGDEN and A. C. PAYNE

Immunobiology Unit, Department of Zoology, University of Edinburgh

Abstract Ageing mice show some immunological defects, including a progressive impairment of the capacity to form 7S antibodies after primary immunization with sheep erythrocytes. This begins to be evident before 12 months of age in CBA mice. Cell transfer experiments show that there is no decline in the numbers or quality of the bone marrow precursors of lymphocytes such as could account for the immunological decline. Other experiments, involving competitive proliferation of two chromosomally distinguishable cell populations in lethally irradiated recipients, show that there are some age-related changes in haemopoietic stem cells which can be assessed as differences in the size of the cell populations which they produce. These age-related changes seem unlikely normally to be a significant factor in senescence.

AGEING AND IMMUNITY: PHENOMENA AND THEIR POSSIBLE EXPLANATION

Many studies have established that immunological competence, at least in mice and men, tends to diminish with age. The best-documented system is the antibody response of mice to xenogeneic erythrocytes. The formation of both 19S (IgM) and 7S (IgG) antibodies is affected, the latter (as judged by the sensitivity of the antibodies to 2-mercaptoethanol) the more strikingly (Makinodan & Peterson 1966). Our own data, based on the 'direct' and 'indirect' haemolytic plaque assay (Dresser & Wortis 1967) for estimating the numbers of 19S and 7S haemolysin-secreting cells, confirm the particular sensitivity of 7S antibody formation to ageing factors. Table 1 shows peak numbers of 19S and 7S plaque-forming cells (PFC) in male CBA/H mice of various ages. Similar data on (C57BL × C3H)F1 mice have recently been reported by Makinodan *et al.* (1971*a*). Comparison with the results of Metcalf *et al.* (1967) and Kishimoto *et al.* (1969) suggests that male CBA mice begin to show signs of ageing later than C57BL, but earlier than (C57BL × C3H)F1 hybrids. Our unpublished data on

TABLE 1

Direct and indirect splenic PFC responses of male CBA mice of various ages, assayed at or near peak

Experiment	Group	Age (months)	Log$_{10}$ PFC/spleen (mean $\pm$ s.e.)	Ratio to Group 1
(A)				
Direct	1	3	4.33 $\pm$ 0.32	1.0
	2	9	4.70 $\pm$ 0.03	2.3
	3	16	4.81 $\pm$ 0.14	3.0
Indirect	1	3	4.82 $\pm$ 0.02	1.0
	2	9	3.69 $\pm$ 0.15	0.07**
	3	16	3.98 $\pm$ 0.14	0.14**
(B)				
Direct	1	3	4.98 $\pm$ 0.13	1.0
	2	7	5.28 $\pm$ 0.03	2.0
Indirect	1	3	4.32 $\pm$ 0.27	1.0
	2	7	3.92 $\pm$ 0.42	0.39
(C)				
Direct	1	3	5.05 $\pm$ 0.06	1.0
	2	18	3.88 $\pm$ 1.14	0.07
	3	22	4.10 $\pm$ 0.24	0.11*
Indirect	1	3	4.83 $\pm$ 0.05	1.0
	2	18	3.72 $\pm$ 0.25	0.08*
	3	22	3.20 $\pm$ 0.44	0.02*

*   significant at 5 % level
** significant at 1 % level.

C57BL and (C57BL $\times$ CBA)F1 mice are concordant, and also indicate that males develop deficiencies of 7S antibody formation earlier than females. Although we have no accurate information on the lifespan of CBA/H mice in this laboratory, it does not differ substantially from the 870 days (median) reported for CBA/H mice by Barnes *et al.* (1959*b*). Thus, males of this strain already show immunological decline at an age approximately one-third of their expected lifespan. Data on cellular immune reactivity in relation to age are relatively scanty. Elderly patients without apparent disease have been reported to show reduced responsiveness to a cutaneous sensitizing agent (Waldorf *et al.* 1968), while rejection of experimental tumours in old mice was delayed (Teller *et al.* 1964; Stjernswärd 1966). The capacity of spleen cells from aged donors to induce a graft-versus-host reaction in young recipients may be impaired (Krohn 1962). The phenomena of ageing in relation to immunity are well reviewed by Makinodan *et al.* (1971*b*).

TABLE 2

Possible mechanisms underlying immunological decline in senescence

---

(A) *Haemopoietic and lymphoid cell deficiencies*
  1) Pluripotential stem cells (CFU, bone marrow repopulating cells)
  2) Bone marrow progenitors of thymus lymphocytes
  3) Bone marrow progenitors of B lymphocytes
  4) Mature T lymphocytes: *(a)* numerical
                            (b) functional
  5) Mature B lymphocytes: *(a)* numerical
                            (b) functional
  6) Bone marrow progenitors of macrophages
  7) Macrophages; *(a)* numerical
                    (b) changed distribution in body
                    (c) functional

(B) *Structural deficiencies in lymphoid tissues*
  1) Thymic epithelium
  2) Spleen, lymph nodes, etc.: *(a)* antigen trapping
                                  (b) milieu for lymphocyte migration/cooperation/
                                         proliferation/differentiation

(C) *Generalized deficiencies and changes*
  1) Hormonal regulation: *(a)* adrenocorticoids
                            (b) sex hormones
                            (c) somatotropic hormone
                            (d) thymic hormone
                            (e) other
  2) Other changes – e.g. availability of nutrients, vascular changes, etc.

The various mechanisms to which immunological decline might be related are summarized in Table 2. The assumption is made that at least two distinct kinds of lymphocytes are involved in antibody responses—both derived in the adult from bone marrow stem cells. One is characterized by a period of residence in the thymus, while the other, which includes antibody-secreting cells and their precursors, is not (Micklem *et al.* 1966; Barnes *et al.* 1967; Wu *et al.* 1968; Miller & Mitchell 1969; Davies *et al.* 1971). These are commonly known as T lymphocytes and B lymphocytes, respectively (Roitt *et al.* 1969). In addition macrophages, likewise derived from bone marrow precursors (Volkman & Gowans 1965), may be important in the trapping and subsequent handling of antigens. It is recognized that the T and B lymphocytes may themselves be subdivisible into more than one distinct category (Cantor 1972; Playfair & Purves 1971).

It is not within the scope of this paper to consider in detail all the categories of deficiency listed in Table 2 or to review the evidence pertaining to them. However, the recent cell transfer experiments of Price & Makinodan (1972*a, b*) have enabled them to identify some factors which are intrinsic to a population of splenic lymphocytes and others which are related to the environment in which the cells have to function. These factors would be included in categories A and B-C, respectively, of Table 2. Intrinsic factors included a reduced ability of both T and B cells to respond to antigenic stimulation, although there appeared to be no gross decrease in the numbers of either type in 30–35-month-old mice. The efficiency of antigen handling was also thought to be impaired, since ten times more antigen was needed to evoke a maximal response in the old mice compared to young adult controls. The nature of the environmental factors could not be identified, but the experimental scheme suggested that they had an immediate effect on the capacity of mature lymphocytes to respond to antigen.

HAEMOPOIETIC STEM CELLS

A number of authors have studied the numbers of pluripotent stem cells present in animals in relation to age (Albright & Makinodan 1966; Proukakis & Lindop 1967; Yuhas & Storer 1967; Davis *et al.* 1968, 1971; Coggle & Proukakis 1970; Chen 1971). Chen (1971) found that although the proportion of spleen-colony-forming units (CFU) in the bone marrow of ageing (C57BL × C3H)F1 mice declined progressively, the total marrow cellularity rose, so that the size of the CFU pool remained approximately the same. This does not, however, necessarily imply that the quality of the CFU pool is unchanged. Several differences have been reported between CFU from different sources or recovered under different conditions. For example, Siminovitch *et al.* (1964) found that serial transplantation of CFU rendered them less and less capable of self-renewal. More recently, evidence has accumulated that CFU derived from foetal mice have on average a greater potential for proliferation than do those derived from adult bone marrow (Duplan 1968; Schofield 1970; Micklem *et al.* 1972; Micklem 1972). For example CFU from foetal liver gave rise to larger and more rapidly proliferating spleen colonies, as judged by incorporation of ^{125}I-labelled 5-iodo-2'-deoxyuridine into DNA, than did CFU from adult bone marrow. Moreover, competition experiments with chromosome-marked populations in irradiated mice showed that populations derived from foetal liver increased in number more rapidly than those derived from adult bone marrow; this was true of the bone marrow, spleen, thymus and lymph nodes of the recipient mice (Micklem *et al.* 1972) This differential increase is illustrated for bone marrow and lymph nodes in Fig. 1.

Preliminary experiments failed to demonstrate any comparable difference

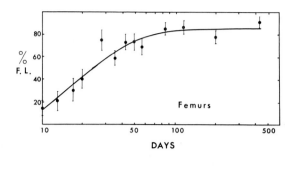

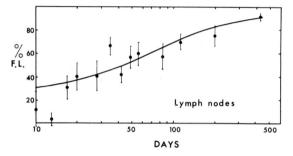

FIG. 1. Increase with time in the proportion of foetal-liver-derived mitoses in femurs and lymph nodes of lethally irradiated CBA mice restored with equal numbers of chromosomally distinguishable adult bone marrow and foetal liver cells. (From Micklem *et al.* 1972.)

between cell populations derived from young and old adult donors. However, serial transfer experiments suggest that 'old' stem cells have poorer proliferative prospects than do 'young' ones. Fig. 2 illustrates an experiment in which equal numbers of CFU from young (3-month) and old (24-month) donors were injected together into lethally irradiated recipients; the bone marrow was then serially passaged at 8–10-week intervals. The young cells progressively increased their share of the total mitotic population in the bone marrow until the fourth passage, when both populations were nearly exhausted and the old one enjoyed a temporary advantage. This last phenomenon is reminiscent of the sequential dominance and decrease of individual haemopoietic clones previously described (Micklem & Loutit 1966). Limited data indicated that the proportion of 'young' mitotic cells in the spleen and lymph nodes also increased progressively.

These data suggest that differences exist between the stem cells of young and old mice, although they are less easy to demonstrate than those between foetal and young adult stem cells.

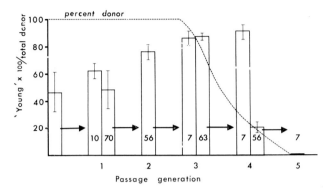

FIG. 2. Proportion of mitotic cells derived from young (3-month) and old (24-month) donors during serial passage through lethally irradiated syngeneic hosts. The host and donor populations were distinguished by the possession of 0, 1 or 2 T6 chromosomes. Each column represents a single animal killed on the day indicated by the number in the column. Vertical bars indicate 95 % confidence limits for the estimated percentage, based on the number of mitoses scored.

THE DERIVATION OF LYMPHOCYTES FROM PLURIPOTENT STEM CELLS

Any difference in the behaviour of CFU or the haemopoietic populations derived from them might be reflected in the populations of both T and B lymphocytes and ultimately in their immune responsiveness to antigens, since there is no doubt that one stem cell (CFU) may differentiate into lymphocytes of both kinds as well as into other blood cells (Barnes *et al.* 1959a; Trentin *et al.* 1967; Wu *et al.* 1968; Edwards *et al.* 1970; Nowell *et al.* 1970).

IS STEM CELL DECLINE AN IMPORTANT FACTOR IN IMMUNOLOGICAL DECLINE?

We have recently sought to determine whether, in practice, any deficit in the pluripotent stem cell compartment is likely to be a limiting factor in immune responses of old mice. In one experiment 3-month-old CBA mice were lethally X-irradiated (900 R) and injected with 5×10^6 bone marrow cells from 3-month-old or 22-month-old syngeneic donors. All the mice received in addition 50×10^6 syngeneic thymus cells from 4-week-old donors. Seventeen days later they were injected intraperitoneally with 4×10^7 sheep erythrocytes. The number of haemolytic plaque-forming cells (PFC) was assayed 3–14 days later. No significant differences were detected between the two groups in either the size or the timing of the responses. Data for the early part of the response are shown in Table 3. Thus, in the fairly short term, the 'old' and 'young' marrow inocula did

TABLE 3

PFC responses of 3-month-old CBA mice to sheep erythrocytes injected 17 days after total-body irradiation and restoration with bone marrow from young or old donors*

Age of donor (months)	Days after antigen	Assay	Log_{10} PFC/spleen (mean ± s.e.)
3	3	Direct	2.87 ± 0.20
22	3	PFC	3.28 ± 0.07
3	5	Direct	4.54 ± 0.12
22	5	PFC	3.77 ± 0.56
3	8	Indirect	4.20 ± 0.05
22	8	PFC	3.92 ± 0.45

* All mice received 5×10^7 thymus cells from 4-week-old donors

not differ greatly in their capacity to generate functional B cells. Further experiments will be necessary to show whether the difference noted on day 5 is significant.

In a second experiment, lethally irradiated 3-month-old CBA mice were injected with 5×10^6 bone marrow cells from 3-month-old or 26-month-old syngeneic donors. The bone marrow suspensions were exposed to anti-theta serum (Raff 1969) and complement to eliminate any mature T cells. Twelve months later the PFC response of the chimeras to sheep erythrocytes was assayed. At the same time counts were made of the number of cells obtained in suspensions from the spleen and from the brachial and axillary lymph nodes of each mouse. Aliquots of each suspension were exposed to anti-theta serum and complement as described by Raff & Wortis (1970), and the proportion of theta-positive cells was calculated. This proportion was assumed to reflect the number of T cells present. The cellular composition and PFC content of the spleens are shown in Table 4. Again, no significant differences were noted between the recipients of young and old bone marrow. The PFC responses were comparable in size with those to be expected, on the basis of other experiments, in normal 15-month-old CBA males. The total cellularity of the lymph nodes was rather variable, but the estimated proportion of T cells (71–86 %) did not appear to differ between the groups.

In a further experiment, we measured the cellular response of chimeras to the cutaneous sensitizing agent oxazolone (4-ethoxymethylene-2-phenyl oxazolone: British Drug Houses). This was done by measuring the incorporation of [125I]iododeoxyuridine into the lymph nodes near the site of sensitization as

TABLE 4

Cellular composition and PFC content of the spleens of male CBA mice immunized with sheep erythrocytes 12 months after lethal total-body irradiation and repopulation with bone marrow from young or old syngeneic donors

Age of marrow donor (months)	Days after immunization	Number of spleen cells ($\times 10^{-6}$) mean $\pm$ S.E.		Log_{10} PFC/spleen (mean $\pm$ S.E.)	
		Theta-positive	Theta-negative	Direct	Indirect
3	0	28.2 $\pm$ 5.6	95.2 $\pm$ 1.7	1.81 $\pm$ 0.13	None
26	0	27.7 $\pm$ 8.2	91.4 $\pm$ 27.9	1.65 $\pm$ 0.05	None
3	2	27.3 $\pm$ 3.3	74.2 $\pm$ 9.1	2.23 $\pm$ 0.09	None
26	2	31.0 $\pm$ 2.9	97.3 $\pm$ 17.9	1.87 $\pm$ 0.17	None
3	7	42.0 $\pm$ 3.3	73.3 $\pm$ 1.9	3.97 $\pm$ 0.16	4.21 $\pm$ 0.31
26	7	44.9 $\pm$ 2.7	86.1 $\pm$ 4.3	4.11 $\pm$ 0.65	4.06 $\pm$ 0.61

described by Pritchard & Micklem (1972). The chimeras were constructed exactly as in the previous experiment, except that the old bone marrow donors were only 24 months of age. Oxazolone (10 mg) was applied 26 weeks after irradiation. The results are shown in Fig. 3, the response of normal 3-month-old CBA males being shown also for comparison. Both groups of chimeras had developed near-normal reactivity to oxazolone as judged by this criterion, and no difference was seen between them. The increase in mitotic activity, and hence by inference in DNA synthesis and incorporation of iododeoxyuridine, in the lymph nodes three days after application of oxazolone is mainly if not entirely attributable to the proliferation of T lymphocytes (Davies *et al.* 1969). Mice which are congenitally deficient in T cells show no response (Pritchard & Micklem 1972). Moreover, in radiation chimeras, injected bone marrow is only able to restore the response if the recipients have not been thymectomized (H. Pritchard, unpublished data). It may therefore be assumed that the response in the present experiment was due to T cells which had matured from theta-negative precursors in the injected bone marrow under the influence of the recipient's thymus. Although it is not yet clear how sensitive the assay is to small reductions in the number of T cells available to react, all these observations indicate that a small fraction (5×10^6 cells) of the total bone marrow of a two-year-old mouse contains sufficient progenitors to endow its recipient with both T and B cells approaching normal in both numbers and functional efficiency. This confirms and extends Metcalf's (1965) findings on the colonization of multiple thymus grafts by bone marrow progenitors in ageing mice.

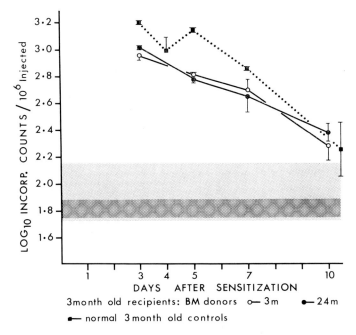

FIG. 3. Uptake of [^{125}I]iododeoxyuridine into regional lymph nodes of male CBA mice after application of oxazolone. Oxazolone was applied 26 weeks after lethal irradiation and restoration with bone marrow from 3-month (○) or 24-month (●) donors. Non-irradiated 3-month-old mice (■) are shown for comparison. Shaded areas indicate 95 % confidence limits for mean uptake of iododeoxyuridine by non-sensitized normal (light shading) or irradiated and restored (dark shading) controls.

IS IT POSSIBLE TO REJUVENATE THE IMMUNE SYSTEM OF OLD MICE?

Approaching the problem from the opposite end, we attempted to enhance the immune responsiveness of ageing mice by injecting them with haemopoietic cells from young syngeneic donors, with or without a neonatal thymus graft in addition. Female CBA mice, 22 months old, were part-body irradiated so that the injected cells could find somewhere to go, the anterior three-quarters of the body being shielded with lead (Ford *et al.* 1966), and the animals were injected intravenously with 5×10^6 bone marrow cells. Twelve weeks later they received 4×10^7 sheep erythrocytes, and the PFC response was assayed on several days. No enhancement of the 7S PFC response was seen after injection of young marrow cells, even when a thymus graft was present (Fig. 4). This confirms that the availability of lymphocyte progenitors is not a limiting factor. Metcalf *et al.* (1967) previously failed to rejuvenate old mice with multiple young thymus or

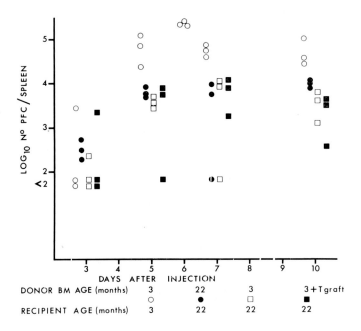

Fig. 4. Indirect haemolytic plaque-forming cells in female CBA mice after injection of sheep erythrocytes. The mice had been part-body irradiated 12 weeks previously and injected with 5×10^6 bone marrow (B.M.) cells.

○   3-month B.M.   →   3-month recipients
□   3-month B.M.   →   22-month recipients
●   22-month B.M.   →   22-month recipients
■   3-month B.M. + neonatal thymus   →   22-month recipients

spleen grafts. However, Makinodan *et al.* (1971*b*) cite preliminary data which suggest that spleen cells which have been primed to *Salmonella typhimurium* antigens afford old recipient mice a measure of protection against challenge with virulent organisms, at least in the short term. If such an approach proves to be generally valid, it will lend further support to the idea that a major defect in old mice is in the initial recognition and handling of antigen. This might itself involve changes in lymphoid tissue architecture, macrophages or hormonal control mechanisms, as well as in T- and B-lymphocytes.

Mice which are deficient in functional T cells (either congenitally or as a result of experimental manipulation) show, like ageing mice, a particularly marked depression of 7S antibody-forming capacity (Taylor & Wortis 1968; Davies *et al.* 1971; Pritchard *et al.* 1973). This might seem to point towards thymic involution as a basic factor in immunological ageing. However, the failure of thymus, spleen or bone marrow-plus-thymus grafts from normal young donors to improve the antibody responses of old mice shows that other factors besides thymic involution and lack of T lymphocytes must be at work.

CONCLUSIONS

No precise picture can yet be drawn of the mechanisms which contribute to age-related changes in immune responsiveness. It seems probable that, as with ageing of the whole mammalian body, different factors will assume major importance under different circumstances. Two conclusions emerge from the present studies.

(1) The capacity to form 7S antibodies during a primary response to sheep erythrocytes is already significantly impaired in CBA male mice at nine months of age—about one-third of the median lifespan.

(2) Haemopoietic stem cells from 24–26-month-old CBA mice manifest no deficiencies in their ability to produce functional lymphocytes when injected into young irradiated recipients. Nor do injected bone marrow cells from young donors improve the immune response of old mice. Thus, although 'old' haemopoietic cell populations may proliferate somewhat less rapidly than 'young' ones when subjected to serial passage, the availability of lymphocyte progenitors in the bone marrow is unlikely normally to limit immune responsiveness in old mice.

ACKNOWLEDGEMENTS

This work was supported by the Medical Research Council.

References

ALBRIGHT, J. F. & MAKINODAN, T. (1966) Growth and senescence of antibody forming cells. *J. Cell. Physiol.* **67** (Suppl. 1), 185–206

BARNES, D. W. H., FORD, C. E., GRAY, S. M. & LOUTIT, J. F. (1959a) Spontaneous and induced changes in cell populations in heavily irradiated mice. *Prog. Nucl. Energy Ser. VI*, **2**, 1–10

BARNES, D. W. H., LOUTIT, J. F. & WESTGARTH, D. R. (1959b) Longevity of radiation-chimaeras. *Gerontologia* **3**, 137–146

BARNES, D. W. H., BRECKON, G., FORD, C. E., MICKLEM, H. S. & OGDEN, D. A. (1967) Fate of lymphoid cells injected into lethally irradiated mice: further experiments, in *The Lymphocyte in Immunology and Haemopoiesis* (Yoffey, J. M., ed.), pp. 207–215, Arnold, London

CANTOR, H. (1972) Two stages in development of lymphocytes, in *Cell Interactions* (Silvestri, L. G., ed.), pp. 172–182, North Holland, Amsterdam

CHEN, M. G. (1971) Age-related changes in hematopoietic stem cell populations of a long-lived hybrid mouse. *J. Cell. Physiol.* **78**, 225–232

COGGLE, J. E. & PROUKAKIS, C. (1970) The effect of age on the bone marrow cellularity of the mouse. *Gerontologia* **16**, 25–29

DAVIES, A. J. S., CARTER, R. L., LEUCHARS, E. & WALLIS, V. (1969) The morphology of immune reactions in normal, thymectomized and reconstituted mice. II. The response to oxazolone. *Immunology* **17**, 111–126

DAVIES, A. J. S., LEUCHARS, E., WALLIS, V. & DOENHOFF, M. J. (1971) A system for lymphocytes in the mouse. *Proc. R. Soc. Lond. B Biol. Sci.* **176**, 369–384

DAVIS, M. L., UPTON, A. C., COSGROVE, G. E. & SATTERFIELD, L. C. (1968) Effect of age of recipient mice on growth and differentiation of transplanted bone marrow cells. *Proc. Soc. Exp. Biol. Med.* **128**, 1149–1153

DAVIS, M. L., UPTON, A. C. & SATTERFIELD, L. C. (1971) Growth and senescence of the bone marrow stem cell pool in RFM/Un mice. *Proc. Soc. Exp. Biol. Med.* **137**, 1452–1458

DRESSER, D. & WORTIS, H. H. (1967) Localized haemolysis in gel, in *Handbook of Experimental Immunology* (Weir, D. M., ed), pp. 1054–1067, Blackwell Scientific Publications, Oxford

DUPLAN, J. F. (1968) Efficacités thérapeutiques comparées des injections de foie foetal ou de moelle osseuse isogéniques chez les souris irradiées. *C.R. Hebd. Séances Acad. Sci. (Paris)* **267**, 227–230

EDWARDS, G. E., MILLER, R. G. & PHILLIPS, R. A. (1970) Differentiation of rosette-forming cells from myeloid stem cells. *J. Immunol.* **105**, 719–729

FORD, C. E., MICKLEM, H. S., EVANS, E. P., GRAY, J. G. & OGDEN, D. A. (1966) The inflow of bone marrow cells to the thymus: studies with part-body irradiated mice injected with chromosome-marked bone marrow and subjected to antigenic stimulation. *Ann. N.Y. Acad. Sci.* **129**, 283–296

KISHIMOTO, S., TSUYUGUCHI, I. & YAMAMURA, Y. (1969) Immune responses in aged mice. *Clin. Exp. Immunol.* **5**, 525–530

KROHN, P. L. (1962) Heterochronic transplantation in the study of ageing. *Proc. R. Soc. Lond. B Biol. Sci.* **157**, 128–147

MAKINODAN, T. & PETERSON, W. J. (1966) Further studies on the secondary antibody-forming potential of juvenile, young adult, adult and aged mice. *Dev. Biol.* **14**, 112–129

MAKINODAN, T., CHINO, F., LEVER, W. E. & BREWEN, B. S. (1971a) The immune systems of mice reared in clean and in dirty conventional laboratory farms. II. Primary antibody-forming activity of young and old mice with long life-spans. *J. Gerontol.* **26**, 508–514

MAKINODAN, T., PERKINS, E. H. & CHEN, M. G. (1971b) Immunologic activity of the aged. *Adv. Gerontol. Res.* **3**, 171–198

METCALF, D. (1965) Multiple thymus grafts in aged mice. *Nature (Lond.)* **208**, 87–88

METCALF, D., MOULDS, R. & PIKE, B. (1967) Influence of the spleen and thymus on immune responses in ageing mice. *Clin. Exp. Immunol.* **2**, 109–120

MICKLEM, H. S. (1972) Cell proliferation in haematopoietic spleen colonies of mice: difference between colonies derived from injected adult bone marrow and foetal liver cells. *Cell Tissue Kinet.* **5**, 159–164

MICKLEM, H. S. & LOUTIT, J. F. (1966) *Tissue Grafting and Radiation*, p. 86, Academic Press, New York

MICKLEM, H. S., FORD, C. E., EVANS, E. P. & GRAY, J. G. (1966) Interrelationships of myeloid and lymphoid cells: experiments with chromosome-marked cells transfused into lethally irradiated recipients. *Proc. R. Soc. Lond. B Biol. Sci.* **165**, 78–102

MICKLEM, H. S., FORD, C. E., EVANS, E. P., OGDEN, D. A. & PAPWORTH, D. S. (1972) Competitive *in vivo* proliferation of foetal and adult haemopoietic cells in lethally irradiated mice. *J. Cell. Physiol.* **79**, 293–298

MILLER, J. F. A. P. & MITCHELL, G. F. (1969) Thymus and antigen-reactive cells. *Transplant. Rev.* **1**, 3–42

NOWELL, P. C., HIRSCH, B. E., FOX, D. H. & WILSON, D. B. (1970) Evidence for the existence of multipotential lympho-hematopoietic stem cells in the adult rat. *J. Cell. Physiol.* **75**, 151–158

PLAYFAIR, J. H. L. & PURVES, E. C. (1971) Antibody formation by bone marrow cells in irradiated mice. *Immunology* **21**, 113–121

PRICE, G. B. & MAKINODAN, T. (1972a) Immunologic deficiencies in senescence. I. Characterization of intrinsic deficiencies. *J. Immunol.* **108**, 403–412

PRICE, G. B. & MAKINODAN, T. (1972b) Immunologic deficiencies in senescence. II. Characterization of extrinsic deficiencies. *J. Immunol.* **108**, 413–417

PRITCHARD, H. & MICKLEM, H. S. (1972) Immune responses in congenitally thymus-less mice. I. Absence of response to oxazolone. *Clin. Exp. Immunol.* **10**, 151–161

PRITCHARD, H., RIDDAWAY, J. & MICKLEM, H. S. (1973) Immune responses in congenitally thymus-less mice. II Quantitative studies of serum immunoglobulins, the antibody response to sheep erythrocytes, and the effect of thymus allografting. *Clin. Exp. Immunol.* **13**, 125–138

PROUKAKIS, C. & LINDOP, P. J. (1967) Age dependence of radiation sensitivity of haemopoietic cells in the mouse. *Nature (Lond.)* **215**, 655–656

RAFF, M. C. (1969) Theta isoantigen as a marker of thymus-derived lymphocytes in mice. *Nature (Lond.)* **224**, 378–379

RAFF, M. C. & WORTIS, H. H. (1970) Thymus dependence of theta-bearing cells in the peripheral lymphoid tissues of mice. *Immunology* **18**, 931–942

ROITT, I. M., GREAVES, M. F., TORRIGIANI, G., BROSTOFF, J. & PLAYFAIR, J. H. L. (1969) The cellular basis of immunological responses. *Lancet* **2**, 367–370

SCHOFIELD, R. (1970) A comparative study of the repopulating potential of grafts from various haemopoietic sources: CFU repopulation. *Cell Tissue Kinet.* **3**, 119–130

SIMINOVITCH, L., McCULLOCH, E. A. & TILL, J. E. (1964) Decline in colony-forming ability of marrow cells subjected to serial transplantation into irradiated mice. *J. Cell. Comp. Physiol.* **64**, 23–32

STJERNSWÄRD, J. (1966) Age-dependent tumor-host barrier and effect of carcinogen-induced immunodepression on rejection of isografted methylcholanthrene-induced sarcoma cells. *J. Natl Cancer Inst.* **37**, 505–512

TAYLOR, R. B. & WORTIS, H. H. (1968) Thymus dependence of antibody response: variation with dose of antigen and class of antibody. *Nature (Lond.)* **220**, 927–928

TELLER, M. N., STOHR, G., CURLETT, W., KUBISEK, M. L., & CURTIS, D. (1964) Aging and cancerigenesis. I. Immunity to tumor and skin grafts. *J. Natl Cancer Inst.* **33**, 649–656

TRENTIN, J. J., WOLF, N., CHENG, V., FAHLBERG, W., WEISS, D. & BONHAG, R. (1967) Antibody production by mice repopulated with limited numbers of clones of lymphoid cell precursors. *J. Immunol.* **97**, 1326–1337

VOLKMAN, A. & GOWANS, J. L. (1965) The origin of macrophages from bone marrow in the rat. *Br. J. Exp. Pathol.* **46**, 62–70

WALDORF, D. S., WILLKENS, R. F. & DECKER, J. L. (1968) Impaired delayed hypersensitivity in an aging population. *J. Am. Med. Assoc.* **203**, 831–834

WU, A. M., TILL, J. E., SIMINOVITCH, L. & McCULLOCH, E. A. (1968) Cytological evidence for a relationship between normal hematopoietic colony-forming cells and cells of the lymphoid system. *J. Exp. Med.* **127**, 455–463

YUHAS, J. M. & STORER, J. B. (1967) The effect of age on two modes of radiation death and on hematopoietic cell survival in the mouse. *Radiat. Res.* **32**, 596–605

Discussion

Metcalf: A combination that might have worked to improve immune responses in the aged mice is a neonatal spleen graft, plus bone marrow cells. I must admit that in our original experiments we did not try this experiment either. Since the stromal elements of the spleen graft remain those of the donor, the internal microenvironment should be satisfactory. Clearly, the bone marrow cells are satisfactory in an old animal, but they need the right environment. Like you, we found that thymus grafts alone did not improve immune responses in old mice, so their deficiency is not simply due to failure of the thymus (Metcalf *et al.* 1967).

Micklem: This would be a very interesting experiment, and would help to sort out whether it was a structural–environmental factor or something to do with overall control, which would presumably act on the spleen graft just as adversely as on the resident spleen. One of the problems with spleen grafts is knowing just how to stimulate them.

Metcalf: Spleen grafts grow best if the host spleen is first removed (Metcalf 1963) so it would be a difficult experiment to compare host spleen with grafted spleen in the same animal. Have you tested spleen cells *in vitro* for their capacity to generate antibody-forming cells to see whether a spleen cell suspension from an aged animal is still deficient *in vitro*?

Micklem: No, I don't think anyone has tried that.

McCulloch: The system you are using requires three cells—B, T, and A cells. Gorczynski *et al.* (1971) have shown that spleens removed from heavily irradiated animals 72 hours after irradiation are an excellent source of A cells. Did you test A cell function in your old recipients?

Micklem: No. I do not know what the results of injecting A cells intravenously would be.

McCulloch: One can test various combinations of all three cell classes.

Micklem: Do they go to the spleen?

McCulloch: Yes.

Stohlman: What is an A cell?

McCulloch: 'A' may stand either for 'accessory' cell or 'adherent' cell. The function of A cells is resistant to ionizing radiation and presumably does not require cellular proliferation. The A cells are required for the humoral response to sheep red cells *in vivo* and in Marbrook chambers.

Thomas: Riches and I have been interested in radioresistant immunologically reactive cells (Riches & Thomas 1970, 1972) and we have tried unsuccessfully to transfer splenic A cells from irradiated donors to irradiated recipients. What are the conditions necessary for the successful transfer of such cells?

McCulloch: Gorczynski *et al.* (1971) injected 10^8 A cells derived from the spleens of animals irradiated 72 hours previously.

Thomas: We used 10^7 cells.

Metcalf: Malcolm Moore and I studied the capacity of stem cells from embryonic or adult animals to undergo extended self-replicating divisions (Metcalf & Moore 1971). No difference was observed between marrow stem cells from young adult or aged mice but foetal liver CFU and particularly those from the yolk sac had a significantly greater capacity for self-generation. It may be that some CFU self-generating divisions are expended in increasing total CFU population size from that in the early embryo to that in the young adult animal.

Micklem: Did you and Moore look at marrow from donors of about four weeks old? The shape of the curve showing the overgrowth of young bone marrow by foetal liver seems to continue for perhaps a couple of months. With very young marrow one might be able to pick out the difference but we have never tried that.

Metcalf: The young adult donors were aged eight weeks.

Micklem: That might be just too late.

Lajtha: Were there identical numbers of CFU in each graft? If not, the growth history of that cell population will be one of an increasingly depopulated milieu. The Toronto workers have shown that if a set number is transferred each time, one is in fact transferring a lower and lower number of CFU (Siminovitch *et al.* 1964). The growth (or repopulation) is slower and slower. However if one allows enough time to make sure that the plateau areas have been reached, and carefully checks that an equal number of active CFU are transferred, one could certainly go up to the sixth passage.

Metcalf: In the experiment I referred to, CFU passages were made from individual spleen colonies at 11–14-day passage intervals.

McCulloch: That does not meet Dr Lajtha's objection. With progressive transfer the doubling time is prolonged. To find out the potential of the CFU to generate new CFU, the prolongation of the doubling time has to be taken into account.

Metcalf: Yes, but at the point where one gets no more colonies induced by passaged spleen colony cells, presumably there are no more CFUs in such colonies.

McCulloch: It is difficult to prevent the experiment from failing, because animals die in the late transfer generation. The ideal way of doing the experiment is to use unirradiated mice of genotype W/W^v. Also, as Dr Lajtha has pointed out, during repeated passages one may pick up endogenous colonies from the recipients.

Metcalf: Not if one uses a T6 marker system.

McCulloch: It is because of the presence of the T6 marker that the Harwell group were able to identify endogenous cells.

Yoffey: Are the Peyer's patches in intestinal lymphoid tissue completely out of all this ageing business? Anatomically that is possibly the most striking area for age changes. The young rabbit has a Peyer's patch with 50 or 60 nodules and in older rabbits one nodule after another seems to drop out. Do intestinal lymphoid tissues have B or T cells?

Micklem: They have both, but perhaps a rather greater proportion of B cells than the lymph nodes. This must be rather variable, depending on the functional state of the Peyer's patch.

Yoffey: They are extremely active proliferation areas, whatever the cells they are producing.

Micklem: Part of the population is certainly a recirculating one.

Lajtha: I was very interested in your finding of the 'bed' effect, i.e. that the young animal offered a better milieu. Maybe this is what matters most in all the ageing phenomena, and it may be the fibroblast or the endothelial populations that really determine the response. The evidence was accepted for residual damage accumulating in the haemopoietic system with chronic irradiation, but somehow nobody looked at the cellular effect as opposed to the 'bed' effect. We did that not very long ago. After four or five doses of 450 rads at monthly intervals, the recovery of the CFU became slower and slower in the femur. However when these cells are grafted into a standard recipient they grow in it at identical rates to identical plateaus. The residual damage of irradiation is clearly a 'bed' effect.

Micklem: As far as ageing of immune systems goes, some of the data of Makinodan & Peterson (1966) show that there is a functional deficiency in spleen cell suspensions transferred from old donors to young adult recipients. It seems probable that this deficiency resides in cells which are readily brought into suspension—i.e. lymphoid cells—although the fact that they are deficient might reflect some irreversible effect of the old 'bed' from which they have come.

Metcalf: I think one must be careful about making generalizations about immune defects in aged mice. There are sufficient differences in detail between the results of Makinodan & Peterson (1964) and our own (Metcalf *et al.* 1967) to make me suspect that the exact nature of the deficiency in old age may vary from strain to strain. In C57BL mice there is no shortage of stem cells capable of seeding in the thymus, as aged mice can repopulate multiple neonatal thymus grafts (Metcalf 1965). The reason why the host thymus is atrophic in old age relates to ageing processes in the epithelial and stromal cells of the thymus. Even in aged animals bearing multiple thymus grafts, the T-dependent areas of the spleen and lymph nodes are still depleted of cells (Metcalf *et al.* 1967) and I conclude from this that the aged stromal elements in these organs are also incapable of supporting normal lymphopoiesis after antigenic stimulation.

Lajtha: In those experiments the grafts usually had a prolonged history in a deficient or damaged host. That history would affect their subsequent fate for potential growth or differentiation.

Micklem: To underline what Dr Metcalf said about strain differences, we have found normal numbers of theta-positive (i.e. presumably thymus-processed) lymphocytes in the lymph nodes of three-year-old CBA mice. It looks as if the deficiency here is at some later stage than the generation of 'T'-lymphocytes.

References

GORCZYNSKI, R. M., MILLER, R. G. & PHILLIPS, R. A. (1971) *In vivo* requirement for a radiation-resistant cell in the immune response to sheep erythrocytes. *J. Exp. Med.* **134**, 1201

MAKINODAN, T. & PETERSON W. J. (1964) Growth and senescence of the primary antibody-forming potential of the spleen. *J. Immunol.* **93**, 886-896

MAKINODAN, T. & PETERSON, W. J. (1966) Secondary antibody-forming potential of mice in relation to age – its significance in senescence. *Dev. Biol.* **14**, 96–111

METCALF, D. (1963) Spleen graft growth in splenectomized mice. *Aust. J. Exp. Biol. Med. Sci.* **41**, 51–60

METCALF, D. (1965) Multiple thymus grafts in aged mice. *Nature (Lond.)* **208**, 87–88

METCALF, D. & MOORE, M. A. S. (1971) *Haemopoietic Cells*, North-Holland, Amsterdam

METCALF, D., MOULDS, R. & PIKE, B. (1967) Influence of the spleen and thymus on immune responses in ageing mice. *Clin. Exp. Immunol.* **2**, 109–120

RICHES, A. C. & THOMAS, D. B. (1970). The effects of X-irradiation and anti-lymphocyte serum on the responses to tumour allografts. *Br. J. Cancer*, **24**, 833–842

RICHES, A. C. & THOMAS, D. B. (1972) The ablation of sensitation of bone marrow allografts. *Proc. Soc. Exp. Biol. Med.* **141**, 731–734

SIMINOVITCH, L., TILL, J. E. & McCULLOCH, E. A. (1964) Decline in colony-forming ability of marrow cells subjected to serial transplantation into irradiated mice. *J. Cell. Comp. Physiol.* **64**, 23–32

Hyperplasia of myeloid and lymphoid tissue (pseudo-leucosis) in mice bearing passaged sarcomas

M. R. BLAND, J. F. LOUTIT and JANET M. SANSOM

MRC Radiobiology Unit, Harwell, Berkshire

Abstract Cancerous human subjects frequently have leucocytosis, occasionally pseudoleukaemia. In mice some passaged tumours are consistently associated with pseudoleukaemia (granulocytic).

Barnes *et al.* (1971) have reported two series of chimerical mice in which sarcomas of subcutaneous connective tissue were induced by either Millipore cellulose filters or silicone rubber plaques. Although there is little to suggest that the animals bearing primary tumours had gross leucocytic abnormalities, the tumours when passaged in series to normal mice frequently, though not consistently, produced at some stage of passage a splenomegaly associated with granulocytic leucocytosis. However, two tumours have for many generations of passage produced a consistent pattern. The first produced splenomegaly with granulocytosis after two weeks; observed metastasis was extremely rare. The second, with variable but slight lymphocytosis in blood, was associated with early hyperplasia of lymphatic tissue excluding thymus and with late metastasis as 'reticulosarcoma' in liver, spleen and mesenteric nodes.

In both, excess colony-forming units (CFU) were found in hyperplastic spleens and in circulating blood—early in the former, late in the latter. No excess of CFU was found in hyperplastic lymph nodes.

Leukaemoid states are well recognized as an occasional feature of malignant disease (Editorial 1967). They are still not fully explained, although 'leukoviruses' have been incriminated in man (Moore & Pickren 1967) and Rous sarcoma virus in rats (Pollard 1970).

In mice Bateman (1951) investigated selected transplanted myoepitheliomas and fibrosarcomas to demonstrate increasing granulocytosis with increasing size of tumour. Delmonte *et al.* (1966) produced either granulocytosis or thrombocytosis according to the mammary carcinoma used. From the former they isolated a 'granulocytosis-promoting factor' which was non-dialysable and protein-free (Delmonte & Liebelt 1965), though a later report (Delmonte *et al.* 1968) puts the molecular weight at less than 2000. This factor thus differs from the leucocytosis-inducing factor of Gordon (Katz et al. 1966).

Smith & Congdon (1957) used the blood of mice bearing carcinoma-A280 to demonstrate that this blood, like normal marrow, was able to correct the radiation syndrome of lethally X-irradiated mice.

THE PRESENT MATERIAL

Recently, having induced sarcomas in murine radiation chimeras by sub-cutaneous implantation of cell-impermeable discs—Millipore filters or silicone rubber—we demonstrated that the tumours arose from host tissue and not from cells derived from the donated myeloid tissue (Barnes et al. 1971). From the records we found that only in the mice with Millipore filters was any spleen enlarged, there being one moderate enlargement ($+$) and six slight enlargements ($\pm$) out of 20 tumorous mice. However, on serial routine passage of the total of 39 tumours arising from both inducing agents, considerable enlargement of the spleen was common as a temporary or persistent phenomenon. This was accompanied usually by granulocytosis, but in one case by generalized enlarge-ment of lymph tissue other than thymus. Like Smith & Congdon (1957), therefore, we investigated whether in such animals the peripheral blood drawn by cardiac puncture contained haemopoietic stem cells in excess of normal (Barnes & Loutit 1967). The colony-forming units (CFU) per million nucleated cells were measured by the method of J. E. Till and E. A. McCulloch as modified by Barnes et al. (1968).

RESULTS

Normal CBA mice 3–6 months old. The mean count of nucleated cells in the blood of 11 mice was 7.0 (range 3.8 to 10.0) $\times$ 10^6 cm^{-3} and of CFU 3.4 (range 1 to 8) 10^{-6} nucleated cells, i.e. from 10–77 cm^{-3} of blood. These figures are higher than reported earlier (Barnes & Loutit 1967), owing to the greater sensitivity of the modified method. For the present purpose more than 10 CFU/10^6 leucocytes and more than 100 CFU cm^{-3} blood will be considered abnormal.

Chimeras bearing induced primary tumours. Only five chimeras were tested, their leucocyte counts ranging from 8 to 13 $\times$ 10^6 cm^{-3}. The CFU numbered 50–305 cm^{-3}, i.e. higher than in young normal adults, but no comparable series of non-tumour-bearing chimeras has been tested.

CBA mice bearing passaged tumours. Twenty tumours were first tested during passages 1 to 5 (two being tested twice), 12 during passages 6 to 10 (three twice), and six during passages 11 to 15 (one twice). The numbers giving more than 100 CFU cm^{-3} blood were 6/20, 8/12 and 2/6 respectively. Those that were repeated either within these series of passage or between series did not necessarily agree in having normal or raised numbers of CFU. The conclusion for the present must be that uncontrolled factors played a part.

Two tumours warrant special mention. (1) M5633 was noted from the first passage to cause marked and consistent splenomegaly (Fig. 1) in the hosts by the time they were killed for passing the tumour. This was associated with granulocytic leucocytosis that frequently qualified for the term pseudoleukaemia ($> 5 \times 10^7$ leucocytes cm^{-3} blood with the presence of primitive cells of the

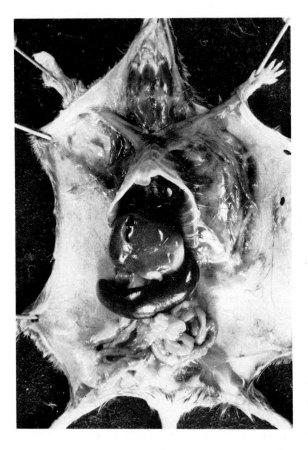

FIG. 1. Tumour M5633 (passage 33) in subcutis of left chest: 25 days' growth; grossly enlarged spleen.

TABLE 1

CFU in peripheral blood of mice bearing tumours M5633 and M5676

Tumour	Passage no.	Residence time : days	WBC cm^{-3} ($\times$ 10^{-6})	CFU 10^{-6} WBC	CFU cm^{-3}
M 5633	7	23	25	32	800
	10	21	40	30	1200
	11	14	7.4	18	130
	12	7	5.3	13	69
	21	34	25	16	400
	23	39	272	10	2700
	30	22	30	18	540
	31	21	20	27	540
	31	28	40	20	800
	32	31	224	24	5400
	32	45	52	36	1900
M 5676	5	45	30	9	270
	22	24	13	7	91
	23	16	5	5	25
	23	41	9.5	31	290
	24	31	10	4	40
	24b	38	9.5	35	330
	24b	45	29	> 42	> 1200

granular series). Passage intravenously of whole blood produced no visible result in recipients. Table 1 shows that after two weeks of residence by the tumour the peripheral blood consistently contained > 100 CFU cm^{-3} (indeed up to 5000) with a concentration of $> 10 \times 10^{-6}$ leucocytes. (2) M5676 was recorded as causing moderate splenomegaly in its hosts from the first passage. On the fifth passage generalized enlargement of lymph nodes, but not thymus, was noted and this was consistent thereafter (Fig. 2). The peripheral blood leucocyte count varied from the normal range to 3×10^7 cm^{-3} with the usual predominance of mononuclear lymphocytic forms, sometimes with a few blast-type cells. The peripheral blood contained > 100 CFU cm^{-3} (Table 1) when the tumour had been resident in the host for five or more weeks.

In the later passages of these tumours, bone marrow, spleen and lymph nodes were tested for their content of CFU and the results are given in Table 2. From the limited information available one can be confident that (1) both tumours induce an increased concentration of CFU in spleen (and up to > 10 times increased mass of spleen with M5633), and (2) the gross enlargement of lymphatic tissue due to M5676 is not associated with an increased concentration of CFU. The concentration in bone marrow may be marginally increased

TABLE 2

CFU in tissues of mice bearing tumours M5633 and M5676

Tumour	Passage no.	Residence time : days	CFU 10^{-5} bone marrow cells	CFU 10^{-6} spleen cells	CFU 10^{-6} lymph node cells
M 5633	30	22	> 25	—	—
	31	21	36	> 170	—
	31	28	31	150	—
	32	31	5	220	—
	32	45	23	150	—
M 5676	22	24	24	—	< 1
	23	16	22	—	—
	23	41	51	—	<0.5
	24	31	25	—	<0.7
	24b	38	42	160	—
	24b	45	57	150	<0.2
	25	30	—	—	<0.3 (axillary) 0.16 (mixed) 0.26 (mesenteric)
Normal		Range	5–30	1–10	< 1

by both tumours.

M5633 with its capacity to induce granulocytosis appears very similar to others already described (e.g. Parsons 1935; Barnes & Sisman 1939; Lappat & Cawein 1964). Histologically there is hyperplasia of granulocytopoietic elements in the bone marrow, intense myeloid hyperplasia, especially for granulopoiesis, in the red pulp of the spleen and scattered collections of granulocyte precursors in liver and other tissues. The original tumour, M5633, was a mass invading muscle and composed of fairly uniform ovoid cells, freely peppered with small round cells, not all of which could be attributed to tumour cells in cross-section, but there was no aggregation of lymphocytes at the margins. In passage it retained its oat-cell character but was always notably infiltrated with granulo-cytes (Fig. 3), and it was prone to central degeneration and liquefaction. Metastasis to local lymph nodes has been observed, on one occasion only, when growth was unduly slow.

M5676 presents different features. Though leucocytosis has not been out-standing, the constant splenomegaly and, since the fifth passage, the generalized

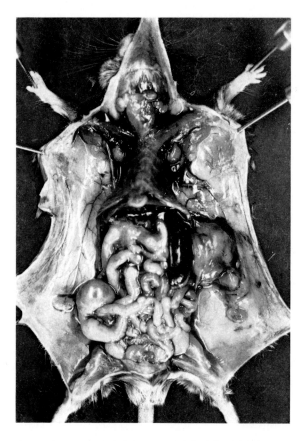

Fig. 2. Tumour M5676 (passage 24) in left abdominal wall: 31 days' growth; moderately enlarged spleen, enlarged lymph nodes—anterior cervical, axillary, inguinal and mesenteric—and prominent Peyer's patches.

enlargement of lymph nodes suggested lymphomatosis. However, on two occasions (passages 15 and 18) concentrated suspensions of axillary lymph nodes passed both subcutaneously and intraperitoneally were without effect on recipients.

The original tumour penetrated the panniculus carnosus and was composed of fusiform cells irregularly arranged and of varying size with some uninucleate and occasionally multinucleate giant cells. There was focal haemorrhage and necrosis and diffuse infiltration by small cells with dense nuclei (probably lymphocytes) and granulocytes but no aggregations of these (Fig. 4). By the fifth passage the cells were loosely woven, stellate and round as well as fusiform; in still later passages (9, 13, 17, 19, 21 and 24) this looseness and anaplastic

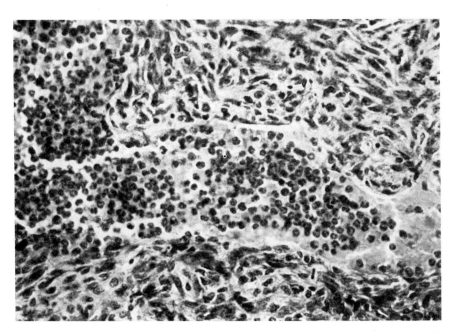

FIG. 3. Tumour M5633 (passage 1), sarcoma composed of irregularly arranged fusiform cells around blood vessel stuffed with granulocytes, many immature (× 450).

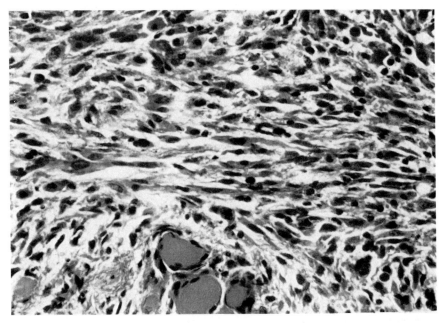

FIG. 4. Tumour M5676 (original): growing edge of sarcoma, fusiform cells invading panniculus carnosus with scattering of small round cells (× 450).

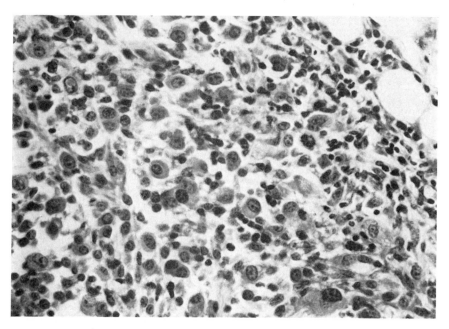

FIG. 5. Tumour M5676 (passage 13): edge invading dermal fat, now of a looser texture with prominent large rounded cells and peppered with small round cells (× 450).

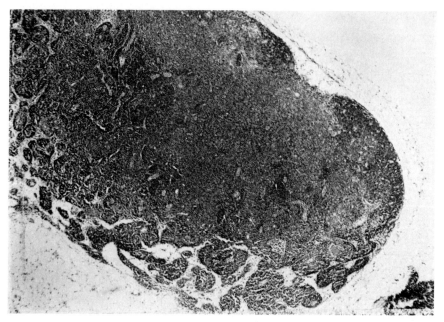

FIG. 6. Mesenteric lymph node of M5676 (passage 25 after 24 days): non-specific hyperplasia especially of paracortical zone (× 40).

rounding of cells seemed still more notable (Fig. 5). Infiltration with granulocytes and lymphocytes was variable but multicentric necrosis was constant.

From the fifth passage onwards the lymph nodes and Malpighian bodies of the spleen appeared diffusely hyperplastic but without notable formation of germinal centres or crescents. In the nodes the paracortical areas were stuffed with slightly leptochromatic small lymphocytes, the medullary cords being rich in plasma cells, with some granulocytes (Fig. 6). In the spleen the red pulp was also hyperplastic, with myeloid tissue in about the normal differential proportions (Fig. 7).

The anatomical and histological appearances, therefore, suggested a diagnosis of pseudolymphomatosis, in accord with the failure for the condition to be passed by suspensions of lymph nodal cells. This provisional diagnosis was revised when the passaged tumour was allowed to remain for about a week longer than the usual month. Then spleen, liver and mesenteric lymph nodes showed histologically miliary 'granulomas', the nodules occasionally coalescing. These lesions consisted of pale-staining cells, indistinct in outline, ovoid or polygonal, sometimes with multinucleate giant cells and, with silver impregna-

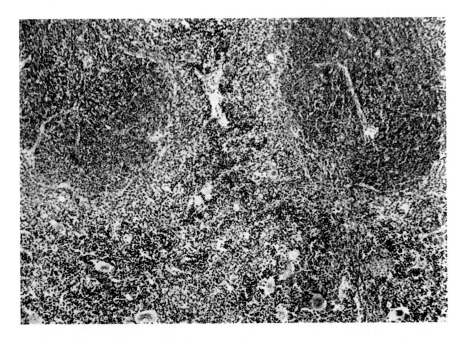

FIG. 7. Spleen of M5676 (passage 25 after 24 days): hyperplasia of both lymphoid tissue in Malpighian bodies and myeloid tissue in red pulp ($\times$ 40).

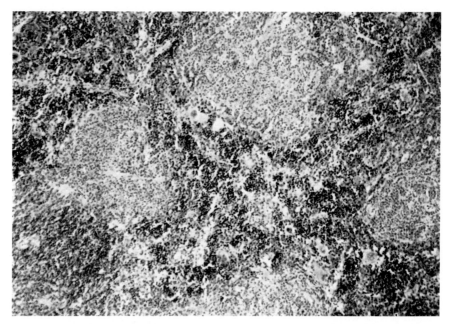

FIG. 8. Spleen of M5676 (passage 24 after 38 days): gross myeloid hyperplasia of red pulp with miliary 'granulomas' composed of epithelioid and giant cells overlaid with eosinophil granulocytes (× 110).

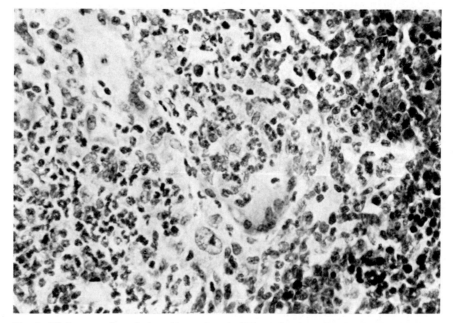

FIG. 9. High power view of edge of 'granuloma' of Fig. 8 abutting red pulp, right (× 465).

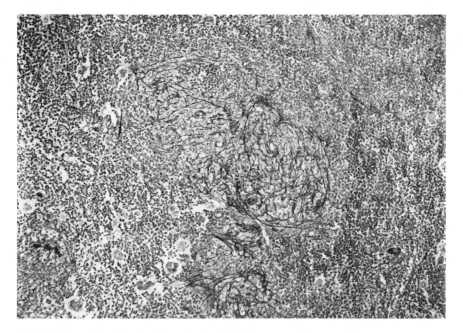

FIG. 10. 'Granulomas' stained for reticulin ($\times$ 110).

tion, many reticulin fibrils; the whole was overlaid heavily with mature and immature granulocytes, often eosinophilic (Figs. 8–10). This picture only remotely resembled that of the primary tumour. However, suspensions of spleen and mesenteric lymph node on passage subcutaneously reproduced at the site of injection the round cell tumour with general lymphatic hyperplasia. The revised diagnosis is now 'reticulosarcoma' with metastasis to abdominal organs with generalized lymphomyeloid stimulation.

DISCUSSION

Sarcomas induced in subcutaneous tissues of radiation chimeras may have had some stimulant action on haemopoiesis and haemopoietic stem cells of bone marrow. However, most of these animals were killed within a few days of the tumours becoming clinically manifest, so that any resulting splenomegaly had little time to develop. When passaged the tumours were allowed to grow to a substantial size and then splenomegaly was commonly but not universally associated with carriage of the tumour. Mostly this splenomegaly was not a persistent phenomenon with continued passage, although it did persist with two tumours, M5633 and M5676.

M5633 was associated regularly with a granulocytic pseudoleukaemia. After a granulocytosis-promoting factor had been isolated from a tumour (Delmonte & Liebelt 1965), Delmonte (1967*a*, *b*) showed that subfractions have a stimulant action on marrow CFU. There is little room in marrow, however, for expansion; indeed Milas & Tomljanovic (1971) show some hypoplasia associated with increased CFU. Here, we show that with perhaps a 20-fold enlargement of the spleen and a tenfold increase in CFU concentration the stimulatory effect is much more marked there than in marrow. Concomitantly a vastly increased traffic of CFU in the peripheral blood has been demonstrated with concentrations of CFU increased 10–100-fold. This tumour seems to require about two weeks of residence for the effects to be demonstrable.

M5676 in the first few passages seemed to be just another tumour which induced moderate splenomegaly but afterwards, additionally and consistently, caused generalized hyperplasia of peripheral lymphatic tissue. (It cannot yet be affirmed whether the current line is a true descendant of the original or a passenger picked up and selected through the multiple passages.) Histologically it now takes the form of 'reticulosarcoma' and certainly it metastasizes late to abdominal organs, in which microenvironment it takes on a different histological appearance. The generalized lymphatic hyperplasia which precedes overt metastasis may represent a reaction to still earlier haematogenous dissemination but failure to colonize at that stage. If this reaction is immunological it is outstandingly fulsome. Alternatively it may be humoral, the lymphatic tissue as well as myeloid tissue in bone marrow and red pulp of spleen being stimulated by a product, or mixture of products, from the tumour. The enlargement of spleen and lymph nodes is evident after two weeks of residence of the tumour, but no increase in traffic of CFU in the blood was seen until the residence time exceeded a month and no pseudoleukaemia was recorded. If the agents responsible are humoral, they must differ from those in M5633.

ACKNOWLEDGEMENTS

We thank Mrs C. Smith and Mr J. W. Asante for histological preparations and Mr G. Wilkins for photographs.

References

BARNES, D. W. H. & LOUTIT, J. F. (1967) Haemopoietic stem cells in the peripheral blood.

Lancet 2, 1138–1141

BARNES, W. A. & SISMAN, I. E. (1939) Myeloid leukemia and non-malignant extramedullary myelopoiesis in mice. *Am. J. Cancer* 37, 1–35

BARNES, D. W. H., EVANS, E. P., FORD, C. E. & WEST, B. J. (1968) Spleen colonies in mice: karyotypic evidence of multiple colonies from single cells. *Nature (Lond.)* 219, 518–520

BARNES, D. W. H., EVANS, E. P. & LOUTIT, J. F. (1971) Local origin of fibroblasts deduced from sarcomas induced in chimaeras by implants of pliable discs. *Nature (Lond.)* 233, 267–268

BATEMAN, J. C. (1951) Leukemoid reactions to transplanted mouse tumours. *J. Natl Cancer Inst.* 11, 671–678

DELMONTE, L. (1967a) Time-and dose-dependent-stimulation of hemopoietic colony-forming potential with granulocytosis-promoting factor (GPF) in inbred mice. *Exp. Hematol.* 12, 57–62

DELMONTE, L. (1967b) Factors modifying the 'hemopoietin'-induced mobilisation of hemopoietic colony-forming units. *Exp. Hematol.* 14, 3–7

DELMONTE, L. & LIEBELT, R. A. (1965) Granulocytosis-promoting extract of mouse tumor tissue: partial purification. *Science (Wash. D.C.)* 148, 521–523

DELMONTE, L., LIEBELT, A. G. & LIEBELT, R. A. (1966) Granulopoiesis and thrombopoiesis in mice bearing transplanted mammary cancer. *Cancer Res.* 26, 149–159

DELMONTE, L., STARBUCK, W. C. & LIEBELT, R. A. (1968) Species dependent concentration of granulocytosis-promoting factor in mammalian tissues. *Am. J. Physiol.* 215, 768–773

EDITORIAL (1967) Annotation: leukaemoid reactions. *Lancet* 2, 408

KATZ, R., GORDON, A. S. & LAPIN, D. M. (1966) Mechanisms of leucocyte production and release. VI. Studies on the purification of leucocytosis-inducing factor (L.I.F.) *J. Reticuloendothel. Soc.* 3, 103–116

LAPPAT, E. J. & CAWEIN, M. (1964) A study of the leukemoid response to transplantable A–280 tumor in mice. *Cancer Res.* 24, 302–311

MILAS, L. & TOMLJANOVIC, M. (1971) Spleen colony-forming capacity of bone marrow from mice bearing fibrosarcoma. *Rev. Eur. Etud. Clin. Biol.* 16, 462–465

MOORE, G. E. & PICKREN, J. W. (1967) Study of a virus-containing hematopoietic cell line and a melanoma cell line derived from a patient with a leukemoid reaction. *Lab. Invest.* 16, 882–891

PARSONS, L. D. (1935) Leukaemia coincident with and transmissable by a spindle-cell sarcoma in the mouse. *J. Pathol. Bacteriol.* 40, 45–50

POLLARD, M. (1970) Leukemoid changes induced in germ-free and conventional rats by Rous Sarcoma Virus. *J. Reticuloendothel. Soc.* 7, 254–263

SMITH, L. H. & CONGDON, C. C. (1957) Leukemoid blood and leucocytes in treatment of radiation lethality. *Arch. Pathol.* 63, 502–507

Discussion

Metcalf: Over the years we have looked at *in vitro* colony-forming cell levels in mice with many types of leukaemia and tumours. All AKR mice with lymphoid leukaemia exhibit a granulocytosis, sometimes with peripheral blood levels as high as 200 000 cells/mm³. When the levels of colony-forming cells in the bone marrow and spleen were determined in such mice, puzzling combinations were sometimes observed. Many mice had large numbers of colony-forming cells, as expected, but some mice with high granulocyte levels had virtually no colony-forming cells. In such mice the intravascular lifespan of granulocytes may have been prolonged.

Then there are certain tumours that characteristically produce splenomegaly without infiltrating the spleen—breast tumours are outstanding in this regard. In almost all such tumour-bearing mice, the content of colony-forming cells in bone marrow is slightly increased, and that in the spleen much more so (Hibberd & Metcalf 1971). The spleen appears to be a more reactive organ in this regard than the marrow. It is difficult to know what provokes this response. All these tumours are antigenic in the mouse, so antigenic stimulation is a possible factor, and antigenic stimulation certainly provokes the appearance of increased numbers of colony-forming cells in the spleen and marrow (McNeill 1970; Metcalf 1971). Many tumours may actually produce colony-stimulating factor (CSF) and so stimulate colony-forming cells. Outstanding in this regard has been the myelomonocytic leukaemia WEHI-3. When WEHI-3 leukaemic cells are mixed in agar culture with bone marrow cells the normal cells are stimulated to form colonies (Metcalf *et al.* 1969).

Lajtha: I have similar evidence that in transplanted RF leukaemias soon after inoculation, a stage is reached when there is a significant increase in absolute numbers of CFU–C in the spleen, but not in the bone marrow. This was rather similar to your finding in virus leukaemia, Dr Metcalf: an increase in the spleen by a factor of 10, without significant changes in the femur. However, this is a transient phase because as the leukaemic population grows—but well before it reaches 10% of the normal bone marrow cellularity—both CFU–C and CFU–S start declining in the spleen and in the femur. This 'milieu' effect is likely to be produced by a humoral product of the tumour. We are trying to reproduce this with some tumour extracts.

Metcalf: Some of the most active tumours in stimulating granulopoiesis in the host have been mixed tumours of the salivary gland (P. M. Bealmear, personal communication). This stimulation occurs also in germ-free mice, which would seem to eliminate microbial flora as a mechanism. It is of interest of course that the salivary gland contains the highest extractable content of CSF (Sheridan & Stanley 1971).

Shreiner: The thrombocytosis that occurs with a variety of tumours in human beings has usually been considered as a reactive thrombocytosis. This does not really explain whether the thrombocytosis is the result of an immunological reaction or perhaps the result of a humoral substance produced by the tumour.

Lajtha: We would like to believe the humoral theory but we have not managed to prove it yet. Tanaka was successful in producing pseudoleukaemias or leukaemoid reactions in a large proportion of appropriately treated RF mice

(Tanaka & Craig 1970). The histopathological picture and the morbid anatomy were remarkably like those of leukaemia, except that pseudoleukaemia was never transferable and was virtually self-limiting.

Winterhalter: What happens if you treat healthy animals with plasma from the tumour-bearing animals, Dr Loutit?

Loutit: This has not been done yet. Neither the tissue fluids nor even the tissues have been assayed chemically or biologically.

Metcalf: A proliferation of granulocytes or macrophages associated with the presence of a tumour need not be too surprising, as these are cells known to react to the presence of foreign material. You showed, however, evidence for an increase in erythropoiesis and this is more puzzling. I wonder whether some mechanism causes an increase in the number of microenvironmental foci in the spleen capable of supporting erythropoiesis? If a tumour-bearing animal had ten spleens, would all of them show increased activity or is there some overall sensor mechanism controlling total spleen cellularity?

Thomas: In albino mice which are rejecting a subcutaneous implant of an allogeneic adenocarcinoma, splenomegaly is associated with extensive myeloid metaplasia and the splenic erythroblast population is greatly enlarged. In such circumstances, it may be that by accommodating extra erythroblasts the spleen relieves the pressure on microenvironments elsewhere, that are required to accommodate cell populations which unlike erythroblasts cannot be maintained satisfactorily in the microenvironment provided by the spleen.

Stohlman: Is there any fibrosis in the bone marrow, Dr Loutit? Does the distribution of white cells in marginal pools, storage pools and so forth change?

Loutit: Ordinary histology of the marrow certainly shows no fibrosis. In the granulocytic pseudoleukaemia the marrow is very markedly granulocytic compared with the normal, just as the spleen is. In the other tumour, the marrow seems to be distributed normally between the various elements, just as the splenic pulp is. There is erythroid hyperplasia, megakaryocyte hyperplasia and, less prominently, granulocytic hyperplasia in this pseudolymphomatous animal.

Yoffey: Do viruses enter into this at all? Dr Metcalf referred to germ-free animals and I don't think these eliminate viruses.

Loutit: Viruses are now commonly associated with tumours, and without a comprehensive survey one cannot say whether there is virus or not. If a virus is isolated it is difficult to show whether it is a passenger or inductive. Of the 40 tumours induced, 38 were tested for circulating CFU on one or more occasions. Increased traffic of CFU so determined was usually associated with splenic enlargement. This could be explained, purely speculatively, by a virus manifestation at that particular time, but no attempt has been made to confirm this speculation. In the two lines with persistent splenomegaly one could say that a viral tumour genome was responsible but again I have not looked at this.

McCulloch: Was necrosis in other areas of the two tumours less extensive than you showed in the figures?

Loutit: Necrosis was constant.

McCulloch: I wonder if tissue necrosis supplies part of the mechanism. Are tumours associated with increased granulocyte production more or less necrotic than other tumours?

Loutit: The granulocyte-producing tumour is fairly typical in appearance. By three weeks or later it is really a bag with an outer rim of tumour tissue and a central core of what looks like pus but is mostly semi-fluid gunk. The other tumour is substantially solid but with multiple foci of necrosis, presumably related to its outgrowing its blood supply in various local regions.

Astaldi: Have you any information on the mechanism of the relationship between the tumour and the myeloid reaction?

Loutit: No.

Metcalf: Our favourite mouse system for studying the response of colony-forming cells and granulopoiesis to the tumour-bearing state is mice carrying certain plasma cell tumours. These tumour cells form distinctive colonies in agar and it is therefore possible to assay precisely the number of tumour cells actually infiltrating the bone marrow or spleen.

Most tumour-bearing animals show an overall reduction in bone marrow cellularity but often a rise in the frequency of *in vitro* colony-forming cells. I am at a loss to explain why the cellularity of the marrow decreases—it does not parallel thymus weight loss.

Lajtha: In the tumours which you described as looking like a bag, how does the reaction compare with that seen after, say, a turpentine abscess, Dr Loutit?

Loutit: They are much larger than any turpentine abscess that I have induced. These tumours can grow to an enormous size, and presumably hold 3 or 4 ml of the fluid. Extensive granulocyte infiltration appears in the oedematous tissue around them.

Winterhalter: Presumably you do the passage by transplanting a piece of the pouch. What happens if you transplant the fluid?

Loutit: I have not tried that. Smears and sections show that the fluid is very largely acellular. Are you thinking of its viral content?

Winterhalter: Yes.

Loutit: One would have to ensure then that it was cell-free fluid that one was passaging.

References

HIBBERD, A. & METCALF, D. (1971) Proliferation of macrophage and granulocyte precursors in response to primary and transplanted tumours. *Isr. J. Med. Sci.* **7**, 202–210

McNEILL, T. A. (1970) Antigenic stimulation of bone marrow colony-forming cells. III. Effect *in vivo. Immunology* **18**, 61–72

METCALF, D. (1971) Antigen-induced proliferation *in vitro* of bone marrow precursors of granulocytes and macrophages. *Immunology* **20**, 727–738

METCALF, D., MOORE, M. A. S. & WARNER, N. (1969) Colony formation *in vitro* by myelo-monocytic leukemic cells. *J. Natl Cancer Inst.* **43**, 983–1001

SHERIDAN, J. & STANLEY, E. R. (1971) Tissue sources of bone marrow colony stimulating factor. *J. Cell. Physiol.* **78**, 951–954

TANAKA, T. & CRAIG, A. W. (1970) A leukaemoid response in 3-methylcholanthrene-treated RF strain of mice. *Neoplasma* **17**, 499–504

General discussion

Loutit: Dr Lajtha and others have suggested that during this final discussion we might make a list of the things that need to be done next and assign some priority to them.

There are also various points arising out of the meeting which people may want to discuss further. For example, Professor Yoffey wants to follow up the problem of pluripotent stem cells, particularly as populations.

POPULATION CONTROL

Metcalf: We all agree, I am sure, that we must develop technology that will allow us to obtain pure populations of haemopoietic cells of various types. The corollary of this is that we should make every effort to purify chemically the regulatory factors which have been detected. In this way it will be possible to work with purified regulators and purified target cells, ideally using *in vitro* cloning systems.

McCulloch: There is no generally accepted technique for studying pluripotent stem cells in cultures.

Dicke: But there is already such an assay available, namely the thin-layer agar technique.

McCulloch: Your procedure is too cumbersome for use even if it proves that CFU–S is being detected. You require pretreatment with vinblastine followed by a separation procedure. Your procedure, therefore, is selective and time-consuming. As an assay it is not very useful.

Dicke: The fact that only in colonies derived from stem cell concentrates can the replication of CFU–S be demonstrated is no argument against the concept that the haemopoietic stem cell is involved in colony formation in the thin-layer agar system. Replication and differentiation are two distinctly different properties of the haemopoietic stem cell and in analogy to the *in vivo* situation those properties may not always be linked to each other and can be influenced separately by various regulators (Dicke *et al.* 1971).

McCulloch: What is needed is a straightforward method that can be applied to marrow, spleen, foetal liver or any other appropriate tissue. If it is necessary to manipulate the donor in advance, the value of this procedure goes way down.

Dicke: You are asking for two things: first an assay which can demonstrate the presence of haemopoietic stem cells in a suspension—a quantitative parameter for haemopoietic stem cells—and secondly, a method by which you can study the two properties of the haemopoietic stem cell: self-replication and differentiation into the different haemopoietic cell lines. In the latter case expression of both properties in such an assay is necessary, whereas in the former situation expression of only one of the properties is sufficient. The thin-layer system is specifically designed as a quantitative assay for haemopoietic stem cells.

McCulloch: There is probably no disagreement between us. A useful, reliable, simple technique that everybody could agree on, that really gave a pluripotent stem cell, would be a tremendous advantage.

MORE ABOUT MORPHOLOGY

Winterhalter: Any disagreement between you seems to be basically, that you, Dr Yoffey, postulate that there is a single type of cell, a pluripotent stem cell, with a unique morphology. But from the earlier discussions at this meeting I concluded that there was a spectrum of morphologies, each type being a potential candidate for the title of pluripotent stem cell. I am less sure that there can be a pool of cells of uniform morphology which all do different things, one of them being to act as a pluripotent stem cell.

Yoffey: The existence of a pluripotent stem cell was first shown by the Harwell group (Barnes *et al.* 1959) using chromosome markers. Dr McCulloch's group, using spleen colonies, later showed that erythroid and granulocytic colonies with the same marker developed from one cell (Becker *et al.* 1963; Wu *et al.* 1967). Did you also get megakaryocytes, Dr McCulloch?

McCulloch: Yes, and markers present in colonies have also been demonstrated in lymphoid cells and in lung macrophages.

Yoffey: I think Dr Dicke and the Bristol group would plump for the same type of cell morphologically. The only difference may be on the question of size, but I do not think Dr Dicke would really differ on this. If the stem cells really are of constant size, then as they differentiate new stem cells must feed in from another source to replace them. But if the stem cells are an independent self-maintaining population, there must be a size spectrum of these cells as smaller cells enlarge and then divide. That is the point at issue, I think.

Dicke: The quantitative studies which I presented earlier (pp. 47–66), demonstrating a clear-cut parallelism between the number of CMOMCs (cell meeting our morphological criteria) and of CFU–S in the mouse, are indicative of the fact that the CMOMC is the multipotential haemopoietic stem cell. And this implies a uniform appearance of the haemopoietic stem cell.

Yoffey: I would extend the pluripotency, in view of all the work showing that CFU production was increased by bacteriological and immunological stimuli. There may be an even wider degree of pluripotency than haematological potency: if we go back far enough we should be able to find a cell which can differentiate either immunologically or haematologically.

Lajtha: My main interest in the stem cell is to understand its regulatory mechanisms. If we could manipulate its proliferation or non-proliferation, differentiation or non-differentiation, we should have an extremely powerful therapeutic method. In order to understand what this cell is doing, how it is being regulated and by what, we must have it *in vitro* in a clean condition. So first we must have an *in vitro* method whereby pure populations of pluripotent CFU can be grown, so that its controlling factors can be titrated, analysed and purified. None of the morphological assays are anything like sufficiently quantitative.

Dicke: I hope that we shall obtain such good morphological pictures that even Dr McCulloch will be convinced that we can quantitate by morphology.

Rosse: It is impossible to show a picture of a cell and call it a stem cell, because we are mixing two very different concepts. One can describe cells in terms of what they look like; one can also present evidence that cells with certain morphological features in common can do certain things. However, one cannot prove that a particular cell is a stem cell; it is already dead when one looks at it, and it will not do the things a stem cell does. Such a claim is as bad as Dr McCulloch's refusal to assign any function to any visible thing. I find both points of view equally disturbing.

Another point to illustrate this pertains to the lymphocyte. We do not keep functional definitions and morphological definitions sufficiently separate. Several people referred to lymphocytes as if equating them with cells capable of doing things which are involved in immunological reactions. But are all cells with immunological functions to be called lymphocytes? And are the cells which on a morphological basis we call lymphocytes, not lymphocytes because no one has yet given evidence that they play a part in immunological reactions?

These difficulties are overcome if we separate these two realms of terminology, which I see no difficulty in doing.

Dr Dicke, Professor Yoffey and you now agree that you are talking about roughly the same kind of cell. You presented evidence that those cells are pluripotent stem cells. Dr Metcalf showed us similar cells which are agar colony-forming units. I showed similar cells which respond to erythropoietin. We therefore have a group of cells which look much the same and may have several different functions. So you are not justified in giving any particular function or label to a morphological picture.

Dicke: I agree.

Yoffey: I was particularly careful to say that we felt fairly confident that the haemopoietic stem cells were to be found *among* the members of a cell population which had a characteristic and readily identifiable morphology. I did not say that *all* the cells of that population were haemopoietic stem cells. Perhaps at our next stem cell conference we may have means of specifically identifying haemopoietic stem cells. At present we can also add that they must possess certain properties on the basis of the experimental findings. Stem cells have to be able to migrate through the bloodstream fairly freely, they have to be able to proliferate at some times more rapidly than others, and so on.

Thomas: When the cell in murine haemopoietic tissues, which we have previously called a transitional cell, emerged as a SCIBTA (stem cell indicated by transplantation assay—if I may adopt the Rijswijk system of terminology), I thought that it would be instructive to compare the appearances which transitional cells exhibit in electron micrographs with those of cells *known* to be multipotent. At first sight the ovum appears to be an excellent example of such a cell but this haploid cell has a number of curious features and the oogonium is a more suitable example of a generalized multipotent cell. A typical oogonium is illustrated in Fig. 1 (p. 325) and the similar appearance of a typical SCIBTA is illustrated in my paper (Fig. 9, p. 91). From its appearance the SCIBTA resembles the cell which is presumably the ultimate generalized multipotent cell of the species!

Loutit: You are still keeping to morphological criteria, although subcellular ones?

Thomas: Yes, I am attempting to define the morphological features which are shared by multipotent cells.

INTRACELLULAR FACTORS

Loutit: Is anyone going to get into the deeper layers of molecular biology?

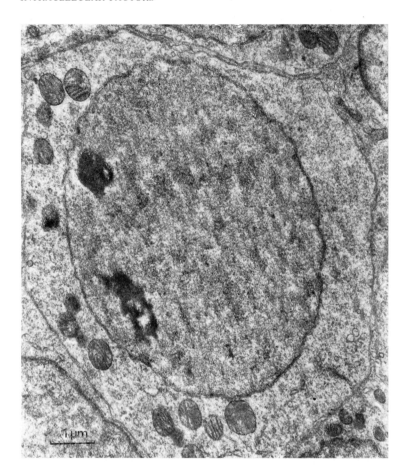

Fig. 1 (Thomas). Oogonium in rat foetal ovary on 17th day of gestation (buffered 1 % OsO₄). Electron micrograph provided through the kindness of Dr. L. L. Franchi. (Compare with Fig. 9, p. 91.)

Presumably all these cells have full genetic equipment. The function for which the pluripotent cell is noted is its capacity to do so many different things, given the right environment or stimulus. Presumably this means switching on or switching off genetic control here and there.

McCulloch: The morphologists and the functionalists will simply have to coexist. If we are to approach the important problem of the molecular biology of the system, good reliable methods are required for studying haemopoietic environments. At the moment all our methods have great drawbacks. None of them has anything like the simplicity of either the *in vivo* or the cell culture methods. We need something like these to allow us to see what the cell, the CFU or the CFU–C, interacts with, so that we can study the interaction. Only in this way, in my view, shall we have any hope of answering your question of what are the molecular elements.

Winterhalter: We shall need to characterize the molecular nature of controlling factors before we study the interaction.

Iscove: We need highly selective assays for the earlier committed progeny of the stem cell, in both the granulocytic and erythroid pathways. Candidate systems exist, but we do not know how close the cells which we are assaying are to the stem cell itself.

Lajtha: We should make it a high priority to determine the precise quantitative kinetics of the granulopoiesis *in vivo*, just as we know the erythroid series from pronormoblast to polychromatic normoblasts. We still do not know what happens from myeloblast to metamyelocyte —the number of divisions, the total maturation time, detailed transit times, etc.

McCulloch: Why do you want that information?

Lajtha: Without that, I will not know whether any *in vitro* system is physiological or not.

Stohlman: If you have both pure populations of cells and pure regulators you do not need that.

Yoffey: The *in vitro* techniques are magnificent—one learns a lot from them and they simplify certain aspects of the problem. However, the ultimate objective is to see how to apply those data *in vivo*. The *in vitro* is the intermediate step.

McCulloch: I think the molecular biologists would disagree with your point of view.

Winterhalter: I do not think they would. At an EMBO conference about the future of molecular biology about two years ago it was decided that man was neither mentally nor technologically equipped to study things *in vivo*, although this is the ultimate aim. One important section of the new EMBO laboratory will have the task of designing new technology enabling us to study *in vivo* phenomena.

Yoffey: 'The proper study of mankind is man'.

Loutit: So far we have referred to the following as needing further research: pluripotent stem cells as populations, techniques for obtaining the pluripotent stem cell in culture, molecular characteristics of controlling factors and assays for early progeny of the stem cell. Can a specific experimental approach be designed for all these items?

Metcalf: These are difficult and time-consuming tasks. We have worked for six years trying to purify CSF from a single source and people have been trying to purify erythropoietin for more than a decade.

One matter of urgency is the need to design simple *in vitro* systems which can mimic some features of tissue microenvironments. This may require a quantum jump in technology but could be approached by a better exploitation of organ cultures and of whole embryo cultures (Moore & Metcalf 1970). This type of culture does support CFU development and it might somehow be possible to simplify it enough to analyse some of the events occurring in the cell–cell interactions leading to derepression of CFU.

EXTRACELLULAR FACTORS

Yoffey: Another item for the list is: what directs cell migration? Streams of lymphocytes or lymphocyte-related cells migrate in vast numbers to and from the bone marrow and the spleen, yet cells in the bloodstream which are capable of repopulating haemopoietic tissues do not, for example, get into thoracic duct lymph. What finally makes them settle in the thymus or in the spleen, and what makes some thymus cells settle in the bone marrow? The only thing I know of is some work on the sialic acid coating and the neuraminidase experiments of some years ago (Woodruff & Gesner 1969).

Hudson: The interplay of the various factors which we are going to characterize *in vivo* should also perhaps be a target for the future.

Thomas: The term 'microenvironment' is currently being used in two different senses, which is beginning to cause some confusion. It is used to designate the environmental compartment which occupies a particular situation, such as the spleen or the medullary cavity of the femur, and to designate the environment in the immediate neighbourhood of a cell. It is clearly important to distinguish between these ecological alternatives, so I think that it would be useful to employ the term *minienvironment* to designate an environmental compartment and the term *microenvironment* to designate the immediate environment of a single cell.

Yoffey: The more mature polymorphs can migrate from the bone marrow under their own steam. Lymphocytes can do likewise and are easily identified as they pass through the sinusoidal endothelium. But what is the mechanism by which red cells escape from the marrow?

Has the sinusoidal endothelium any part to play in the stem cell problem? I do not mean as a source of stem cells—an old concept which has now long been discarded—but as influencing their migration into or out of the marrow. When, for example, stem cells enter the marrow from the bloodstream, their first point of contact with the marrow tissue is actually the sinusoidal endothelium. Is there any kind of biotactic mechanism involved? At the moment we have no actual evidence, but can only speculate on the existence of such a mechanism.

Stohlman: Lichtman & Weed (1972) suggested that the reason why the polymorphs come out in a pipeline fashion in normal circumstances relates to the deformability and stickiness which they acquire as they mature. What the leucocytosis-promoting factor of Gordon (Gordon *et al.* 1964) would do in these circumstances, I don't know. The kinetic studies show that apparently polymorphs are released from the storage pool. At least these changes in physical properties of the polymorphs would give some reason for this. The red cell loses its nucleus in normal circumstances, and becomes more deformable. This may have something to do with release of these cells.

Yoffey: In 1921 Key said that the immature red cells all stuck together. That is a statement which has been repeated in the literature ever since. Do you know of any evidence bearing on that?

Stohlman: There is some evidence for stickiness in the mature cells.

COLONIALISM

Osmond: The large-scale production of lymphocytes in bone marrow requires the existence of a large pool of lymphocyte progenitor cells in the marrow which should be included in any complete model of haemopoiesis. Similarly, a comprehensive assay of pluripotent marrow stem cell function should assay marrow lymphocytopoiesis as well as granulocytopoiesis, erythropoiesis and megakaryocytopoiesis. Unfortunately, marrow lymphocytes do not form colonies *in vivo* or *in vitro*. The reason for this is not clear. One suggestion has been that it reflects the different cell kinetics of lymphoid tissues as compared with erythroid and granulocytic cells. It is true that in peripheral lymphoid tissues such as the lymph nodes, spleen and blood, many small lymphocytes have a long lifespan and post-irradiation recovery of the total small lymphocyte population is slow. However, the majority of bone marrow small lymphocytes are rapidly renewed and there is no kinetic reason why a colony of marrow lymphocytes should not develop in the same sort of time as a granulocytic or erythroid colony. Possibly, the failure of marrow lymphocytes to form clonal aggregates *in vivo* may be related to their migratory properties. There remains a need to develop a convenient system to assay directly the lymphocyte progenitor cells in bone marrow.

Micklem: Something very like a lymphoid colony may develop in the right conditions in the thymus. If small doses of marrow cells are injected into a lethally irradiated mouse, and appropriate chromosome markers are used, one may reach a dose where one lobe of the thymus will be repopulated by a single clone of cells, and the other may not be repopulated until later (V. Wallis, E. Leuchars & A. J. S. Davies, 1972, personal communication). I think that is a kind of colony. Otherwise, apart from the particular microenvironment provided by the thymus, and perhaps (although I do not know) the bone marrow, I believe that the only conditions under which there can be quasi-colonial proliferation of lymphocytes (on a limited scale) occur after antigenic stimulation.

Loutit: We are using the word 'colony' and the word 'clone', which basically are the same thing. I have morphological visions of colonies, whether of granulocytes or of erythroid cells, but I do not have a morphological picture of a lymphoid colony. A whole lobe of a thymus may come from one original progenitor cell, but it does not form a tight colony morphologically, as does the erythroblast or its precursor. Are we perhaps asking for the moon by looking for lymphoid colonies? Perhaps they have a syncytial spread rather than a colonial?

Stohlman: Do colonies exist only in mice, or are there also distinct colonies in monkeys?

Dicke: There are no distinct colonies in the monkey.

Loutit: Histological sections of bone marrow show convincing evidence of a mother cell of some sort, which takes the form of a reticulum cell. Originally it was histologically thought of as the stem cell. Around it are the various progressions of erythroblasts. One still has the picture of a colony of erythroid or granulocytic cells in the marrow, but I do not have a picture of a lymphoid colony in the marrow; it is spread out.

Yoffey: In sections of over 1000 guinea pig marrows—some normal, some unstimulated, some stimulated to erythropoiesis and some to granulopoiesis — we just have not seen lymphoid colonies. In a few monkey marrows I occasionally saw a few small aggregates of lymphocytes. In most normal human marrows there are no lymphoid masses although they are seen in pathological conditions. Normally the marrow lymphocyte is a scattered population.

Stohlman: Occasionally lymph follicles are seen in normal human marrow.

Yoffey: They are rare.

Dicke: I agree with you, Dr Yoffey, but we do not want to call these small lymphocyte clones in the monkey 'colonies'.

McCulloch: There is unequivocal chromosomal evidence that lymphoid cells, identified either morphologically or by immunological methods, can belong to the same clone as CFU–S in the mouse (Wu *et al.* 1968; Trentin *et al.* 1967; Edwards *et al.* 1970). Perhaps the situation in man may be different.

Small lymphoid colonies can be detected in the spleen using a technique worked out by Kennedy *et al.* (1965).

Perhaps we should be surprised and gratified that colonies of haemopoietic cells are ever obtained since one of the characteristics of the haemopoietic system is the tendency of its cells to migrate. Failure to detect large lymphoid colonies may be explained if lymphoid cells are less likely to stay in aggregates. While it would be delightful to have a colonial technique for the lymphoid system, I would not suggest halting investigation until it is discovered.

Stohlman: I am not sure about this 'unequivocal' information. Is the CFU also a precursor of 'lymphocytes' and plasma cells—immunologically reactive cells?

McCulloch: In this respect there may be a genuine species difference between mouse and man. I agree that the evidence from chronic myelogenous leukaemia (CML) indicates that in man the myeloid and lymphoid populations may be maintained independently. Trentin's single colony transplant experiments (Trentin *et al.* 1967), Wu's marker experiments (Wu *et al.* 1968) and Edwards' combination of rosette formation with chromosomal markers (Edwards *et al.* 1970) together provide unequivocal evidence that at least some lymphoid cells with immunological capacity may belong to the same clone as CFU–S in the mouse.

Thomas: Dr Loutit, lymphoid aplasia in lethally irradiated recipients of syngeneic haemopoietic cells (Barnes *et al.* 1962; Šljivič 1966), could be attributed to the existence of a stem cell population which maintains the production of erythrocytes, granulocytes and megakaryocytes, and of a separate stem cell population which maintains the production of lymphocytes. How do you interpret its occurrence in the light of your subsequent work?

Loutit: I still interpret them in the same way. The environment favoured erythrocytic and granulocytic production, but somehow the interaction of environment and seed did not favour lymphocytic development under those conditions. I have done no further work to attempt to sort out this interaction.

Thomas: You emphasize the role of the host environment rather than the differentiation potential of the transplanted cells?

Loutit: Both are important.

Iscove: The genetic evidence obtained by Gandini & Gartler (1969) would favour the common stem cell origin of lymphoid, granulocytic and erythroid cells in man. Gandini & Gartler examined these cell populations in adult females heterozygous for the X-linked glucose 6-phosphate dehydrogenase types A and B. In each such individual tested, the relative amounts of the two enzyme types were always concordant in the three cell populations—that is, if most erythrocytes in such an individual contained enzyme type A, then the same was true for that individual's granulocytes and lymphocytes. The finding would suggest that these three populations are maintained by a common stem cell pool into adult life; separate stem cell pools might be expected to diverge in composition during adult life.

Lajtha: This is not necessarily so. Even if there is a genuinely dualistic maintenance population of stem cells in the adult, it has come not very far back from
some common precursor.

Iscove: These are adults; these are people 30 years after Lyonization.

McCulloch: Yes, but Lyonization occurs very early.

Winterhalter: It has also been shown repeatedly that all cells in a given solid
tumour are of either one or the other type.

McCulloch: That is not a good argument; during the growth of a tumour
such strong selection pressures are present that a single clone could easily be
dominant by the time the tumour is studied.

Stohlman: The difference in respect to the Ph chromosome in CML between
the lymphoid element and the other three elements in man, is the strongest
argument to suggest that at some point in development there is a stem cell
common to these three but not common to lymphocytes. This does not mean
that further back there could not be a common line.

Hudson: In discussing controlling factors, we should remember there are
other kinds of granulocyte besides the neutrophils, and one thinks particularly
of the eosinophil granulocyte. Recent work by Beeson's group has shown that
in the eosinophilia caused by *Trichinella spiralis*, T-type lymphocytes are important in attracting eosinophils (Basten & Beeson 1970; Walls *et al.* 1971), and
complement may also be important in chemotaxis of eosinophils (Ward 1969;
Kay 1970). Our own work has suggested rather indirectly that local factors in
the bone marrow can also be involved (Hudson *et al.* 1972). At the moment, we
know very little about the factors controlling eosinophils as compared with
neutrophil granulocytes.

Stohlman: There are conditions in which there is normal eosinophil formation with abnormal neutrophilic formation. There are diseases in which there
are abnormalities in the development of granulocytes. Perhaps you have studied
some of these?

Metcalf: We have not been able to grow eosinophilic colonies from human
marrow cells, or at least to prove to our satisfaction that the eosinophil-like cells
in some colonies are really eosinophils.

One disease state which would be very valuable to recognize and analyse is a
leukaemia involving genuine multipotential stem cells. Many leukaemias are
classified as 'stem cell' simply because the cells are undifferentiated, but to prove
such a classification one would need to be able to demonstrate multipotentiality.
Such a leukaemia would allow some fascinating studies on haemopoietic cell
differentiation. The closest we have come to such a leukaemia has been the
myelomonocytic leukaemia (WEHI-3) which is only bipotential and seems to

be a neoplasm of relatively differentiated (progenitor) cells (Warner *et al.* 1969).

Lajtha: There is such a leukaemia, acute erythroleukaemia, in which a patient at one stage can show large numbers of erythroblasts in the marrow and peripheral blood and two to three weeks later a clear-cut myeloblastic picture and myeloblasts. Later on the patient returns to the erythroblastic phase.

Metcalf: One has to be rather critical about what one calls a leukaemic population. There is a growing feeling that in acute granulocytic leukaemia, for example, the erythroid cells can also exhibit karyotypic abnormalities, but does this make the erythroid cells neoplastic (Killmann 1970)? The same problem exists in chronic myeloid leukaemia where the erythropoietic cells show the abnormal Philadelphia chromosome.

Lajtha: In these specific cases marrow puncture showed over 80% of an almost homogeneous population of very early normoblasts. Equally the peripheral blood contained the same population in excess of $60\ 000/mm^3$.

Stohlman: In the cases di Guglielmo (1917) originally described there were clear-cut abnormal erythroid and myeloid elements. One presumes that something happened back down the line. In some acute myelocytic leukaemias, disorders of erythropoiesis may be seen. These seem to be true leukaemias originating with the CFU. Abnormalities of CFU may also be manifested as aplastic anaemias. Unfortunately we have no way of demonstrating CFU in human beings.

Metcalf: This is why it is so important to screen mice with spontaneous and induced leukaemia for genuine stem cell leukaemias, because in the mouse techniques exist for proving cells are CFUs.

McCulloch: I am sure the correct techniques would demonstrate multipotent neoplastic cells.

Stohlman: Most of the mouse leukaemias are lymphoid.

Loutit: This is an extremely difficult problem to sort out. Most of the mouse leukaemias that I know about are of the mononuclear round cell type, which we are conventionally calling, on morphological grounds, lymphoid. By the same token, on morphological grounds I have no doubt that many of Yoffey's group would draw analogies to transitional cells. Morphologically could these be leukaemias of the stem cell type? One cannot prove it because they do not differentiate far enough in any different direction for anyone to say that they are multipotential.

Metcalf: I doubt whether mouse stem cell leukaemias have in the past been confused with lymphoid leukaemia, for two reasons: (*a*) lymphoid leukaemic cells selectively home to lymphoid tissue and this is not a property of CFUs, and (*b*) most lymphoid leukaemias carry the theta and TL antigens allowing them to be identified as thymus-derived cells. Maybe some of the non-lymphoid leukaemias in RF mice would be better candidates but these have not yet been looked at properly.

McCulloch: That is what is required—a proper technique must be used.

Metcalf: The Shay leukaemia is a transplanted leukaemia that I think has long since committed itself to the granulocytic pathway. One would be much better off examining primary leukaemias in the search for a stem cell leukaemia, not leukaemias which have been transplanted for years and must have undergone many secondary mutations and selections.

EPILOGUE

Loutit: The beauty of a symposium is that not only is it, in the phrasing of the Oxford English Dictionary 'a convivial meeting for drinking, conversation and intellectual entertainment' (all aspects of which the Ciba Foundation fosters so well), but unlike a committee it does not have to reach a consensus or draw conclusions. The reader of the general discussion may note that some of us attempted to see whether we could formulate some recommendations to our individual selves. I do not think we accomplished this and I believe this to be a healthy sign. We have not reached the end of the road to the Haemopoietic Stem Cell, nor yet a road block. We have indeed made remarkable progress since the Ciba Foundation symposium on *Haemopoiesis* (1960). In no small measure is this attributable to those who have contributed to the present symposium and whom for the present we can describe as anatomists on the one hand and physiologists on the other. Neither group has been frustrated by the lack of suitable means for furthering its endeavours. By painstaking graft and ingenuity in developing new methods the field is being narrowed down. The morphological characteristics of candidates for stem cells are recognizable at least when the cells are 'fixed' and dead: we must now learn their form while living. Living stem cells can now be made to perform by producing colonies under defined experimental conditions *in vivo* and notably now *in vitro:* we must characterize them still further and relate them to natural conditions of health and disease. As with cancer we must avoid the pitfall of expression only in the singular, and rightly in this symposium we have talked of CFU–S and CFU–C. This does not exhaust the variants, nor exclude a still more multipotential precursor (even if, as noted, we have to go back as far as the fertilized egg). I guess, and hope, that the failure to reach an agreed *modus operandi* will act as a stimulant to each contributor, and reader, to find a new twist that will lead to the further elucidation of haemopoiesis and so warrant another Ciba Foundation symposium on the subject in the not too distant future.

References

BARNES, D. W. H., FORD, C. E., GRAY, S. M. & LOUTIT, J. F. (1959) Spontaneous and induced changes in cell populations in heavily irradiated mice. *Prog. Nucl. Energy Ser. VI* **2**, 1–10

BARNES, D. W. H., LOUTIT, J. F. & MICKLEM, H. S. (1962) 'Secondary disease' in lethally irradiated mice restored with syngeneic or allogeneic foetal liver cells, in *Mechanisms of Immunological Tolerance*, Publishing House of the Czechoslovak Academy of Sciences, Prague

BASTEN, A. & BEESON, P. B. (1970) Mechanism of eosinophilia. II. Role of the lymphocyte. *J. Exp. Med.* **131**, 1288–1305

BECKER, A. J., McCULLOCH, E. A. & TILL, J. E. (1963) Cytological demonstration of the clonal nature of spleen colonies derived from transplanted mouse marrow cells. *Nature (Lond.)* **197**, 452–454,

CIBA FOUNDATION SYMPOSIUM (1960) *Haemopoiesis: Cell Production and its Regulation*, Churchill, London

DICKE, K. A., PLATENBURG, M. G. C. & VAN BEKKUM, D. W. (1971) Colony formation in agar: *in vitro* assay for haemopoietic stem cells. *Cell Tissue Kinet.* **4**, 463–477

DI GUGLIELMO, G. (1917) Richerche di ematologia. I. Un case di eritroleucemia. *Folia Med. (Napoli)*, **13**, 386

EDWARDS, G. E., MILLER, R. G. & PHILLIPS, R. A. (1970) Differentiation of rosette forming cells from myeloid stem cells. *J. Immunol.* **105**, 719

GANDINI, E. & GARTLER, S. M. (1969) Glucose-6-phosphate dehydrogenase mosaicism for studying the development of blood cell precursors. *Nature (Lond.)* **224**, 599

GORDON, A. S., HANDLER, E. S., SIEGEL, C. D., DORNFEST, B. S. & LOBUE, J. (1964) Plasma factors influencing leukocyte release in rats. *Ann. N.Y. Acad. Sci.* **113**, 766–779

HUDSON, G., CHIN, K. N. & MOFFATT, D. J. (1972) Changes in eosinophil granulocyte kinetics in severe hypoxia. *Acta Haematol. (Basel)* **48**, 58–64

KAY, A. B. (1970) Studies on eosinophil leucocyte migration. II. Factors specifically chemotactic for eosinophils and neutrophils generated from guinea pig serum by antigen-antibody complexes. *Clin. Exp. Immunol.* **7**, 723–737

KENNEDY, J. C., SIMINOVITCH, L., TILL, J. E. & McCULLOCH, E. A. (1965) A transplantation assay for mouse cells responsive to antigenic stimulation by sheep erythrocytes. *Proc. Soc. Exp. Biol. Med.* **120**, 868

KEY, J. A. (1921) Studies on erythrocytes, with special reference to reticulum, polychromatophilia, and mitochondria. *Arch. Intern. Med.* **28**, 511–549

KILLMANN, S. A. (1970) A hypothesis concerning the relationship between normal and leukemic hemopoiesis in acute myeloid leukemia, in *Hemopoietic Cellular Proliferation* (Stohlman, F., Jr., ed.), pp. 267–277, Grune & Stratton, New York

LICHTMAN, M. A. & WEED, R. I. (1972) Alteration of the cell periphery during maturation. *Blood J. Hematol.* **39**, 301–316

MOORE, M. A. S. & METCALF, D. (1970) Ontogeny of the haemopoietic system: yolk sac origin of *in vitro* and *in vitro* colony forming cells in the developing mouse embryo. *Br. J. Haematol.* **18**, 279–296

ŠLJIVIČ, V. S. (1966) Studies on 'secondary disease' in syngeneic mouse radiation chimaeras. *Int. J. Radiat. Biol.* **11**, no. 3, 273–286

TRENTIN, J., WOLF, N., CHENG, V., FAHLBERG, W., WEISS, D. & BONHAG, R. (1967) Antibody production by mice repopulated with limited numbers of clones of lymphoid cell precursors. *J. Immunol.* **98**, 1326

WALLS, R. S., BASTEN, A., LEUCHARS, E. & DAVIES, A. J. S. (1971) Mechanisms for eosinophilic and neutrophilic leucocytosis. *Br. Med. J.* **3**, 157–159

WARD, P. A. (1969) Chemotaxis of eosinophils. *Am. J. Pathol.* **54**, 121–128

WARNER, N. L., MOORE, M. A. S. & METCALF, D. (1969) A transplantable myelomonocytic leukaemia in BALB/c mice: cytology, karyotopic and muramidase content. *J. Natl Cancer Inst.* **93**, 963–982

WOODRUFF, J. J. & GESNER, B. M. (1969) The effect of neuraminidase on the fate of transfused lymphocytes. *J. Exp. Med.* **129**, 551–568

WU, A. M., TILL, J. E., SIMINOVITCH, L. & McCULLOCH, E. A. (1967) A cytological study of the capacity for differentiation of normal hemopoietic colony-forming cells. *J. Cell. Physiol.* **69**, 177–184

WU, A. M., TILL, J. E., SIMINOVITCH, L. & McCULLOCH, E. A. (1968) Cytological evidence for a relationship between normal hematopoietic colony forming cells and cells of the lymphoid system. *J. Exp. Med.* **127**, 455

Index of contributors

Indexes compiled by William Hill

Subject index